Space
and
Space Travel

First Edition

By Erika Harnett and Robert Winglee
University of Washington

cognella®
academic publishing

Bassim Hamadeh, CEO and Publisher
Michael Simpson, Vice President of Acquisitions
Jamie Giganti, Managing Editor
Jess Busch, Senior Graphic Designer
Kristina Stolte, Acquisitions Editor
Michelle Piehl, Project Editor
Alexa Lucido, Licensing Coordinator

First published in the United States of America in 2015 by Cognella, Inc.

Trademark Notice: Product or corporate names may be trademarks or registered trademarks, and are used only for identification and explanation without intent to infringe.

Cover Image: Copyright © 2011 Depositphotos Inc./mmaxer.
         NASA, "Endeavour STS-130 Earth Limb." Copyright in the Public Domain.
         Copyright © 2013 Depositphotos Inc./Shtanzman.

ISBN: 978-1-62661-250-1 (pbk)/ 978-1-62661-251-8 (br)

www.cognella.com   800-200-3908

Contents

All Systems Go

1.1. Introduction

It is a dark and stormy night. Looking about one could easily be convinced that there is no one about, but with a flash of lightning you can see out the horizon and know that there is more beyond what you can actually see. Then, the clouds clear, you see the moon glow and the stars come out and then you are reminded that we're only a small part of the universe. The question then becomes: "Do we stay on Earth or do we try to leave this perfect environment and head out into space?" In the science fiction movies the answer always appears to be simple - we go for no better reason than it is just there.

The answer to the question of "do we stay or do we go?" is very much more complicated. First and foremost if we go to space, it means that we will leave the comfortable environment of the Earth to one that is lethal to life in almost every conceivable fashion possible. Most obvious of these threats is that no breathable air beyond our atmosphere exists anywhere in the entire solar system. If one can contrive a solution for this inconvenience, then one has to face the fact that unless some sort of radiation shielding is in place, humans will be subjected to energetic particles with sufficient energies to be lethal with only a few month of exposure, though the particles are at a relatively low density. And if the radiation doesn't kill you, then the lack of gravity in space is going to ensure degradation of the human body, with a multitude of health problems.

Now if you think all these problems solvable, and in fact they are with sufficient financial resources, then there is only the last issue of distance. The distance scales are unimaginable relative to our everyday life experiences. Going to work or school typically involves distances of a few to tens of kilometers. Going cross-country involves scales of a few thousand kilometers. Going to our nearest neighbor in the solar system, the Moon, is only a mere 400,000 km. And if you want to go to one of the nearest planets you can start adding multiple zeros to the distances and even more zeroes if you travel to one of the gas giants. And as we all know from our own travel experiences, the cost greatly increases with distance.

So why go to space if it is that dangerous and expensive? The answer is that our lives are already much more richer due to the development of space travel, and there is still huge potential as future developments occur. For example, space technology has allowed communication satellites, more accurate prediction of weather, including extreme events such as hurricanes and tornadoes, the development of global locations using the global positioning system (GPS), environmental monitoring with real-time data, and a vast number of spinoff technologies including electronics, materials, computers and internet.

On a more philosophical note, those of who have traveled to low Earth orbit and beyond, often speak of the perspective one gains from traveling to space. Astronauts speak of not truly understanding how fragile our protection is from the hazards of space until they can see the thin blue line of the atmosphere from above. Astronauts also speak to the realization that one truly can not distinguish political boundaries from space. To an astronaut, the inhabitants below are not Americans or Australians or Africans, they are Earthlings and we are all one.

In this course, we examine many of these and other issues involved in space and space travel. This includes past, present, and future scientific developments spearheaded by NASA, the science of the solar system itself and what benefits may arise from such studies. Additionally, it is important to consider the new technologies being developed by the private sector, which will provide more access to space. This may include the development of advanced systems that may allow us to go into space much more cheaply and quickly than is presently possible.

1.2 The Human Relationship with Space

Probably since the dawn of humans, have people looked up at the night sky and wondered what is out there. In an area lacking human produced light, the Milky Way is a dominant feature in the night sky (Figure 1.2.1). Early astronomers in Europe, and Central and South America (circa 3000 BC) left record of their observations in the form of structures that track the Sun, and in some cases, marking out the solstices (such as Newgrange in Ireland).

The Arabian region (including Persia, Greece, Northern Africa) was one center of astronomical observation and research. Many of the constellations we know today, are referred to in early Greek and Babylonian writings. Most of the names of the brightest stars that we use today originate from the Arabic names given by Persian astronomers.

Early records show that active astronomical observations through out much of China's early recorded history. Early Chinese rulers actively sought out collaboration with Indian and Arabian astronomers. Chinese astronomers also recorded the supernova in 1054 that created the region we now call the Crab Nebula.

Many objects in the night sky were dutifully catalogued by Charles Messier, a French astronomer that lived between 1730 and 1817.

FIGURE 1.2.1. THE MILKY WAY, AS SEEN FROM THE PARANAL OBSERVATORY IN CHILE. THE RED LASER FROM THE OBSERVATORY ON THE GROUND IS POINTING AT THE GALACTIC CENTER.

In his search to separate "fixed" diffuse objects from possible comets, he recorded over a 100 objects that we now know range from galaxies to nebulae within our own galaxy. At the time, it was not known that our Universe is composed of many billions of galaxies. It took the observations of a particular type of variable star by Edwin Hubble in the 1920s for the scientific community to accept that many of the objects observed by Messier, are outside of our own galaxy.

Coming a little closer to home, one of the more profound observations of planets within our solar system came when Galileo Galilei trained his refined telescope design upon Jupiter and discovered four moons orbiting around the planet (now know as the Galilean moons – Io, Europa, Ganymede and Callisto). That he discovered something orbiting around an object other than the Earth, helped to upend the belief of heliocentrism (that the Earth is the center of the Universe and everything orbits around it).

The question of the uniqueness of planets forming around stars, and if our solar system was alone in the Universe, remained unanswered until 1995 when the first planet was found around another main sequence star, 51 Pegasus, by Mayor and Queloz [1]. Planet hunters have now found hundreds of planets round hundreds of stars. It seems like almost every day a new planet is found. The early discoveries of planets were very large planets (like Jupiter) very close to their home stars (closer than Mercury is to the Sun). With improvements in technology and longer observation times though, the types of planets found are getting smaller while the types of solar systems discovered are looking a little bit more like ours, and planets more similar to Earth. A current tabulation can be found at http://exoplanets.org.

All of these observations were made by people looking up from the surface of the Earth. Humans did not make their first foray into space until 1957, when Sputnik 1 became the first human made object to orbit the Earth. Its launch ushered in the beginning of the "Space Age", over a decade of expansive growth in humans' knowledge of space travel, and what can be found when we are out in space. Much of original theory and science needed to build the rockets capable of launching objects into orbit was developed by Konstantin Tsiolkovsky, Robert Goddard and Hermann Oberth, all working in the late 19th century and early 20th century.

The first object to orbit around a body other than the Earth was the Soviet satellite Luna 10, which went into orbit around the Moon on April 3, 1966 [2]. It made measurements of magnetic fields, plasmas, radiation and micrometeorites. It was soon followed by the US Apollo missions, with the first human setting foot on the Moon, when Neil Armstrong stepped on to the lunar surface, on July 20, 1969, uttered him immortal words about making a giant leap for mankind. So far six countries or entities have sent either orbiters or landers to the Moon – USSR/Russia, the USA, the European Space Agency, Japan, China and India. The question now, is who will be the next person to set foot on the Moon?

The first satellite mission to another planet that succeeded in returning data was the USSR's Venera 7 spacecraft, which landed on the surface of Venus. It probably landed incorrectly, which lead to only a partial transmission of a few minutes of temperature data. The first fully successful satellite mission to another planet occurred when NASA's Mariner 9 spacecraft went into orbit around Mars in November of 1971. It returned data for almost a year, providing our first nearly complete mapping of the Martian surface from orbit. Many missions followed, some successful, some not. The important part is that the missions have continued, with a growing number of countries launching satellites and sending missions to other planets.

But all great journeys begin with a single step, and for us, that means understanding the scales and sizes we must contend with before we can travel through the solar system.

1.3. Scientific Notation

The properties of the solar system are characterized by many extremes. There are regions that are sufficiently hot to produce fusion and regions that are so cold that methane is a solid. There are regions where the density of the material is 10 times higher than lead, while other regions in space are nearly empty - in a volume the size of your thumb, the number of atoms present can be counted on your fingers. Large scale-planetary or stellar processes are often controlled or defined by processes that are occurring in atomic scale sizes. In order to quantify these extremes, we use scientific notation as a shorthand way of writing out and multiplying large- and small-scale numbers. For those that are already familiar with scientific notation, this section can be skipped.

The point of using scientific notation is to convert all the numbers to powers of 10 so that it is easier to see the relative magnitude of the numbers, as well as to simplify simple arithmetical operations. Some common magnitudes of scientific notation are shown in Table 1.3.1. For numbers less than unity (one), the index, or exponent, of the power of 10 is derived by counting the number of digits from the decimal to the place just right of the first non-zero digit. The negative index indicates that the number is a decimal or less than unity. Numbers larger than unity have a positive exponent determined by counting the number of places between the decimal and the place just to the right of the highest-order digit.

Table 1.3.1. Common numbers placed in scientific notation and their scientific designation along with their common terms. For numbers less than unity, the exponent is a negative number whose value is the number of decimal places to reach the right of the first significant figure. Numbers greater than unity have a positive exponent whose value is equal to the number of decimal places to the left to reach the first significant figure. Units bigger than a thousand are typically designated by capitals, while the other units are designated by lowercase letters.

Number	Scientific Notation	Designation	Common Term
0.000000001	10^{-9}	nano (n)	billionth
0.000001	10^{-6}	micro (µ)	millionth
0.001	10^{-3}	milli (m)	thousandth
1	10^0	unity	
1000	10^3	kilo (k)	thousands
1,000,000	10^6	Mega (M)	millions
1,000,000,000	10^9	Giga (G)	billions
1,000,000,000,000	10^{12}	Tera (T)	trillions

An example would be the speed of light, which is written as 3×10^8 m/s or 300,000,000 (i.e. 3 with 8 zeros behind it). From these simple examples it is seen that scientific notation offers a simple clean way of writing down both big and small numbers. Of equal importance, scientific notation offers the ability to simplify the mathematical manipulation of these numbers. In particular, multiplication by a power of 10 simply means adding the relevant exponents while division means of subtracting exponents.

An example of this is to find the thickness of a pile of 20 CDs, in meters, given that the thickness of a CD which is 1.2 mm. To start off with the note that:

$1 \text{ mm} = 10^{-3} \text{ m}$

Thickness 1 CD $= 1.2 \text{ mm} = 1.2 \times 10^{-3} \text{ m}$

Number of CDs $= 20 = 2 \times 10^1$

Thickness of 20 CDs $= (2 \times 10^1) \times (1.2 \times 10^{-3}) \text{ m}$
$= (2 \times 1.2) \times (10^1 \times 10^{-3}) \text{ m}$
$= 2.4 \times 10^{(1-3)} \text{ m}$
$= 2.4 \times 10^{-2} \text{ m}$

Adding and subtracting is equally simple if one remembers to ensure that the exponent for the two numbers is the same before performing the operation. For example, suppose you wanted to find the mass of hydrogen, which is made up of a proton and an electron:

Mass of a proton $= 1.67262 \times 10^{-27} \text{ kg}$
Mass of an electron $= 9 \times 10^{-31} \text{ kg}$
$= 0.0009 \times 10^{-27} \text{ kg}$
Mass of hydrogen $= 1.6726 \times 10^{-27} \text{ kg} + 0.0009 \times 10^{-27} \text{ kg}$
$= 1.6735 \times 10^{-27} \text{ kg}$

(Note that this number is slightly less than the mass of hydrogen quoted in periodic tables since the latter includes a small percentage of isotopes that are present in naturally occurring hydrogen; this discussion will come later).

The other trick about using scientific notation is to ensure that the numbers being manipulated are in the right units. For example, suppose we wish to calculate the travel time it takes light to propagate from the Sun to the Earth. This time is given by the simple formula:

Travel Time = Distance/Speed

The speed is given above and is equal to 3×10^8 m/s. The distance from the Sun to the Earth is called the astronomical unit (1 AU) and is equivalent to approximately 150,000,000 km or 1.5 x 108 km. Note that distances are typically quoted in kilometers while the speed in this example is quoted in meters per second. In order to solve for the time, you need to ensure the units of distance match the speed units, which requires us to convert kilometers to meters, i.e.,

$$1 \text{ AU} = 1.5 \times 10^8 \text{ km or } 1.5 \times 10^8 \times 10^3 \text{ m}$$
$$= 1.5 \times 10^{11} \text{ m}$$

Hence, the

$$\text{Travel time} = \frac{1.5 \times 10^{11} \ m}{3 \times x10^8 \ m/s} = \frac{1.5}{3} \times 10^{(11-8)} s$$
$$= 0.5 \times 10^3 s$$
$$= 8.3 \text{ minutes.}$$

This example also illustrates one of the enormous problems in moving about the solar system. Light takes about eight minutes to travel from the Sun to the Earth. On Earth, we are used to almost immediate electronic communications because our distances are small compared with space. Suppose you are an astronaut on Mars, which sits at 1.5 AU. The closest approach between Mars and the Earth is about 0.5 AU, and when it is on the far side of the Sun, the distance is 2.5 AU. Suppose there is a critical air leak or health crisis on Mars and you radio back to Earth for help; that signal could take somewhere between four and 20 minutes to reach Earth. Suppose Earth then radios back for more details, so now we are definitely talking tens of minutes, and a response that could be on the order of an hour. A person can bleed out on a much shorter time scale, and similarly a loss of structural integrity can lead to depressurization of buildings on timescales of less than an hour.

1.4. The Solar System

The solar system includes the planets (four rocky inner planets and the four outer gas giant planets) and their moons, dwarf planets (including Pluto), and other solar system objects including the asteroid belt, which lies between Mars and Jupiter, and the Kuiper belt, which lies beyond Neptune and consists of small icy bodies.

The properties of the main bodies are given in Table 1.4.1. The problem is how to put this information into a perspective that is both meaningful and memorable.

The issue of scale sizes within the solar system is of immense importance because many of the popular images underplay the true scales; even when portrayed accurately, it is very hard for a human to perceive the consequences of the disparate scale sizes from our everyday experiences. As an example, which of the images in Figure 1.4.1 is to scale, given the information in Table 1.4.1?

The image in the top right is probably the most pleasing because the planets are resolved, and most of the main solar system objects are fitted into the one image. The reality, though, is that the planets are not drawn to scale, since Jupiter is ten times the size of Earth, yet only 1/10 the size of the Sun. While the planets are correctly aligned in position, the actual positions of the planetary orbits are not to scale. The bottom image has the orbits to scale, but the size of the planets relative to the Sun or their orbits is not. The sci-fi image in the top gives you the impression that you are close to the Sun, and it most definitely looks cool. But, in fact, if the spacecraft was as close as the image implies, then the real spacecraft would be sub pixel in size in the image—and therefore would not look cool at all. So the answer is that none of the images is actually to scale.

So let us try a different approach and map the solar system onto objects within the state of Washington. Suppose that the Sun is the size of the football playing field in Seattle. On this

Table 1.4.1. Main characteristics of the larger objects within the solar system. Data are from http://www.aai.ee/planets/nineplanets/ and http://planetfacts.org/the-solar-system/.

Solar System Object	Orbit (AU = 1.5×10^8 km)	Radius (km)	Mass (kg)	Surface Materials and Atmosphere
Sun	0	700,000	2.0×10^{30}	92% hydrogen, 7% helium
Mercury	0.38	2439	3.3×10^{23}	Basaltic rocks and regolith trace atmosphere of hydrogen, helium
Venus	0.72	6052	4.9×10^{24}	Basaltic rocks and altered materials, thick atmosphere of CO_2, N_2
Earth	1	6378	6.0×10^{24}	Basaltic and granitic rock and altered materials, atmosphere of N_2, O_2
Mars	1.5	3397	6.4×10^{23}	Basaltic rock and altered materials, CO_2, N_2
Jupiter	5.2	71492	1.9×10^{27}	90% hydrogen, 10% helium
Saturn	9.5	60268	5.7×10^{26}	97% hydrogen, 3% helium
Uranus	19	25559	8.7×10^{25}	83% hydrogen, 15% helium
Neptune	30	24764	1.0×10^{26}	74% hydrogen, 25% helium

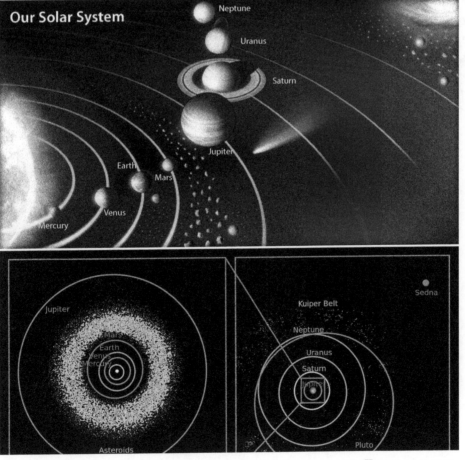

FIGURE 1.4.1. THREE IMAGES OF OBJECTS IN OUR SOLAR SYSTEM. THE QUESTION IS, WHICH IMAGE IS TO SCALE?

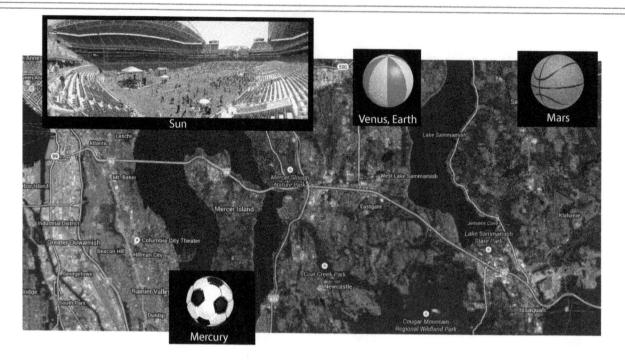

FIGURE 1.4.2. THE INNER SOLAR SYSTEM TO SCALE, WHERE THE SIZE OF THE SUN IS ASSUMED TO BE THE SIZE OF A FOOTBALL STADIUM.

scale, Mercury would be the size of a soccer ball located on Mercer Island, about 6.5 miles away. Venus would be near Eastgate, and Earth near Cougar Mountain. Both would be about the size of a beach ball. Mars would be out near Newport as the size of a basketball.

The point is that the size of the inner planets is less than 1% of the size of the Sun and less than 0.001% of the orbital distance. As for the outer planets, one must go to a larger-scale map.

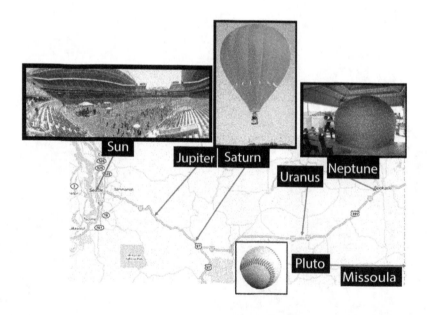

FIGURE 1.4.3. MAPPING OF THE OUTER SOLAR SYSTEM USING THE SAME SCALE AS FIGURE 1.4.2.

Using the same scale for the Sun, Jupiter and Saturn would have the size of a hot-air balloon. Uranus and Neptune would be about a third of this size, with Neptune being at the other end of the state and Pluto found in the next adjoining state. Jupiter and Saturn are sometimes referred to as substellar giant planets, in that with a few times more mass, they could potentially generate energy like a star as opposed to absorbing energy like a planet.

For humans traveling from the Earth to Mars, the task seems huge. But from a solar system perspective, this is only a small hop. If you have ever driven the route from Seattle to Spokane, you would agree that this is much more arduous than doing a small hop between the outer suburbs of Seattle. So, the difficulty in having humans move through space is literally as immense as the solar system.

Assignment Question 1.1. *If the solar system we scale in Figure 1.4.3, with the Sun positioned in Seattle and Neptune located at Spokane, where would the near star Alpha Centauri be located?*

Now that we have a qualitative perspective, let us put some of the numbers in Table 1.4.1 into a quantitative perspective. One of the most important aspects is to recognize the exact size

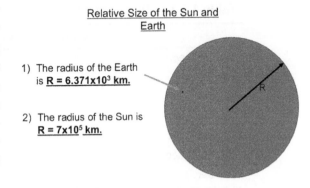

Relative Size of the Sun and Earth

1) The radius of the Earth is **R = 6.371x10³ km.**

2) The radius of the Sun is **R = 7x10⁵ km.**

FIGURE 1.4.4. RELATIVE SIZE OF THE SUN AND EARTH.

of the Earth relative to the Sun, as shown in Figure 1.4.4.

From the given information, the radius of the Earth is only about 0.9% of that the Sun. Figure 1.4.4 is to scale and shows the Earth and the solar disk. Figure 1.4.5 shows an image of the Sun taken in white light with some typical sunspots on the surface. It is seen that our Earth is only as big as some of the smaller sunspots, and accordingly, the Earth pales relative to the largest sunspots.

Table 1.4.1 shows that the Sun contains 99.9% of the total mass of the solar system and that Jupiter makes up the bulk of the missing 0.1% of the solar system's mass. Interestingly enough, the ratio of the electron mass to the proton mass is about 0.5%. So, if you like similes, one could say that Jupiter to the Sun is like the electron and proton are to the hydrogen atom and that from a mass perspective, maybe the Earth doesn't count.

There are additional similes between the atom and the solar system. For example, the atomic radius[1] is about 10,000 times the radius of its nucleus. If we go out to 10,000 times the solar radius, we would be at $(1 \times 10^4) \times (7 \times 10^5)$ = 7×10^9 km or 46 AU. So, the atomic radius relative to the proton radius is like the position of Neptune (or Pluto) relative to the radius of the Sun. And, of course, the electron orbits

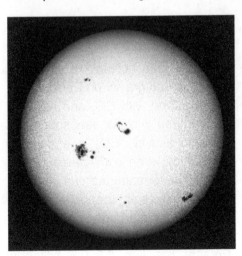

FIGURE 1.4.5. IMAGE OF THE SUN WITH SUNSPOTS PRESENT.[2]

---

1 http://en.wikipedia.org/wiki/Atomic_radius

2 http://solar.physics.montana.edu/ypop/Classroom/Lessons/Sunspots/

Table 1.5.1.   Timescales for the Earth.

Time Scales for the Earth	
$10^3 - 10^4$ sec.	Storms
$10^4 - 10^5$ sec.	Day-Night Cycle—Tides
10^7 sec.	Seasons
$10^9 - 10^{10}$ sec.	Typical Human Life Span
$10^{11} - 10^{12}$ sec.	Ice Ages/Climate Shifts
$10^{15} - 10^{16}$ sec.	Continent Drift/Magnetic Field/Life
10^{17} sec.	**Age of Earth (4.5 billion years)**

the nucleus as the planets revolve around the Sun; in some sense, the structure of the atom is being repeated within the solar system, but at much larger scale lengths.

1.5. Timescales

So far we have concentrated just on spatial scales, but there is another scale that must be taken into account, and that is timescale. From the human perspective, there are only small changes occurring. For example, weather comes and goes, but the composition of the atmosphere itself basically doesn't change from day to day. Similarly, the continents look fixed in place, whereas in reality they are moving at well-defined speeds that are too small for a human to perceive. To see these changes, one has to focus on the relevant timescale. To put these into perspective, we have placed the terrestrial processes and their timescales in Table 1.5.1 all in seconds. Day-to-day events occur on much shorter timescales than the typical human life span, but the latter is very much shorter than many of the geological processes that have shaped the Earth, including ice ages and the development of continental drift. Because our timescale is short relative to these geological timescales, we end up thinking that these geological processes are not occurring;

this controls how humanity thinks and operates in the present.

For example, there is a tendency to think that our atmosphere has always been like it is today. Table 1.4.1 shows that our atmosphere is unique among the planets, which should cause anyone to stop and wonder why that is so. The fact is that the Earth has had three different atmospheres:

The Early Earth Atmosphere:

- Atmosphere similar to the solar composition—primarily hydrogen and helium;
- 100 times bigger than today;
- Present between 4.5–3.5 billion years ago.

The Young Earth Atmosphere:

- Hydrogen and helium are lost to space due to limited gravity on Earth;
- Oceans form with CO_2 and nitrogen being pumped into the atmosphere due to volcanic activity; CO_2 is a greenhouse gas[3] which, even in low percentages, can control the temperature of a planet;
- CO_2 dissolves in the oceans, allowing habitable temperature conditions to start to develop;
- Present between 3.5–0.5 billion years ago. At this stage, the atmospheric com-

---

3   http://en.wikipedia.org/wiki/Greenhouse_gas

Table 1.5.2. Timescales for the Sun.

Timescales for The Sun	
10^4 sec.	Convection at Visible Surface
$10^5 - 10^6$ sec.	Flares–Solar Events–Oscillations
2×10^6 sec.	Solar Rotation
$10^7 - 10^8$ sec.	Magnetic Cycle
$10^{15} - 10^{16}$ sec.	Energy Transport—Changes in Core
10^{17} sec.	**Age of Sun (4.5 billion years)**
2×10^{17} sec.	Sun Becomes a Red Giant/Stellar Death. Inner Solar System Is Destroyed.

position is similar to that of present-day Venus and Mars, but the actual concentrations are different between the planets.

The Living Earth Atmosphere:

- Nitrogen dominates as CO_2 is removed from the atmosphere and reaches modern densities;
- Plants evolve, enabling photosynthesis to occur, causing oxygen to be released into the atmosphere;
- Animals evolve to utilize the oxygen in the atmosphere and move from the oceans to the land;
- Oxygen in the atmosphere is a smoking gun for life and does not occur (at least within the solar system) without life being present.
- Present between 0.5 billion years and the present day.

How the atmosphere continues to develop is unknown, but it is going through significant changes due to the production of CO_2 from industrial processes. We know what the past conditions have been like from the rock/geological record. We see the evolution of life from fossils. We see earlier conditions in the types of rocks that are present. Some types of rocks, dating from billions of years ago, will not form in the presence of an oxygen-rich atmosphere. It is even suggested that the presence of life itself is due to an early atmosphere poor in oxygen. While very beneficial for life now, oxygen likes to bind with other elements. If it had been present in higher quantities early in Earth's history, it may have prevented the complex molecular chains from forming that went on to become self-replicating life.

Like the Earth, the Sun continues to evolve and is not static, as seen in Table 1.5.2. Its surface is controlled by convection (hot gas rising from below, releasing energy that we see as light), much in the same way the weather on Earth is controlled by convection cells. The Sun also has storms, which are called solar flares; these storms can last one or two orders of magnitude longer than on Earth because of the larger distance scales involved. The Sun, like the Earth, rotates, with a period of about 27 days (or about 2 Msec), and its magnetic field flips polarity every 11 years. Material from the core can move to the surface, but this can take hundreds of thousands of years. Finally, the Sun cannot last forever since it is constantly emitting power. It is, in fact, presently halfway through its power cycle. When its power source is depleted, the Sun will become a red giant[4] with its outer atmosphere occupying much of the region presently occupied by the inner planets. At this point, the Earth will also come to an end, so our fate is completely tied to that of the Sun.

_____

4   http://en.wikipedia.org/wiki/Red_giant

Assignment 1.2. Calculate the timescale of light to travel from the Sun to the Earth. Calculate the time for a radio signal to travel from the Earth to Mars when they are in closest approach, and then recalculate the time when the Earth and Mars are on the opposite sides of the Sun. Now calculate the time if the signal is traveling at the maximum speed of the Space Shuttle of 8 km/s. What would the time be if the signal were traveling at the speed of a car, 60 miles/hour?

1.6. Electromagnetic Spectrum and Blackbody Radiation

At this point, one should pause and ask the question, how do we actually know the composition of the planets and the Sun when no one has actually been there? Indeed, the composition and temperature of the atmosphere of the planets and stars have been known since long before the advent of space travel. How is this information obtained? It comes from the electromagnetic (EM) waves (including visible light) emitted from the object. These techniques, called remote sensing, were developed with the advent of the telescope in the late 1600s and continues today. Even the most modern spacecraft uses the same methods, and they are one of the main diagnostic tools for the rovers that are presently on Mars.

There are many types of waves in nature. A spring oscillating up and down and the ripples on a pond generated by a thrown stone are two common examples. Another example is sound waves[5], which are pressure oscillations in the transporting medium, typically air, in human experience. In all these cases, it's a mechanical way in which the speed of the wave is determined by the properties of the medium.

The electromagnetic spectrum[6] consists of oscillating electric and magnetic fields that make up the wave. These waves can propagate in the vacuum at the cosmic speed limit of $c = 3 \times 10^8$ m/s. Mechanical waves can be generated in space, but they are highly tenuous, given the nature of space and travel at the inherent speed of the material. In air, the speed of sound[7] is much slower at 343 m/s. It is for this reason that you will see the lightning strike several seconds before you typically hear the associated thunder (if there is no delay, then you are too close).

The electromagnetic spectrum is divided up according to the properties of the waves:

- Speed (*v*): how much distance late moves the unit time
  (for an EM wave $v = c = 3 \times 10^8$ m/s)
- Frequency (*f*): number of oscillations that pass a location in a given time
  (units: Hertz [Hz] or per second or s^{-1})
- Wavelength (λ): distance between two consecutive peaks
  (units: km, m, mm, μm, nm, etc.)
- Amplitude (A): intensity or height of the oscillations
  (Units: volts/meter; many times or relative intensity is given).

An example of the difference between two waves with differing wavelengths is shown in Figure 1.6.1. A key feature of all waves is that speed, frequency, and wavelength are related by the equation:

$$f = \frac{v}{\lambda}$$

This equation means, for example, that longer wavelength waves have a lower frequency.

The energy to generate an individual EM wave increases with frequency in much the same way it takes more energy for a person to make a skipping rope go to a higher frequency or rotation at the same amplitude. The

---

5   http://en.wikipedia.org/wiki/Sound_wave

6   http://en.wikipedia.org/wiki/Electromagnetic_spectrum

7   http://en.wikipedia.org/wiki/Speed_of_sound

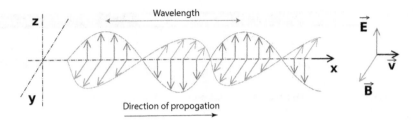

FIGURE 1.6.1. SCHEMATIC OF AN EM WAVE SHOWING THE DIFFERENCE BETWEEN (A) A LONG WAVELENGTH WAVE; AND (B) A SHORT WAVELENGTH WAVE.

relationship between then energy of a single packet of light, or photon[8], of electromagnetic energy is given by

$$E = h \times f \quad \text{(where h is Planck's constant} = 6.6 \times 10^{-34} \text{ J.s).}$$

The key components of the electromagnetic spectrum are shown in Figure 1.6.2 and include

- radio waves[9], which have the longest wavelengths because our atmosphere is transparent to these waves, and because they have the lowest energies, these waves are most commonly used for communications;
- microwaves[10], which are also useful in communications, particularly with the advent of fiber-optic lines. It overcomes absorption effects in the atmosphere of the high end of the microwave spectrum; wavelength is such that it can produce strong heating of organic material as well;
- infrared[11] is associated with heat; our bodies generate heat and can be seen in the infrared—if a body becomes hot, it will start to become visible in the red; hence the term "infra," which means "just below";

- visible[12], which is the dominant part of the electromagnetic emissions from the Sun;
- ultraviolet[13] (UV), which means "above violet" and has sufficiently short scale length and sufficiently high energy that it can directly interact with molecules and can produce harmful effects to life; fortunately, nearly all of the most harmful part of the spectrum is blocked by the ozone layer;
- X-rays[14] are emitted from the Sun during periods of strong solar activity (along with UV and gamma rays); they are also naturally produced on Earth, for example, during lightning storms; because of their short wavelength, they are able to penetrate soft material and hence their extensive use in medical diagnostics; their energy is sufficiently high that excessive exposure can lead to increased cancer rates and eventually death;
- gamma rays[15] are produced through solar activity as well as by the radioactive decay of elements, including uranium and plutonium; they are also seen during galactic events such as supernovas[16] and through cosmic showers produced by galactic cosmic rays[17].

---

8   http://en.wikipedia.org/wiki/Photon
9   http://en.wikipedia.org/wiki/Radio_waves
10   http://en.wikipedia.org/wiki/Microwave
11   http://en.wikipedia.org/wiki/Infrared

12   http://en.wikipedia.org/wiki/Visible_light
13   http://en.wikipedia.org/wiki/Ultraviolet
14   http://en.wikipedia.org/wiki/X-ray
15   http://en.wikipedia.org/wiki/Gamma_ray
16   http://en.wikipedia.org/wiki/Supernova
17   http://en.wikipedia.org/wiki/Galactic_cosmic_ray

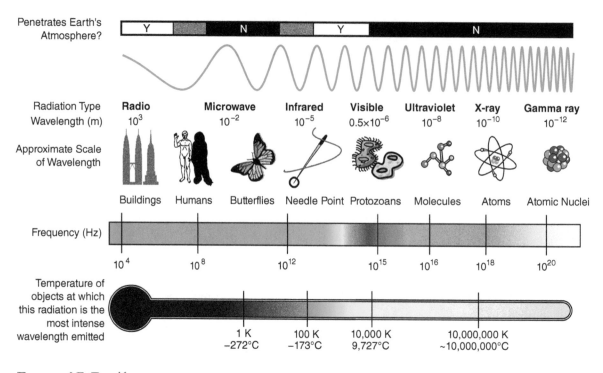

FIGURE 1.6.2. KEY PROPERTIES OF THE ELECTROMAGNETIC SPECTRUM.

All bodies emit electromagnetic radiation. The exact form of this radiation is entirely dependent on the temperature of the body and is called blackbody radiation[18]. Some example curves are shown in Figure 1.6.3. Colder bodies emit predominantly in the infrared (which follows from the statement that the infrared is relatively low energy and is associated with heat). As a body's temperature increases, it is capable of emitting light—hence, red-hot is actually colder than white-hot. The Sun has its dominant emissions in the visible, which means that its surface temperature is about 6000K.

This dependence of the characteristics of the blackbody radiation was discovered by Wilhelm Wien[19] in 1893, and this work eventually won him the Nobel Prize. He showed that the wavelength at which the blackbody radiation peaks is inversely proportional to the temperature of the body:

$$\lambda_{max} \propto \frac{1}{T_K}$$

Note that the units for temperature in this equation are in Kelvin[20], which has absolute zero (i.e., zero thermal motion) as the null for the temperature scale, as opposed to Celsius[21], where zero is the freezing point of water.

With this established relationship, astronomers have been able to look at different stars to see how they compare with our star. An example is shown in Figure 1.6.4, the varying colors of the stars, from red, to yellow, to blue, is a function of their different blackbody temperature. The blue stars will have a blackbody temperature around 20,000K and will be approximately ten times more massive than the Sun. An example of such a star is Spica[22], which has a blackbody temperature of

18   http://www.astro.washington.edu/courses/labs/clearinghouse/labs/Spectclass/spectralclassweb.html
19   http://en.wikipedia.org/wiki/Wien's_displacement_law

20   http://en.wikiphttp/en.wikipedia.org/wiki/Kelvinedia.org/wiki/Kelvin
21   http://en.wikipedia.org/wiki/Celsius
22   http://en.wikipedia.org/wiki/Spica

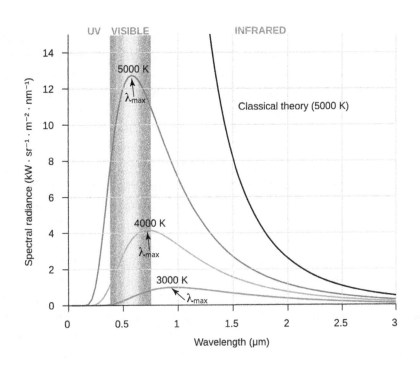

FIGURE 1.6.3. BLACKBODY SPECTRUM.

23,000K. The red stars have a blackbody temperature around 3,000K. An example of such a star is Antares[23], which is a red supergiant into which the Sun will eventually evolve.

A fun point to think about is that our Earth is perfectly designed for the Sun in that the peak emission from the Sun is able to propagate through the terrestrial atmosphere. The bulk of the electronic radiation propagates through our atmosphere to heat the ground, which then sets up the convection cells that control our weather. If we had Spica as our star, most of its energy would be absorbed by the atmosphere, and the planetary

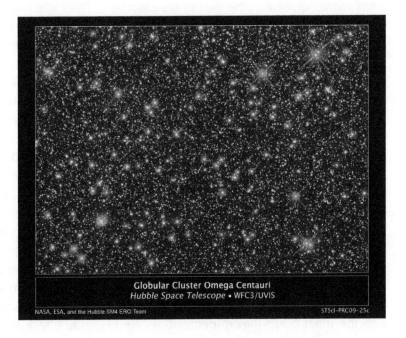

FIGURE 1.6.4. A HUBBLE SPACE TELESCOPE IMAGE OF A STAR CLUSTER IN THE MILKY WAY. THE IMAGE SHOWS APPROXIMATELY 100,000 STARS. CREDIT: NASA, ESA, AND THE HUBBLE SM4 ERO TEAM.

---

23 http://en.wikipedia.org/wiki/Antares

surface would be dark at least in the visible part of the spectrum. On the other hand, if the Sun were a red giant—well, the Earth wouldn't be around at all.n addition to the shape of the spectrum changing, the intensity (or the total energy radiated per unit area per unit time) of the radiation also increases with temperature. The relationship between power and temperature is known as the Stefan-Boltzmann law[24],

$$j = \sigma T^4$$

where j = total power, T is temperature in Kelvin, and σ is a proportionality constant; the exact number is not needed here, but for those who like details, the value of σ is

$$5.64 \times 10^{-8} \ W \ m^{-2} \ K^{-4}.$$

This means that not only does Spica emit in the UV, but it produces $(23/6)^4$, or nearly 216 times more power than the Sun (if we assume the two are the same size). So, any planet at 1 AU around such a star would be mighty toasty.

1.7. Visible Light as a Remote Diagnostic Tool

Visible light spans a range of wavelengths, which our eyes interpret as different colors. We know that different colors are present by looking at different objects. The full spectrum of colors is seen naturally in the form of rainbows, with the main colors being identified as Red, Orange, Yellow, Green, Blue, Indigo, and Violet (an acronym to help remember it is Roy G Biv) as seen in Figure 1.7.1.[25]

The spectrum from any particular object can be seen using a glass prism as seen in Figure 1.7.2. The prism, similar to a rainbow, uses a process called refraction to separate the individual parts of the spectrum. Refraction[26] is based on the fact that the speed of light changes as it moves through different mediums, with the shortest wavelengths (i.e., violet) more strongly interacting with the constituent atoms than the longer wavelengths and moving more slowly. So, when light strikes a glass prism at an angle, the shorter wavelength colors (blues) are turning at a larger angle than the longer wavelength colors (red).

The image in Figure 1.7.2 is from a small prism. Back in the day when the discipline of optics was beginning to be developed and understood, high-precision prisms were developed. In 1814, Joseph von Fraunhofer[27] noted that the solar spectrum was not pristine and had hundreds of dark bands as seen in Figure 1.7.3. This discovery was not initially accepted; the Sun, at this time, was assumed to be perfect; thus, the observed imperfections must come from imperfections in Fraunhofer's prisms and not in the solar spectrum. This was a major setback because he was trying to become a world leader in the manufacture of optics. As happens with many scientific discoveries, Fraunhofer was required to repeat the experiment to verify the results were real and not an artifact of his construction. He rebuilt his prism and still found the same results. If the dark bands were caused by imperfections in the instrumentation, the bands' locations in the spectrum would move when viewing each of the different objects such as the Moon and each of the planets, which reflect the Sun's light. However, since it was a real effect, the black bands did not move. So, after much hard work, Fraunhofer eventually proved that the black bands were, in fact, real.

The original of the Fraunhofer fringes remained a mystery for nearly 45 years, until

---

24　http://en.wikipedia.org/wiki/
Stefan%E2%80%93Boltzmann_law
25　http://www.fas.org/irp/imint/docs/rst/Sect20/
A7.html

26　http://www.britannica.com/EBchecked/
media/3124/Refraction-of-light-by-a-prism-having-
index-n2-immersed
27　http://en.wikipedia.org/wiki/Fraunhofer_lines

	Red	Orange	Yellow	Green	Blue	Indigo	Violet
Wavelength (nm)	750	590	570	520	475	445	400
Energy (eV)	1.6	2.1	2.2	2.4	2.6	2.8	3.1

FIGURE 1.7.1. THE VISIBLE SPECTRUM IN TERMS OF COMMON NAMES AS WELL AS ACTUAL WAVELENGTHS AND FREQUENCIES.

Robert Bunsen[28] (the inventor of the Bunsen burner) teamed with Gustav Kirchhoff[29] to develop the first spectrometer. They showed that individual elements produce light emission at discrete wavelengths. Examples of line emissions from different elements are shown in Figure 1.7.4. Basically, each line represents a possible electron orbit around the nucleus. The lightest elements have just a few line emissions, while the noble gases with their full electron shells have much more complicated spectral emissions. The device that is able to identify these different light emissions is known as a spectrometer. In the present day, a much more sophisticated spectrometer is on board the *Curiosity*[30] rover and is being used to analyze minerals within Gale Crater on Mars.

The story goes that Bunsen and Kirchhoff used their newly developed spectrometer to analyze the composition of material being emitted during a large fire near Heidelberg. After that success, they decided that if they could analyze these fires, then they could analyze the fire of the Sun. They did, and they showed that many of the dark bands discovered by Fraunhofer matched exactly the line emissions associated with the various elements, including hydrogen and helium. This is how we know the composition of the atmospheres of the Sun and other planets of the solar system, as well as other stars within the galaxy.

Assignment Question 1.3. Walk through a shopping mall and take a picture of three

FIGURE 1.7.2. SEPARATION OF WHITE LIGHT INTO ITS INDIVIDUAL COLOR COMPONENTS THROUGH THE USE OF A GLASS PRISM.

28   http://en.wikipedia.org/wiki/Robert_Bunsen
29   http://en.wikipedia.org/wiki/Gustav_Kirchhoff
30   http://en.wikipedia.org/wiki/Curiosity_rover

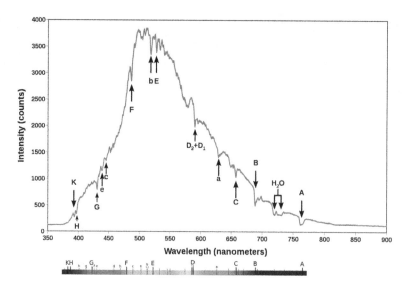

FIGURE 1.7.3. THE FRAUNHOFER FRINGES SHOWING THE PRESENCE OF DARK BANDS IN THE SOLAR SPECTRUM.

different lighting signs. Using the emission spectrum in Figure 1.7.4 or other online spectra, determine the elements most likely being used to create the lights.

1.8. Emission versus Absorption

An astute student might say, "Wait a minute, not so fast. Bunsen is seeing bright line emissions from the elements, whereas Fraunhofer is seeing dark bands; how do the two relate to each other?" The answer is not actually that difficult. Light is emitted from objects that are hot. Objects that are cold tend to absorb radiation, and atoms like to absorb the radiation at the same wavelengths or frequencies at which they can emit. Thus, whether an object emits or absorbs radiation is dependent on the relative temperature of the object. The situation for the Sun is shown in Figure 1.8.1. There is a hot source below the surface of the Sun that is emitting blackbody radiation in the form of a continuous spectrum, which is determined by the temperature of the source.

If there was nothing between the source and us on the Earth, then it would be detected unaltered as a continuous spectrum with no structure. However, if it passes through a colder atmosphere, then the atmosphere will absorb some of the emissions at the lines inherent to the elements that make up that atmosphere. This absorption manifests itself as the dark lines within the Fraunhofer spectrum. If the atmosphere were hotter than the surface, the reverse would be true, and we would see discrete line emissions. The Fraunhofer fringes not only tell us the composition of the Sun, but they also tell us that the Sun has a structure in which there is an atmosphere that is cooler than the surface of the Sun. This type of spectral information is one of the key diagnostic tools used to remotely determine the composition of essentially all objects in the solar system.

One thing that is important to note here is that the dark bands discovered by Fraunhofer are not completely black. There is still light

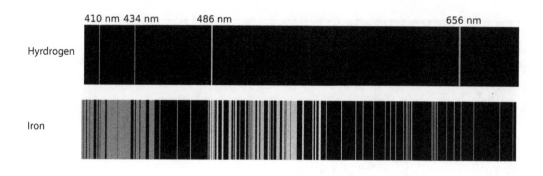

410 nm 434 nm   486 nm   656 nm

Hyrdrogen

Iron

FIGURE 1.7.4. LINE EMISSIONS FROM TWO COMMON ELEMENTS. EACH ELEMENT HAS A VERY DISTINCT SET OF OPTICAL EMISSIONS THAT CAN LEAD TO ITS UNIQUE IDENTIFICATION.

arriving at the Earth in those wavelengths; it is just much reduced in intensity as compared to the rest of the wavelengths. The cooler atmosphere absorbs light originally directed at the Earth. After a short time period, that energy is reemitted—but in all directions—only some of which is directed at the Earth.

inner rocky planets have elemental compositions that are deficient in these light elements, since they have insufficient gravity to hold onto these light elements when they are in their gaseous forms.

So, this is the physical description of the solar system. In the next chapter, we investigate how we power up the entire solar system.

1.9. Composition of the Sun

Using the relative intensity of the different line emissions, one can then determine the elemental abundances within the Sun. These abundances are shown in Figure 1.9.1 and demonstrate that, like the outer planets, the dominant constituents of the Sun are hydrogen and helium. The presence of these two elements is directly related to the fusion cycle, which generates the power output from stars and is discussed in the next chapter. Some of the light elements are thought to be generated by the collapse of low-mass stars. The heavier elements between magnesium and nickel are thought to be derived from supernova events.

In the development of the solar system, the gas giants have the composition that most resembles the solar system abundances, with H and He dominating their composition. The

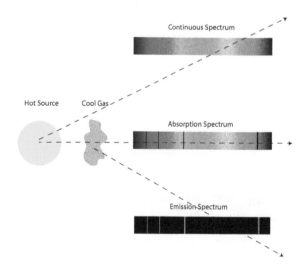

FIGURE 1.8.1. SCHEMATIC SHOWING THE DIFFERENCE BETWEEN SPECTRA SHOWING ABSORPTION FEATURES (BLACK LINES) THAT ARE ASSOCIATED WITH LIKE MOVING THROUGH COLD OBJECT AND EMISSION FEATURES (BRIGHT LINES) ASSOCIATED WITH RELATIVELY HOT OBJECTS.

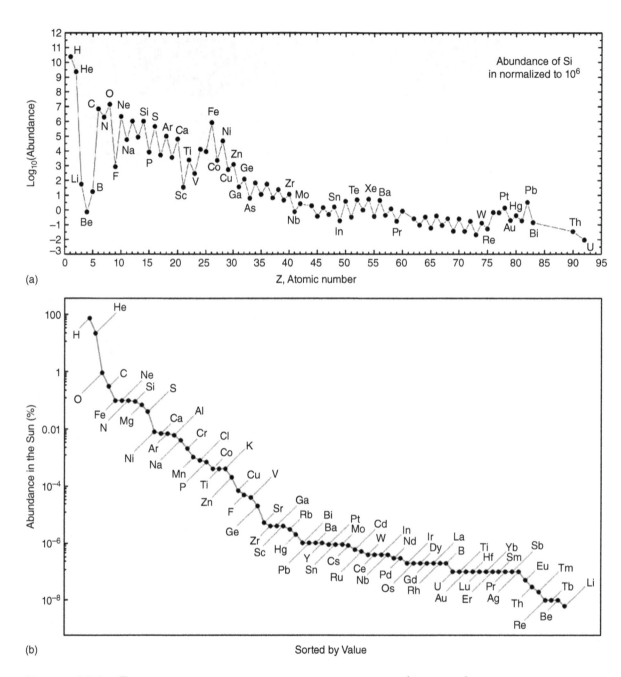

FIGURE 1.9.1. Elemental abundances sorted by atomic number (top panel) and by relative importance (lower panel).

References

[1] Mayor, M., & Queloz, D. (1995). "A Jupiter-mass companion to a solar-type star." *Nature*[31] 378 (6555): 355–359.

Bibcode[32]: 1995Natur.378.355M[33]

DOI[34]: 10.1038/378355a0[35]

[2] http://nssdc.gsfc.nasa.gov/nmc/spacecraft-Display.do?id=1966-027A

Image Credits

Chapter 1 Opening Image: NASA/ESA/Hubble Heritage Team, "A rose made of galaxies," http://www.spacetelescope.org/images/heic1107a/. Copyright in the Public Domain.

Figure 1.2.1: Copyright © ESO/Yuri Beletsky (CC by 4.0) at http://www.eso.org/public/images/eso0733a/.

Table 1.3.1: Copyright in the Public Domain.

Table 1.4.1: Data from: http://planetfacts.org/the-solar-system/ and http://www.aai.ee/planets/nineplanets/

Figure 1.4.1a: NASA, "Our Solar System," http://solarsystem.nasa.gov/planets/images/splash-planets.jpg. Copyright in the Public Domain.

Figure 1.4.1b and c: NASA, "Oort cloud Sedna orbit," http://commons.wikimedia.org/wiki/File:Oort_cloud_Sedna_orbit.jpg. Copyright in the Public Domain.

Figure 1.4.2a: Copyright © by Google Maps.

Figure 1.4.2b: Copyright © Andrew Hitchcock (CC by 2.0) at https://commons.wikimedia.org/wiki/File:Seahawk_Stadium.jpg.

Figure 1.4.2c: flomar, "Football (soccer ball)," http://commons.wikimedia.org/wiki/File:Football_(soccer_ball).svg. Copyright in the Public Domain.

Figure 1.4.2d: Copyright © Falstaff (CC by 3.0) at http://commons.wikimedia.org/wiki/File:Blender259BeachBall.png.

Figure 1.4.2e: Reisio, "Basketball," https://commons.wikimedia.org/wiki/File:Basketball.png. Copyright in the Public Domain.

Figure 1.4.3a: Copyright © by Google Maps.

Figure 1.4.3b: Copyright © Andrew Hitchcock (CC by 2.0) at https://commons.wikimedia.org/wiki/File:Seahawk_Stadium.jpg.

Figure 1.4.3c: Copyright © Kropsoq (CC by 3.0) at http://commons.wikimedia.org/wiki/File:2006_Ojiya_balloon_festival_011.jpg.

Figure 1.4.3d: Copyright © TomTheHand (CC by 2.0) at https://commons.wikimedia.org/wiki/File:Baseball_%28crop%29.jpg.

Figure 1.4.3e: Copyright in the Public Domain.

Figure 1.4.5: Copyright © Hans Bernhard (CC BY-SA 3.0) at https://commons.wikimedia.org/wiki/File:Sun_with_sunspots.JPG

Figure 1.6.1: Adapted from: Copyright © SuperManu (CC BY-SA 3.0) at http://en.wikipedia.org/wiki/File:Onde_electro-magnetique.svg

Figure 1.6.2: Copyright © Iductiveload (CC BY-SA 3.0) at http://en.wikipedia.org/wiki/File:EM_Spectrum_Properties_edit.svg

Figure 1.6.3: Adapted from: Darth Kule, "Black body," http://en.wikipedia.org/wiki/File:Black_body.svg. Copyright in the Public Domain.

Figure 1.6.4: NASA, ESA and the Hubble SM4 ERO Team, "Omega Cntauri globular cluster stars," http://hubblesite.org/gallery/album/star/star_cluster/pr2009025q/. Copyright in the Public Domain.

Figure 1.7.1: Adapted from: Copyright © Meganbeckett27 (CC BY-SA 3.0) at http://commons.wikimedia.org/wiki/File:Colours_of_the_visible_light_spectrum.png

Figure 1.7.2: Copyright © D-Kuru (CC BY-SA 3.0) at http://en.wikipedia.org/wiki/File:Light_dispersion_of_a_mercury-vapor_lamp_with_a_flint_glass_prism_IPNr%C2%B00125.jpg

Figure 1.7.3a: Adapted from: Cepheiden, "Fraunhofer lines," http://en.wikipedia.org/wiki/File:Fraunhofer_lines.svg. Copyright in the Public Domain.

Figure 1.7.3b: Adapted from: Copyright © Eric Bajart (CC BY-SA 3.0) at http://en.wikipedia.org/wiki/File:Spectrum_of_blue_sky.svg

Figure 1.7.4a: Adapted from: Merikanto, Adrignola, "Emission spectrum-H labeled," http://commons.wikimedia.org/wiki/File:Emission_spectrum-H_labeled.svg. Copyright in the Public Domain.

Figure 1.7.4b: Adapted from: nilda, "Emission spectrum-Fe," http://en.wikipedia.org/wiki/File:Emission_spectrum-Fe.svg. Copyright in the Public Domain.

Figure 1.8.1a: Adapted from: Sassospicco, "Spectral lines continuous," http://en.wikipedia.org/wiki/File:Spectral_lines_continous.png. Copyright in the Public Domain.

Figure 1.8.1b: Adapted from: Sassospicco, "Spectral lines absorption," http://en.wikipedia.org/wiki/File:Spectral_lines_absorption.png. Copyright in the Public Domain.

Figure 1.8.1c: Adapted from: Sassospicco, "Spectral lines emission," http://en.wikipedia.org/wiki/File:Spectral_lines_emission.png. Copyright in the Public Domain.

Figure 1.9.1a: Copyright © 28bytes (CC BY-SA 3.0) at http://en.wikipedia.org/wiki/File:SolarSystemAbundances.png

Figure 1.9.1b: Adapted from: "Abundance in the Sun of the elements," http://periodictable.com/Properties/A/SolarAbundance.html. Copyright in the Public Domain.

31 http://en.wikipedia.org/wiki/Nature_%28journal%29

32 http://en.wikipedia.org/wiki/Bibcode

33 http://adsabs.harvard.edu/abs/1995Natur.378..355M

34 http://en.wikipedia.org/wiki/Digital_object_identifier

35 http://dx.doi.org/10.1038%2F378355a0

Chapter 2

Energy, Power, and the Atom

So, now we have some idea of the distance and timescales involved in the composition of the sources. The next important question is that of energy and power. Energy controls everything in the solar system. It is the most important issue in terms of the properties of the solar system and the space beyond, and how we can potentially move through space. Power is the rate at which energy is expended. The two terms are often used similarly and yet are significantly different. For example, most people have sufficient energy to climb the steepest hill, but if one has insufficient fitness so that we cannot burn the energy sufficiently fast, then one can't actually get up the hill. The same is true for missions to the planets. The reality is that there is plenty of energy presently available to make planetary missions—even interstellar missions—possible. The real difficulty is obtaining systems that can deliver sufficient power to overcome the gravity of the planet in order to reach escape velocity and have a sufficiently short mission time and cost to be worth undertaking.

As noted in Chapter 1, the distance scales are literally astronomical. As a consequence, the power and energy requirements are equally astronomical, if you'll forgive the pun. In the industrial age, we face an almost parallel issue about how we obtain the necessary power to produce a sustainable future. Insight into how we might solve these future problems can be obtained by spending a little time looking backward. Thus, in this chapter we describe not only the science of power, but also some of the history that went into figuring out the sources of power, in the hope that we might be able to better predict our future possibilities.

2.1. Powering the Sun

There are several forms of energy:

- Kinetic energy[1] (energy of motion)
- Thermal energy[2] (energy in the form of heat)
- Electromagnetic energy[3] (radiation)
- Gravitational energy[4] (gravity)
- Nuclear energy[5] (fission and fusion)

From a modern perspective, the answer to what is required to power the Sun is obvious. For the different ages, this problem did not appear to have a solution. For example, if you lived in a pre-nuclear age, a common belief would have been that the Sun was literally a ball of fire. However, it was recognized early enough that if the Sun was composed entirely of coal, and if it had a sufficient supply of oxygen to burn all the coal, then the Sun would generate light for only 4000 years. Way too short a time!

In 1842, Robert Mayer proposed that the Sun could gain its energy by swallowing meteorites, using the fact that kinetic energy can be converted into thermal energy. The assumption of meteorites would have matched the cratering seen on the Moon, for example. However, calculations showed that the increase in the mass of the Sun produced by this process would increase the orbital period of the Earth by two seconds per year. This change in period, while small, would have been easily detectable even in the 1800s and it is not observed, so this theory also went by the wayside.

Since the Sun is evolving, it was suggested by Sir William Thomson, and later by Lord Kelvin, that maybe the Sun had swallowed a planet in the past and that we in the present would therefore not notice any change in our planetary period. However, Thomson's own calculations showed that if the Sun captured Mercury, it would deliver seven years of power; Venus, 84 years of power; and consuming all the planets (with the largest contributions form Jupiter and Saturn) equally, only 46,000 years of power.

The short duration in power from outside sources suggested that the power source has to be internal. So instead, in the mid-1850s, it was proposed that the power could come from the gravitational collapse of the Sun. An infall of only 150 ft. per year would suffice to generate sufficient power, and the change in the scale of the Sun would not be noticed for thousands of years [1]. This infall could support power for 22 million years. As a result, this could achieve a much longer period, but still be very much shorter than the lifetime of the Sun.

A good question at this point is: How do we know the power output of the Sun? First, power is the rate at which work is done, or simply

Power = Energy / Time

Units

Power is in Watts (W = J/s)

Energy is on Joules (J)

Time in seconds (s)

Since power is often the dominant consideration for engineers, another unit for energy use is in terms of a kilowatt hour (kW hrs = power × times). The typical household bill, for example, is in this type of unit.

The power of the Sun can be determined on Earth by measuring how much energy is delivered into a known area over a given time. This gives the local power deposited, and then by

---

1   http://en.wikipedia.org/wiki/Kinetic_energy
2   http://en.wikipedia.org/wiki/Thermal_energy
3   http://en.wikipedia.org/wiki/Electromagnetic_energy
4   http://en.wikipedia.org/wiki/Gravitational_energy
5   http://en.wikipedia.org/wiki/Nuclear_Energy

calculating the total area for a full sphere, one can obtain the global, or total, power generated by the Sun.

This is actually a simple calculation and has been known since the late 1700s. All you have to do is take a one-inch ice cube, place it in the Sun such that it is insulated from the ground, and measure how long it takes to melt. The energy required for this feat can be measured by calorimeters[6]. It turns out that it takes about two hours and 12 minutes for the Sun to perform this task. This might seem pretty lame because if you hold it in your palm, you can melt the same ice block in about ten minutes. The difference, though, is that the Sun can melt this same ice block at each one-inch square over the entire sphere that enclosed Earth's orbit (approximately 4×10^{26} ice cubes). If one were to collapse this inch-thick spherical shell onto the surface of the Sun, it would be a km thick. Melting this entire ice cube in two hours, then, is a real feat.

The actual numbers are that the Sun provides 1.36 kW/m^2 (which is known as the solar constant[7]) at 1 AU. This means that the Sun is emitting 4×10^{26} watts of power. Again, let us try and put this big number into perspective. A typical electrical power station[8] generates about 1000 MW (or 10^9W). A typical household might use 1000 W (i.e., just ten old-style electric light bulbs), so a typical power plant would support about one million people. If each inhabitant of the Earth were given ten million of these power plants each, then we could match the power of the Sun. Now that would be a lot of power.

Assignment Question 2.1: *The Ice Melter.*
Part 1: Try performing the above experiment yourself by placing an ice cube on a Styrofoam plate so that it is insulated from any contact surfaces. If it is too cold outside, place the ice cube under a 100 W lightbulb and measure the time for the cube to melt.

Part 2: Take some cold water and heat it in a stove or microwave. Try to estimate how much power was used to heat the water, and then place the ice cube in the water to see how long it takes to melt. Estimate the time to melt/per watt used. Is this more or less efficient than the Sun?

Part 3: Place an ice cube on a cement floor of a heated building. Does the ice cube melt faster on the floor or under the lamp/in the Sun?

Discussion Assignment 2.1—The Solar Constant: Why might the value we measure for the solar constant at the surface of the Earth actually vary with time?

2.2. Early Ideas of the Atom

If you wish to go nuclear, then one first needs to understand something about the structure of the atom. The first ideas of the atom date back to nearly 400 BC to Leucippus[9], a Greek philosopher who proposed that all matter is made up of "tiny indivisible bodies—*atoms*." The word atom comes from the Greek word *atomos*, meaning not divisible. Democritus[10], considered the father of modern science, went further to say that atoms were not all alike, but had different shapes and sizes in order to make up different types of matter. While this may seem obvious to us, these ideas were actually opposed by other famous Greek philosophers, including Aristotle[11]. He proposed that there were five elements: Earth (solid), Water (liquid), Air (gas), Fire (heat), and Aether (making up the heavenly bodies). The heavenly bodies were assumed to be perfect objects moving in perfect circles around the Earth. The idea that

---

6   http://en.wikipedia.org/wiki/Calorimeter
7   http://en.wikipedia.org/wiki/Solar_constant
8   http://en.wikipedia.org/wiki/Power_station
9   http://en.wikipedia.org/wiki/Leucippus
10   http://en.wikipedia.org/wiki/Democritus
11   http://en.wikipedia.org/wiki/Aristotle

there were five elements dominated science for many centuries, lasting all the way up to the Middle Ages. Aristotle's idea of perfect heavenly bodies was eventually called into question by Nicolaus Copernicus, and later in detailed calculations by Johannes Kepler. In the early 1600s, Galileo Galilei[12] made the first observations to support the idea that the Earth revolved around the Sun, by discovering the moons of Jupiter. This idea brought nothing but trouble for Galileo, but it was eventually accepted. The point is that sometimes acceptance of new ideas can be a very slow process, something that is often forgotten in today's highly connected electronic society.

Development of our present understanding of the atom did not occur until the late 1800s and the beginning of the 20th century. A key step in these developments occurred in 1897, when J. J. Thomson[13] discovered the "corpuscles" (eventually relabeled as electrons, as suggested earlier by George Johnstone Stoney[14] in 1894). Thomson was able to show that electrons had to have about 1/1000th the mass of hydrogen and that their properties were independent of the material from which they were emitted.

At this time, the lead model for the atom was called corpuscularianism[15], where all matter is composed of minute particles that possess an inner and outer layer of minute particles, or corpuscles. This model differs from the model of the atom in that corpuscular matter can be subdivided, while atoms are indivisible. Thomson proposed a "plum pudding" model of the atom, where the atom is charge neutral with the corpuscles/electrons mixed into a sea of more massive positive charges. The "plum pudding" fits into our human perception that matter is completely solid—i.e., no empty space. After all, everyone knows that you can't pass through a solid.

This idea of a solid atom was to be discarded very shortly after, due to the work of Ernest Rutherford[16] and his studies on radioactive material. In the early 1900s, it was known that radioactive materials are associated with the emission of alpha particles[17] (later to be identified as helium nuclei) and beta particles[18] (later identified as electrons). So, if you have a source of energetic particles, why not point it at something and see what happens? Rutherford performed the experiment by shooting alpha particles at some gold foil. The expected behavior was a small angle scattering of all the alpha particles as they interacted with solid material. To his surprise, Rutherford found that almost all the alpha particles penetrated the foil with little or no scattering, except for the occasional alpha particle that was completely backscattered. The only interpretation for his results was that matter was, in fact, mostly empty space and that there had to be a small positive nucleus causing the occasional backscattering of the alpha particles.

2.3. Modern Version of the Atom

There was a problem with the Rutherford model, though, in that it predicted an atom would emit a continuous spectrum of electromagnetic waves, whereas we saw in Chapter 1 that Bunsen and Kirchhoff discovered that atoms only produce discrete line emissions. To overcome this problem, Niels Bohr[19] proposed the Bohr model of the atom[20] in 1913. This model is the basis of the modern version of the atom, shown schematically in Figure 2.3.1. In

12   http://en.wikipedia.org/wiki/Galileo_Galilei
13   http://en.wikipedia.org/wiki/J._J._Thomson
14   http://en.wikipedia.org/wiki/George_Johnstone_Stoney
15   http://en.wikipedia.org/wiki/Corpuscularianism

16   http://en.wikipedia.org/wiki/Ernest_Rutherford
17   http://en.wikipedia.org/wiki/Alpha_particles
18   http://en.wikipedia.org/wiki/Beta_particles
19   http://en.wikipedia.org/wiki/Niels_Bohr
20   http://en.wikipedia.org/wiki/Bohr_model

this model, the electrons are only allowed to a *limited* set of motions. Specifically:

- Electrons associated with an atom orbit the nucleus in a discrete number of orbits (shown shaded with discrete energy levels);
- No electromagnetic emissions occur when the electron is in one of these orbits;
- Electrons can only gain and lose energy by jumping from one allowed orbit to another;
- If an electron goes from a low-energy state (e.g., E1) to a high-energy state (e.g., E2), it has to absorb a photon with as much energy as that obtained from a collision with an energetic particle;
- When an electron in a high-energy state (e.g., E2) decays to a lower-energy state (e.g., E1), the frequency of the photon is given by

$$\upsilon = \frac{E2 - E1}{h}$$

where h is the proportionality constant known as Planck's constant.

Therefore, the very light emission of an atom, as seen by Bunsen's spectrometer, is directly related to the energy levels within an atom. Thus, the light emissions not only tell us about the elemental composition of the atmospheres of distant planets and stars, but they tell us information about the very structure of the atom.

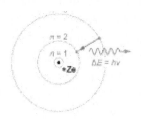

FIGURE 2.3.1. SCHEMATIC SHOWING THE BOHR MODEL WITH THE ATOM AND THE PROCESSES THAT LEAD TO THE EMISSION OF ELECTROMAGNETIC RADIATION FROM AN ATOM. (ANIMATION: HTTPS://COMMONS. WIKIMEDIA.ORG/WIKI/FILE:BOHR_ATOM_ANIMATION. GIF)

Some processes occurring on the very largest distance scales are closely linked to some of the very smallest scale processes that one can imagine.

2.4. Structure of the Nucleus

The final missing piece (at least at the subatomic level) to our understanding of the atom is the structure of the nucleus. The structure became clear with the discovery of:

- The proton[21] in 1918 by Rutherford, with a mass about 2000 times that of the electron and with the opposite charge. This discovery utilized the use of a radioactive material that was a known source of alpha particles by shooting it at nitrogen. What was observed coming out was oxygen and a proton, i.e.,

  Alpha particle (He nucleus) + Nitrogen → Oxygen + proton

  The experiment was one the first human-produced nuclear reactions.

- The neutron[22] in 1932 by James Chadwick. The neutron is an uncharged particle with a mass slightly larger than that of the proton. This discovery utilized a head-on collision between a proton and electron to produce a neutron plus an additional particle, called the neutrino[23], or the "little neutral one" in Italian. The reaction can be written as

  Proton + electron → neutron + neutrino

21 http://physics.about.com/od/glossary/g/proton. htm

22 http://physics.about.com/od/glossary/g/neutron. htm

23 http://en.wikipedia.org/wiki/Neutrino

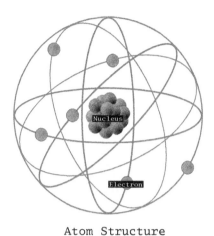

Atom Structure   Detail of Nucleus

FIGURE 2.4.1. STRUCTURE OF THE ATOM INCLUDING THE NUCLEUS, WHICH INCLUDES BOTH PROTONS AND NEUTRONS.

In addition to conserving charge, all nuclear reactions must conserve momentum. Additional experiments showed that a free neutron (one not bound in a nucleus) will decay into a proton and an electron. The problem is that the electron and proton can travel off in a similar direction once the neutron decays. On its own, this would violate the conservation of momentum if something else didn't travel off in the opposite direction. That other particle was eventually found to be the neutrino. Actual discovery of the neutrino itself, however, did not occur until 1956, when it was detected by Cowan and Reines (for which they won the Nobel Prize in physics).

The neutrino has special properties in that it has very weak interactions with matter. As discussed in the next chapter, interaction is so weak that you have a better chance of winning the mega-ball lottery than a neutrino has of being stopped as it passes through the entire Earth.

Both neutrons and protons reside in the nucleus (cf. Figure 2.4.1). The number of protons sets the numbers of electrons that the atom can support and it is these electrons that determine the chemical behavior of the element. One can generate the periodic table of the elements[24] by starting with hydrogen and adding protons—each proton added is a new element on the table.

2.5. Isotopes

While neutrons do not affect the chemical behavior of an element, they do affect the nuclear reactivity. As a result, atoms with the same number of protons at different numbers of neutrons are given a special name called isotopes[25]. Different isotopes of an element have the same place in the periodic table and the same chemical properties.

An example showing the difference between isotopes and elements is shown in Figure 2.5.1. The most common form of hydrogen is a single proton in the nucleus of a single

24   http://en.wikipedia.org/wiki/Periodic_table
25   http://en.wikipedia.org/wiki/Isotope

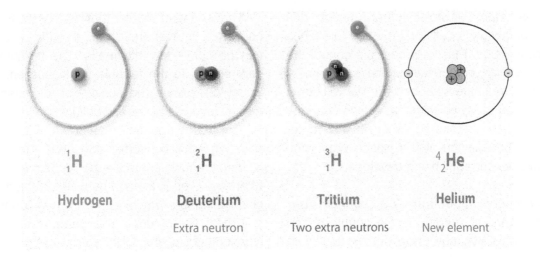

^1_1H ^2_1H ^3_1H ^4_2He

Hydrogen   Deuterium   Tritium   Helium

Extra neutron   Two extra neutrons   New element

FIGURE 2.5.1. THE ISOTOPES OF HYDROGEN AND HOW THEY DIFFER FROM HELIUM.

electron orbiting at a proton. The first isotope of hydrogen is called deuterium[26], where the extra neutron is present in the nucleus. There are no other changes to the structure of the atom. Deuterium is actually very rare on Earth and represents only about 0.015% of the hydrogen in the oceans. Tritium[27] is the second isotope of hydrogen and has one proton and two neutrons in its nucleus, still with the single electron orbiting the nucleus. Tritium is highly unstable, and thus radioactive, with a half-life of about 12 years. It exists naturally on Earth only in trace amounts.

Helium is not an isotope of hydrogen, as it has two protons in its core and two electrons orbiting the nucleus. As a result, it has very different chemical properties from hydrogen, despite the fact that its nucleus bears a closer resemblance to tritium than the tritium nucleus does to the hydrogen nucleus.

2.6. Plasmas

In everyday life, we typically only encounter three states of matter: solid, liquid, and gas. The three states have a common characteristic: the electrons are bound to the nucleus in the fixed orbits described above. While on a summer day we may consider conditions as "hot," for the electron, these are cold days with little action. If one starts to raise the temperature and/or pressure, other states of matter can be encountered. In particular, at a temperature of about 10,000 K, the outer electrons can be stripped from an atom to produce a mixture of neutral atoms, free electrons, and positively charged ions (i.e., atoms without their full complement of electrons). As one increases the temperature to above 100,000 K, all the atoms can become stripped of electrons, creating a sea of positively charged ions and negatively charged electrons. This sea of charged particles is called a plasma[28]. The threshold energy for creating a plasma is the energy needed to remove the electron from orbit around the nucleus; it is called the ionization energy.

Plasmas have different properties from the neutral gas because ions and electrons can be accelerated by electric and magnetic fields,

26   http://en.wikipedia.org/wiki/Deutrium
27   http://en.wikipedia.org/wiki/Tritium

28   http://en.wikipedia.org/wiki/Plasma_(physics)

whereas atoms or molecules of a neutral gas are completely unaffected by the presence of these fields. Plasma processes control the Sun's energy output and space environment that fills the entire solar system. We will come back to discussing plasmas when we talk about the processes occurring in the center of the Sun and the new in-space propulsion techniques currently being developed.

Assignment Question 2.2: *Build your own model of matter.* Get a couple dozen ping-pong balls. Lay them on the floor with a random amount of spacing. Throw a ping-pong ball from a distance, and measure the probability of hitting one of the balls on the floor. How does this probability change as the spacing between the balls decreases? Is the probability the same for hitting a ball on the edges as that of hitting a ball in the center? Explain your answer.

2.7. The Road to the Solar Nuclear Reactor

Going from the structure of the nucleus to figuring out how the energy of the Sun is produced is a difficult process. It took one person to put together several separate scientific discoveries and the audacity to overcome multitudes of skeptics. The individual discoveries that led to the modern model of the solar interior were made around the early 1900s. These include:

Albert Einstein[29] in 1905 develops his theory for the equivalence of mass and energy in the famous equation

$$E = mc^2$$

where m is mass (in kg) and c is the speed of light (in m/s).

This equation means that all mass can be converted into energy, and similarly, energy can be converted into mass. The formula is very similar to the formula for kinetic energy ($= mv^2/2$), except the conversion of mass to energy involves the speed of light.

The above equation means that if 1 gm of anything were converted into pure energy, it would be equivalent to 9×10^{13} J. This amount of energy is equivalent to burning 1000 tons of coal. Talk about watching your calorie count!

Ernest Rutherford[30] discovered during his development of the initial model of the atom that certain types of nuclear transformation reactions also generated gamma rays (which, as we noted above, are part of the electromagnetic spectrum).

Francis Aston[31], who won the 1922 Nobel Prize in chemistry for his discovery of isotopes in nonradioactive elements, showed that the mass of helium is slightly less than the mass for four protons.

Putting these clues together, Sir Arthur Eddington[32] proposed a model for stellar interiors in the 1920s in which the fusion of protons creates helium, and that the mass difference found by Aston produces the energy of the Sun. The process occurs as follows:

- Some process causes a gas cloud to begin to collapse and form the beginnings of the Sun.
- Gravitational forces at the center of the Sun result in an interior temperature of approximately 40 million degrees (later observations indicate 15 million degrees).
- This temperature is sufficient to create enough pressure to prevent the Sun from further collapsing.
- The high temperatures strip electrons off the atoms, producing a plasma sea of free protons and electrons.
- The free protons collide and fuse, thereby forming helium nuclei.

29   http://en.wikipedia.org/wiki/Albert_Einstein

30   http://en.wikipedia.org/wiki/Ernest_Rutherford
31   http://en.wikipedia.org/wiki/Francis_Aston
32   http://en.wikipedia.org/wiki/Arthur_Eddington

Table 2.9.1. Summary of subatomic particles relevant for fusion.

Name	Symbol	Charge (coulombs)	Mass (kg)	Divisible
Electron	e^-	-1.6×10^{-19}	9.1094×10^{-31}	No
Positron (antielectron)	e^+	1.6×10^{-19}	9.1094×10^{-31}	No
Proton	p	1.6×10^{-19}	1.6726×10^{-27} ($m_p = \sim 2000\, m_e$)	Yes 2 up quarks and 1 down quark
Neutron	n	0	1.6749×10^{-27} ($m_n \sim m_p$)	Yes 1 up quark and 2 down quarks
Neutrino		0	Unknown ($m > 0$)	No
Photon		0	0	No

- The reduction in mass, produced in the formation of helium, generates the energy required to power the star.

In today's society, it is easy for us to talk about fusion. But when this theory was first proposed, it received a blistering review. First, crashing two positively charged nuclei together is extremely difficult and requires a substantial amount of energy. Second, the math did not add up—four protons going to a helium nuclei means that two positive charges are missing that have to be accounted for. And finally, nuclear reactions generate gamma rays, whereas a star's emission is typically dominated by emissions in the visible, so the question of how to convert a gamma ray to a visible photon also needed to be addressed.

These questions had no real answers in the 1920s. It took nearly two more decades to solve all the problems, but the overall model developed by Eddington was shown to be indeed correct, even if he had insufficient information. It goes to show that a little bit of intuition can go a long way.

2.8. The Positron

The missing link comes with the discovery of the positron[33]. The positron was originally proposed by Paul Dirac[34] in 1928, with subsequent work in 1931 that refined the properties of the positron. (This work led to Dirac receiving the Nobel Prize in 1932.) The positron has the same mass as an electron, but it has the opposite charge—hence the term "antielectron." The positron itself was discovered by Carl D. Anderson[35] using a cloud chamber that is used to identify energetic particles moving through the atmosphere from space, called galactic cosmic rays. Positrons have the important characteristic wherein when they collide with an electron, all matter is completely annihilated (or converted into energy) with the emission of two gamma rays (two are required for conservation of momentum). This reaction can be written as

$$e^- + e^+ \rightarrow 2\,\gamma$$

Protons, like electrons, also have an antimatter[36] component, called an antiproton. Antimatter is annihilated almost instantaneously in the

---

33 http://en.wikipedia.org/wiki/Positron
34 http://en.wikipedia.org/wiki/Paul_Dirac
35 http://en.wikipedia.org/wiki/Carl_D._Anderson
36 http://en.wikipedia.org/wiki/Antimatter

presence of matter and, as such, is only seen in high-energy particle collisions. Some are generated in intense lightning storms[37] and by the interaction of galactic cosmic rays with atoms in our atmosphere, creating a shower of particles[38]. It can also be generated under controlled conditions using large particle accelerators that operate under a high-integrity vacuum. Antimatter produced by these collisions can be confined in a magnetic bottle. Presently, about ten nanograms per year[39] are generated by particle accelerators.

2.9. Inventory of Subatomic Particles

A summary of the subatomic particles and their properties are listed in Table 2.9.1.

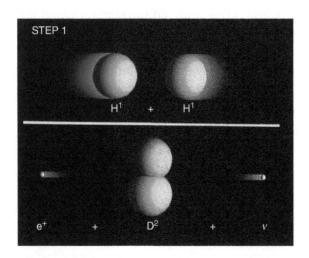

FIGURE 2.10.1. STEP 1 OF THE PROTON-PROTON CHAIN, WHERE TWO PROTONS COLLIDE TO PRODUCE DEUTERIUM, A POSITRON, AND A NEUTRINO. THE LARGE RED SPHERES INDICATE PROTONS AND THE GREEN SPHERE INDICATES A NEUTRON. THE SMALLEST SPECIES ARE DESIGNATED BELOW THE LOW-MASS PARTICLES.

2.10. Solar Fusion via the Proton-Proton Chain

In 1939, Hans Bethe[40] was able to complete the details that Eddington could not, thus discovering the details of fusion within the stellar interiors. The process Bethe discovered is called the proton-proton chain[41]. This work earned Bethe the Nobel Prize in 1967. The proton-proton chain has three major steps:

Step 1 (Figure 2.10.1): Two protons collide to produce a deuterium nucleus (i.e., a proton bound to a neutron). The extra positive charge comes off as a positron. To conserve lepton number, a neutrino is also generated. Colliding two protons together is exceptionally difficult because the positive charges of the protons repel each other. Thus, a glancing collision between protons will only produce deflection and no reaction.

For this reaction to occur, we need not only a head-on collision, but we also need sufficient energy to overcome the repulsive force of the positive charges. It is for this reason that Eddington proposed a 40-million-degree temperature in the core of the Sun. Bethe showed that with quantum mechanical effects (specifically, the wave nature of the protons), the temperature of the core only needs to be 15 million degrees. Even with the reduction in energy threshold, the reaction rate is very slow, with the probability of collision occurring on a timescale of 1.4×10^{10} years. Note that the age of the solar system is 4.5 billion years, so we are actually about one-third of the way through material in the entire core.

With the reaction, there is the annihilation of mass and the release of energy. This energy is typically written in terms of electron volts (eV), which is the energy that a particle with the charge of an electron gains when it moves

---

37   http://science.nasa.gov/science-news/
science-at-nasa/2011/11jan_antimatter/
38   mailto:http://en.wikipedia.org/wiki/Cosmic_ray
39   http://www.engr.psu.edu/antimatter/

40   http://en.wikipedia.org/wiki/Hans_Bethe
41   http://en.wikipedia.org/wiki/
Proton-proton_chain_reaction

through a potential drop of 1 V. The conversion from electron volts to Joules is given by

$$1 \text{ MeV} = 1.6 \times 10^{-13} \text{ J}.$$

The first step of the proton-proton chain generates about 0.42 MeV of energy.

Additional energy is released when the positron immediately annihilates with an electron and is converted into two gamma ray photons. Thus, the first step in the proton-proton chain can be summarized as follows:

$$p + p \rightarrow D + e^+ + \upsilon_e \text{ (0.42 MeV)}$$

$$e^- + e^+ \rightarrow 2\gamma \text{ (1.02 MeV)}$$

Step 2 (Figure 2.10.2): In Step 2, the deuterium generated in Step 1 fuses with another proton to produce a He^3 nucleus and a gamma ray. This reaction occurs much faster than in Step 1 due to the presence of the neutron in the deuterium core. The neutron provides both an attractive force on the incident proton and shielding from the positive charge of the proton already in the core. This reaction occurs on a timescale of 0.6s, so that any deuterium produced by Step 1 is unable to propagate any distance before it is consumed. The reaction of the step can be written as:

$$D + p \rightarrow He^3 + \gamma \text{ (5.49 MeV)}$$

$$\text{(pn)} \qquad\qquad \text{(ppn)}$$

Step 3 (Figure 2.10.3): In this last step of the proton-proton chain, two He^3 collide to produce He^4 (or an alpha particle) plus two energetic protons, i.e.,

$$He^3 + He^3 \rightarrow He^4 + 2p \text{ (12.86 MeV)}$$

$$\text{(ppn)} \quad \text{(ppn)} \quad \text{(ppnn)}$$

This reaction is slow, but not as slow as the first step with a timescale of about 10^6 yrs. The

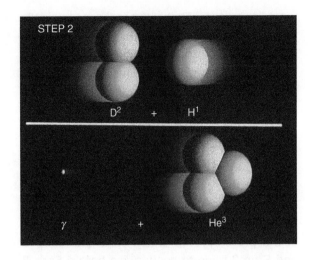

FIGURE 2.10.2. STEP 2, WHERE DEUTERIUM FROM STEP 1 COLLIDES WITH A PROTON TO PRODUCE A GAMMA RAY AND A HE3 NUCLEUS.

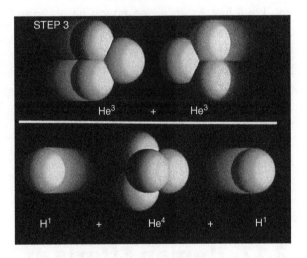

FIGURE 2.10.3. STEP 3, WHERE TWO HE³ COLLIDE TO PRODUCE TWO ENERGETIC PROTONS AND A HE⁴ NUCLEUS.

reason for the extended timescale is that the collisions now have to overcome the two positive charges of each nucleus, but the process is aided by the presence of a single neutron in each He^3 nuclei. As a result, the timescale is intermediate between the proton/proton reaction and the deuterium/proton reaction.

This reaction also explains why proton/helium atmospheres are prevalent in the formation of the solar system. These atmospheres basically are being built by by-products of the proton-proton chain along with unspent hydrogen.

Total Reaction: If one sums up all the components in the total reaction, the energy is:

$$4p + 2e^- \rightarrow He^4 + 6\gamma + 2\upsilon_e \ (\sim 26 \text{ MeV}).$$

So, the sum total reaction is very close to what was originally proposed by Eddington, except that he was missing the electrons being annihilated by positrons associated with Step 1 of the proton-proton chain. Note that Step 1 and Step 2 have to occur twice before Step 3 can occur.

This fusion sequence and related variants is at the heart of all main sequence stars[42].

Question 2.3: *How much mass is that worth?* You have just eaten a one-pound hamburger, which has a calorie count of 1000 calories. Using online resources, convert this energy to its equivalent in Joules. Similarly, convert the 26 MeV from the proton-proton chain into Joules. How much total mass is required for the proton-proton chain to create the same amount of energy as the 1000 calories of the hamburger?

2.11. Human Efforts at Fusion

Given the high-power yields from fusion, efforts to produce controlled nuclear fusion[43] on Earth have been ongoing almost since the end of World War II. The problem that we have on the Earth is the inability to create sufficiently hot and dense plasma for proton-proton fusion to occur. Because of the high potential energy that

is needed to initiate the proton-proton chain, controlled fusion efforts seek to utilize isotopes of hydrogen that are more reactive and easier to accomplish. These reactions include:

- D-D fuel cycle:

    $$D + D \rightarrow T \ (1 \text{ MeV}) + p \ (3 \text{ MeV})$$

    50–50 probability split

    $$\rightarrow He^3 \ (0.8 \text{ MeV}) + n \ (2.5 \text{ MeV})$$

- D-T fuel cycle:

    $$D + T \rightarrow He^4 \ (3.5 \text{ MeV}) + n \ (14 \text{ MeV})$$

- D- He^3 fuel cycle:

    $$D + He^3 \rightarrow He^4 \ (3.7 \text{ MeV}) + p \ (14.7 \text{ MeV})$$

Each of the above fuel cycles has its advantages and disadvantages. The D-D fuel cycle has the advantage that the deuterium needed occurs naturally in the oceans, so the raw materials are easily available. The downside is that there is relatively small energy released relative to the other fuel cycles. In addition, a substantial fraction of the energy is released in the form of a neutron. The energy of the neutron is so high that if a human were exposed to this type of energy particle, it could produce disruption of DNA and produce mutations at the cellular level. If the neutrons are instead captured by a nucleus in the reactor walls, that atom could then become radioactive. This reaction also has a 50% chance of producing tritium, which, as we have seen, is radioactive. Efficiently extracting this energy while keeping the plasma confined and eliminating harmful radiation by-products remains a difficult problem to solve.

The D-T fuel cycle offers higher energy yields and lower energy thresholds. However, tritium does not occur naturally on the Earth at any significant concentration, and even a

---

42 http://en.wikipedia.org/wiki/Main_sequence_stars
43 http://en.wikipedia.org/wiki/
Controlled_thermonuclear_fusion

larger energy fraction produced by the reaction is carried by neutron by-products.

The D-He^3 fuel cycle offers the highest yield, with all the energy being carried away in the form of charged particles which can be guided/controlled by magnetic and electric fields. A big problem, though, is that He^3 also does not occur naturally on Earth. As discussed later, the helium that is presently on the Earth is generated by the radioactive decay of heavy elements like uranium. This process of radioactive decay only generates alpha particles, i.e., He^4 nuclei. However, the *Apollo* missions found that He^3 is present on the lunar surface. This He^3 is generated in the core of the Sun, and because of the long reaction time in the last step of the proton-proton chain, there is sufficient time for a small fraction of the He^3 to escape the core and eventually reach the surface of the Sun. At the surface, it is blown off into space and can directly impact the Moon and other solar system objects that have no atmosphere. The speed of the He^3 at impact is sufficiently high that it becomes trapped in the regolith of the object.

The energy content of He^3 is about 2×10^8 kWh/kg. An average person uses about 250 kWh each month. This means that 1 kg of He^3 could provide power for 10^5 people for a year. If a kWh of energy costs about \$0.10, He^3 is worth about \$600,000 an ounce. Now we just need to figure out a way to go to the Moon and mine it.

Question 2.4: *How much power do you use*? Find an old household power bill and determine how much power is used in terms of electricity and gas. Using this value, how much power is required for the entire population of the state? If you assume that a typical power plant generates 1000 MW, how many such power plants are required to power the state, and how many are required to power the nation?

So, the ability to developed controlled nuclear fusion is very important, despite the fact that the answer to the problem remains elusive at this time. The problem is that the required temperatures are so high that none of the plasma can be in contact with any walls that provide the containment of the plasma. Contact with walls leads to erosion of the walls themselves, which in itself can cause catastrophic events. At the same time, the plasma will cool and become contaminated by debris from the walls, which causes additional energy losses of the plasma.

There are basically two main ways that are being investigated to confine the plasma for controlled fusion. The first is through a magnetic confinement, where magnetic fields guide the plasma inside the container without the plasma actually touching the walls. Unfortunately, most magnetic configurations allow some loss of particles to the chamber walls, and present efforts are investigating the development of very large devices where such effects are minimized. The largest ongoing experiment is the International Thermonuclear Experimental Reactor (ITER)[44]. This fusion reactor is designed to produce 500 MW using 50 MW of input power to create the initial plasma. It is anticipated that this device will be online in 2019.

Controlled fusion systems in which the plasma is confined magnetically have all shown that there is substantial diffusion of particles from the core of the plasma to the edges, contributing to loss at the walls of the chamber. The most popular form is called tokamak[45], where the magnetic field is in the shape of the torus or a hollow doughnut. A spheromak[46] also uses a toroidal shape for the plasma formation, but the chamber itself is spherical rather than toroidal. The torus shape was expected to allow the plasma to circulate without the possibility of interacting with the walls. In so doing, the particles were expected to have very long lifetimes without the need of producing lead-like densities as in the core of the Sun. Various methods such as radio-frequency heating are used to continue to energize the particles to

44   http://www.iter.org/
45   http://en.wikipedia.org/wiki/Tokamak
46   http://en.wikipedia.org/wiki/Spheromak

bring them up to the energy intensity needed for fusion reactions.

The reality, though, is that the plasma is subject to a variety of processes that cause particles to diffuse across the system until they eventually reach the walls and are lost in the system. This type of particle transport has many analogues within the Sun's fusion reactor. In order to reduce the particle losses, present theories suggest that the reactors need to be made larger so that the surface-to-volume ratio is smaller, and therefore particle losses should be smaller. It is for this reason that the ITER[47] reactor is the largest tokamak system ever built. The problem is, of course, that the systems are now exceptionally expensive and cannot be developed by a single nation. The expense also means that research on the systems is exceptionally slow—even small mistakes can be very expensive. A system as large as ITER would also be unfeasible for launching into space.

The second method for trying to achieve controlled fusion is known as inertial confinement fusion (ICF)[48]. High-powered lasers are used to compress pellets of deuterium and tritium in much the same way as gravity causes the compression and heating of the plasma in the core of the Sun. The problem at this time lies in obtaining sufficiently high-powered lasers that can generate the compression on fast enough timescales that the resulting plasma does not diffuse away before fusion occurs. Most of this work is occurring at U.S. national laboratories that have access to high-powered lasers developed during the 1980s for the military Star Wars program.

These systems most closely follow the above processes for the core of the Sun, except that instead of gravity pulling the plasma to the core, intent lasers are used to push the plasma to the core as shown in Figure 2.10.4.

By using fast-pulsed lasers, the expectation is that the fuel pellet, typically made up of cryogenically frozen hydrogen/deuterium or deuterium/tritium, will be crushed to a point where it reaches densities 20 times that of lead and temperatures up to 100,000,000 K to produce conditions even harsher than within the solar core.

Most of the technical challenges in the development of sufficiently energetic pulsed lasers with sufficient pointing accuracy and uniformity of emission have been solved. The plasma transport associated with the movement of different density plasmas causes the loss of particles and energy, which prevents sustained fusion from occurring. In some sense, the issue remains one of scales, which we focused on in Chapter 1. The physical scales are so large on the Sun that particle transport timescales are relatively slow, while in the terrestrial applications, the size of the fusion plasma is so small that the particle transport processes prevent controlled nuclear fusion.

The inertial confinement method also has physical size issues when thinking in terms of powering spacecraft. Currently, in order to power the lasers, large banks of capacitors are needed to store up energy over time. That energy reserve is then released over a very short period of time. All of this infrastructure is typically contained in several large buildings—again, much too big to launch into space.

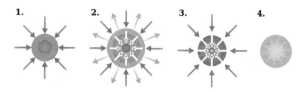

FIGURE 2.10.4. SCHEMATIC SHOWING CONTROL FUSION THROUGH THE INERTIAL CONFINEMENT. A FUSION PELLET IS CRUSHED BY MULTIPLE **PLACES** THAT ARE INDICATED BY THE BLUE ARROWS. THERE IS INITIAL BLOW OFF OF SOME OF THE MATERIAL, WHICH IS SHOWN BY THE ORANGE ARROWS IN STEP 2. THE REMAINING MATERIAL IS FORCED TO MOVE INWARD, PRODUCING A CORE MATERIAL SHOWN IN PURPLE AND BLUE IN STEP 2. WITHIN THE CORE, THE DENSITY IS EXPECTED TO REACH 20 TIMES THAT OF LEAD AT A TEMPERATURE OF 100,000,000 K, AND THEREBY PRODUCE FUSION AND YIELD AN ENERGY OUTPUT MUCH GREATER THAN THE ENERGY INPUT.

47   http://en.wikipedia.org/wiki/ITER
48   http://en.wikipedia.org/wiki/
Inertial_confinement_fusion

In the next chapter, the study of the Sun's interior provides a unique opportunity to understand how nature is able to sustain the solar system power plant. It shows that these processes are very complicated and dynamic and occur within a highly structured object. It is this structure that allows the conversion of mass to energy across the full electromagnetic spectrum and production of bulk thermal motions of the plasma within. We are still waiting to see if these processes can be successfully scaled to enable controlled nuclear fusion on Earth.

2.12. Nuclear Fission

While controlled nuclear fusion has yet to be achieved, power from controlled nuclear fission has been available since the 1950s. Presently, there are 439 nuclear reactors[49] in operation around the world. Fission involves the splitting (i.e., creating a fissure) of very large nuclei to create intermediate-sized nuclei, which is opposite to fusion in the sense that the latter is using smaller nuclei to create immediate nuclei. However, in both processes, the intermediate nuclei have less mass than the initial nuclei so that there is energy released.

Nuclear fission was discovered by Otto Hahn[50], Lise Meitner[51], and Fritz Strassmann[52] in 1938. In the experiment, neutrons were used to bombard uranium in the hope of creating even heavier elements. To their surprise, heavier elements were not observed. Instead, barium was seen to be created from the bombardment. The conclusion was that the uranium nucleus might resemble a wobbly unstable drop ready to divide itself at the slightest provocation, which was being provided by impacts from

the bombarding neutrons. For this work, Hahn received the Nobel Prize for chemistry in 1944. A slightly modified version of this process is used in today's nuclear power plants.

In particular, a fissile material is one that is capable of sustaining a chain reaction of nuclear fission. One of the most common radioactive elements is uranium, but not all radioactive material is fissile, that is, capable of nuclear fusion. For example, the most common isotope of uranium, Uranium 238[53] (U^{238}), which amounts to 99.3% of natural uranium, is not considered fissile. It can spontaneously decay into different light elements through the reaction

$$U^{238} \rightarrow Th^{234} + He^4 \,(4.2\text{ MeV})$$

$$(92P + 146N) \,(90P + 144N) \,(2P + 2N)$$

but the reaction rate for this is very slow, with a 4.5-billion-year half-life. Note that helium is a byproduct of this reaction and is the alpha particle, which is the signature of radioactive decay. However, this same helium, when generated underground, is captured in the rock formations that capture oil. This helium is often extracted with the oil and it is this helium that is used to fill the gas bottles for party balloons; in other words, when you play with helium balloons, you are playing with by-products from nuclear fission.

U^{238} can be subject to fission through the absorption of an energetic neutron, but the neutrons generated by the reaction have insufficient energy to continue the reaction; i.e., U^{238} is a net absorber of neutrons. The story is very different for the lighter isotope of uranium, Uranium 235[54] (U^{235}). This isotope is considered fissile (it generates more neutrons than it absorbs) so that there is the potential of a self-sustaining chain reaction to develop if there is sufficient U^{235} available. The specific reaction is

49 http://en.wikipedia.org/wiki/Nuclear_power_plants
50 http://en.wikipedia.org/wiki/Otto_Hahn
51 http://en.wikipedia.org/wiki/Lise_Meitner
52 http://en.wikipedia.org/wiki/Fritz_Strassmann

53 http://en.wikipedia.org/wiki/Uranium-238
54 http://en.wikipedia.org/wiki/Uranium-235

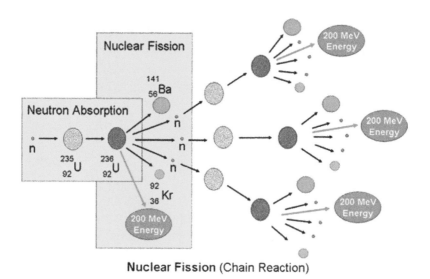

Nuclear Fission (Chain Reaction)

FIGURE 2.12.1. CHART SHOWING HOW A CHAIN REACTION IS CREATED WITHIN U^{235}. IMAGE CREDIT: WOODBANK COMMUNICATIONS LTD.[60]

$$^{235}U_{92} + {}^{1}n_{0} \rightarrow {}^{236}U_{92} \rightarrow {}^{140}Ba_{56} + {}^{96}Kr_{36} + 3\ {}^{1}n_{0}$$
$$(202\ \text{MeV})$$

and is also shown graphically in Figure 2.12.1. A fast (or energetic) neutron is absorbed by U^{235} and temporarily forms U^{236}. This isotope has a very short time scale and quickly breaks apart into barium, krypton, and three fast neutrons, releasing ~200 MeV of energy. If there is nothing in the way to absorb the three new neutrons, then they can react with other U^{235} to produce a self-sustaining runaway nuclear reaction. A nuclear bomb minimizes the amount of absorbing material to produce a runaway nuclear reaction. A nuclear power plant introduces moderators to absorb some of the energy so that the reaction occurs at a controllable rate. There are many variants on this process, though, which can be seen in the zoo of reactor types[55] employed around the world.

Light water reactors[56] use enriched uranium in which the fuel contains 5% U^{235}. Control rods are made up of material that can absorb the neutrons, such as carbon, and thereby control the nuclear reaction rate. Water is used to absorb some of the neutrons, take the heat out of the reactor, and generate electricity. Meltdown of the reactor occurs when there is a loss of coolant because the U^{235} reaction is always occurring and generating heat. Without the presence of the coolant, the fuel rods melt, often with the release of radioactive material. An example of meltdown occurred with the Fukushima nuclear disaster[57] following the Tohoku earthquake and tsunami of March 11, 2011. The resultant destruction of the power plant can be seen on YouTube[58]. The Chernobyl disaster[59] of 1986 is another infamous example of a nuclear meltdown with significant human and environmental consequences, but this disaster was partially due to the use of a different, highly unstable reactor design.

Note that while the energy produced in the above reaction is much higher than an individual fusion reaction, fission generates about 1 MeV per atomic mass unit (AMU), while fusion generates about 4 MeV/AMU. So, from a mass budget point of view, fusion requires fewer resources than fission.

55   http://en.wikipedia.org/wiki/Nuclear_reactor
56   http://en.wikipedia.org/wiki/Light_water_reactor
57   http://en.wikipedia.org/wiki/Fukushima_Daiichi_nuclear_disaster
58   http://www.youtube.com/watch?v=B3_ZRO5oATk
59   http://en.wikipedia.org/wiki/Chernobyl_disaster
60   http://www.mpoweruk.com/nuclear_theory.htm

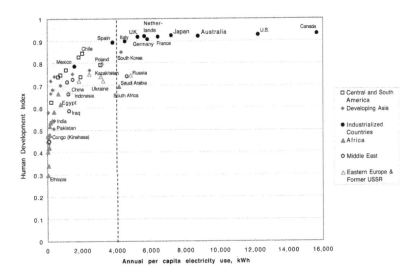

FIGURE 2.13.1. HUMAN DEVELOPMENT INDEX, WHICH IS A MEASURE OF THE QUALITY OF LIFE AS A FUNCTION OF ANNUAL POWER CONSUMPTION PER CAPITA. EIGHTY PERCENT OF THE WORLD POPULATION OF NEARLY 7 BILLION PEOPLE HAVE AN INDEX BELOW 0.8, AND THE POPULATION ONLY HAS AVAILABILITY TO IT IN ANNUAL POWER CONSUMPTION OF BETWEEN 2,000 AND 4,000 KWH/CAPITA.

Another downside of fission reactors is that the spent fuel rods are highly radioactive. A different type of reactor is called the breeder reactor[61]. This reactor converts non-fissile material like U^{238} into fissile material such as plutonium 239 and produces much less harmful nuclear waste. The downside with these systems, though, is that they have to run at much higher temperatures, so instead of having a coolant of water, they have to have a coolant of liquid metal, including lead, mercury, or sodium. Handling these systems is very much more complicated at this time, as they have fewer built-in safeguards for slowing down the reactions should a problem occur.

Power is one of our main issues for spacecraft. The cheapest and safest power source for orbiting spacecraft around the Earth is through the use of solar panels[62], which convert solar energy into electrical energy. However, for spacecraft moving away from the Sun, the efficiency decreases, so that either spacecraft has to be designed to use very little power. Historically, any mission traveling to Jupiter or beyond has used radioisotope thermal generators[63] (or RTGs) for power. In these systems, material that will radioactively decay such as plutonium 239 generates heat. This heat is then converted into electrical energy via devices called thermocouples. The timescale for this radioactive decay is of the order of tens of years so that the energy generated can be easily handled, at the same time providing a long-lived energy source. The lifetime of the *Voyager* spacecraft, based on their RTGs alone, is on the order of 50 years.

---

61   http://en.wikipedia.org/wiki/Breeder_reactor

62   http://en.wikipedia.org/wiki/Photovoltaic_module

63   http://en.wikipedia.org/wiki/Radioisotope_thermoelectric_generator

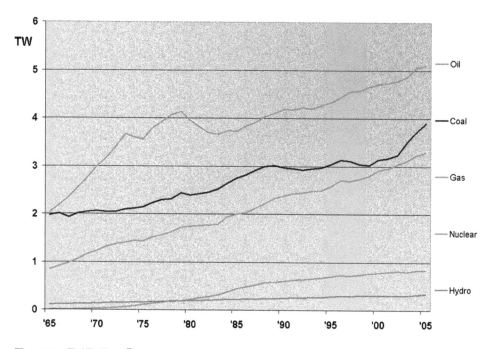

FIGURE 2.13.2.   BREAKDOWN OF POWER GENERATION AROUND THE WORLD IN THE DIFFERENT TYPES OF FUELS, INCLUDING OIL, COAL, GAS, NUCLEAR, AND HYDROELECTRIC SYSTEMS.

2.13. Future Developments for an Industrial Era

Our energy needs follow very closely the discussion in this chapter on the generation of energy for the Sun. There are different choices to be made about which fuel type one would like to use to produce power on Earth. The different choices yield different timescales and different consequences for the evolution of the Earth. This is an important question. In the McFarlane 2006 study for the United Nations Development Program, it was noted that those with high amounts of annual power consumption per capita had a higher quality of life (measured by the human development index[64], HDI) as shown in Figure 2.13.1. We can see that many of the developing countries have both low HDI and low power consumption per capita. Having more power doesn't necessarily improve HDI as seen by the relatively

small change in HDI between countries that use 8000 kWh per capita versus those that are using nearly 14,000 kWh.

If everyone on the planet were to have an HDI of 0.9, and if this was associated with an annual power consumption of 8,000 kWh/capita, then the present population of 7 billion would require

$$\text{Total World Power} = \frac{8,000 \text{ kWhr}}{365 \times 24 \text{ hr in a year}}$$
$$= 6.4 \text{ TW}$$

This total power consumption is presently available to the world through a mixture of all fossil fuel burning, nuclear power, and hydroelectric power systems.

At this time, the main elements for power production are from fossil fuels: oil, coal, and gas. Powers similar to that produced by the Sun can be achieved by fossil fuels, but this cannot be sustained indefinitely. There are two limitations that must be taken into consideration.

64   http://en.wikipedia.org/wiki/Human_Development_Index

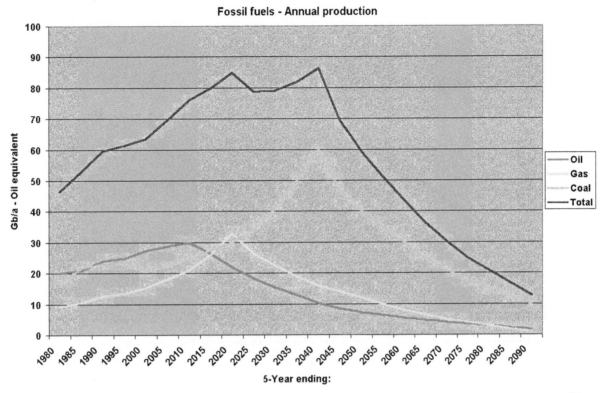

FIGURE 2.13.3. PROJECTED PRODUCTION OF FOSSIL FUELS. SOURCE: HTTP://WWW.AFTER-OIL.CO.UK/[66]

A projection for fossil fuel annual consumption is shown in Figure 2.13.3. It should be noted that technology developments such as fracking[65] continually add to the reserve so that projections can change radically. But even so, all fossil fuel reserves are expected to be significantly depleted by the end of the century, and the present consumption rate is not sustainable.

In particular, we could derive all the power needed for the industrial era using coal/fossil fuels. Like the problem with solar power generation, this will work, but only for a limited timescale. Estimates for fossil fuel usage suggest that there may be only 100 or so years available for power production by this means. The questions, then, are: what do we do to conserve those resources, and what we do for future power production?

The other reason why fossil fuel burning is probably not sustainable is that we are adding CO_2 to the atmosphere. CO_2 is a greenhouse gas, and its increased concentration in the atmosphere from fossil fuel burning is correlated with an increase in the global temperature as shown in Figure 2.13.4.

Despite the fact that the increase is only a few degrees globally, locally there can be larger seasonal swings in temperature, which is causing melting of the polar ice packs. This, in turn, can lead to increased sea levels that can induce changes with sea currents and leads to the extreme weather events we are now seeing on a regular basis. These extreme weather events lead to destruction of homes, industry, and food production capabilities.

So, fossil fuel burning at the present rate—whether from a resource basis or from an environment stance—can only be considered a temporary solution.

Wind turbines and solar electric systems utilize renewable energy sources, but the question is whether they can generate sufficient power for the seven billion inhabitants of the Earth. Fusion offers a huge potential for energy production, but, like Rutherford, who

---

65   http://en.wikipedia.org/wiki/Hydraulic_fracturing

66   http://www.after-oil.co.uk/CCS.htm

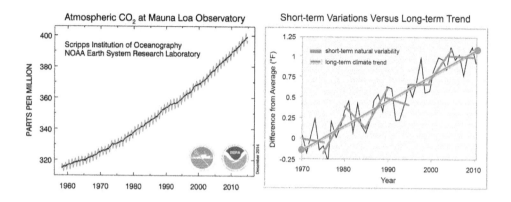

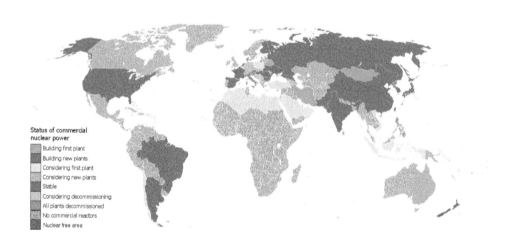

FIGURE 2.13.4. CORRELATION BETWEEN GLOBAL TEMPERATURE CHANGE AND CO_2 CONCENTRATION IN THE ATMOSPHERE.

FIGURE 2.13.5. NUCLEAR POWER PLANTS IN OPERATION AND PLANNED CONSTRUCTION AROUND THE WORLD. THERE IS THE POTENTIAL THAT THE NUMBER OF OPERATIONAL PLANTS WILL DOUBLE IN THE NEXT DECADE.[67]

67   http://www.guardian.co.uk/environment/datablog/2009/aug/14/nuclear-power-world

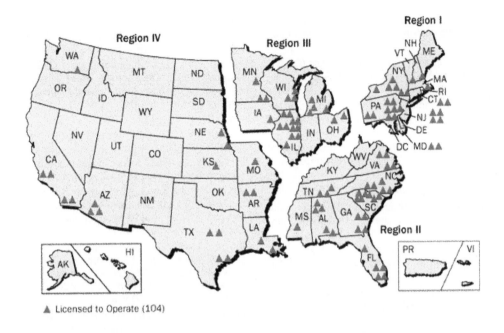

FIGURE 2.13.6. NUCLEAR POWER PLANTS IN THE UNITED STATES.

proposed the initial fusion model for the Sun, we presently do not know how to make a controlled fusion system work economically at this time. Fission reactors offer a working alternative, but environmental issues associated with waste products and accidental failures within the reactor have yet to be solved as well. New reactor designs have many more safeguards than current reactors (most of which were built in the 1970s), but production of some of those reactors would require renegotiating nuclear nonproliferation treaties that were signed in the 1980s. Nevertheless, many countries around the world are investing in new nuclear power plants to solve their country's energy issues as shown in Figure 2.13.5.

Figure 2.13.6 shows the distribution of the existing nuclear power stations across the United States. We can see they are concentrated in the highest populations areas, which makes sense from a commercial perspective. Regardless of which way power is to be produced in this century, we will definitely have an interesting time with multiple issues to be solved.

References

[1] Herbert Friedman. (1985). Sun and Earth, *Scientific American*, New York.

Image Credits

The Solar Interior

Nature's Fusion Reactor

One of the problems we have yet to address is that the proton-proton chain generates gamma rays and not visible light. This conversion to the visible spectrum occurs through the layers of the Sun beyond the region where fusion occurs. We will find that many processes occur within the Sun, leading to dynamics that rival the weather conditions on Earth. As a result, we will demonstrate that there are solar storms that occur that regularly lead to the ejection of matter from the Sun into the solar system, so that space is not actually empty. Instead, space is filled with a tenuous population of particles that are very much more energetic than the particles that comprise our atmosphere. Because of their energy, these energetic particles leave their mark on many of the solar system objects. Moreover, they can provide a harmful radiation environment for any space travel between the planets. In this chapter, we therefore look at the overall structure of the Sun and how the Sun imposes its mark on the rest of the solar system.

3.1. Energy Transport

So far, we've talked a lot about power and energy, but we haven't talked about how these quantities are moved about in the solar system. Transport of energy dominates all aspects of everything in the solar system. For humans, the same processes play crucial roles in determining whether a person gets frostbite in cold conditions or whether a person gets heatstroke in hot conditions. It can occur via four processes that are illustrated in Figure 3.1.1:

- **Conduction**[1], in which heat moves from regions of high temperature to one of lower temperature by direct contact: At the microscopic level, adjacent particles or atoms in the hotter regions have larger thermal motions which cause them to collide with adjacent particles to move the energy from the hotter regions to the cold regions; there is no physical movement of any material in this process; metals are great heat conductors, while insulators are poor conductors;
- **Convection**[2], in which a hot fluid (typically more buoyant) moves or rises into a cold region of less buoyant material so that there is a physical exchange of material between hot and cold regions—unlike conduction, where the material itself is completely static.
- **Radiation**[3], in which heat is converted to electromagnetic radiation (hence the term radiation) that propagates away from the source;
- **Phase Transition**[4], in which heat is either absorbed or released as a result of a change in the state of the material. For example, the evaporation of sweat or alcohol from a person leads to the cooling of the person.

3.2. The Solar Interior

The solar interior[5] is structured in a similar fashion to the hard rocky inner planets. This is because all solar system objects are under the influence of gravity, which is trying to draw all the material into the very center of the object. The gravitational pull generates heat that in turn slows the gravitational collapse. This tug-of-war causes the hydrogen to have different properties, as the density and temperature of the material change with depth within the Sun.

The main regions are illustrated in Figure 3.2.1 and include the core, the radiative zone, and the convection zone. These different regions can be identified in terms of density, temperature, or temperature gradient (i.e., the rate at which the temperature changes with distance). Because of variations in these quantities, the physical processes that control the dynamics of these regions can be very different, despite the fact that they are all made up of hydrogen.

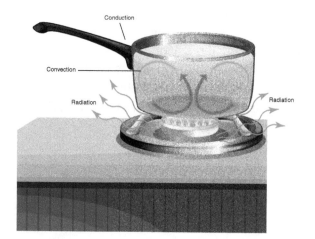

FIGURE 3.1.1. EXAMPLE SHOWING THE DIFFERENCE BETWEEN CONDUCTION, CONVECTION, RADIATION, AND PHASE TRANSITION.

1   http://physics.info/conduction/
2   http://physics.info/convection/
3   http://physics.info/radiation/

4   http://physics.info/heat-latent/
5   http://solarscience.msfc.nasa.gov/interior.shtml

3.3. The Core

The core[6] is at the center of the Sun with the highest density and temperature. It is defined by the region where fusion occurs. The profiles for the density and temperature are shown in Figure 3.3.1. The temperature at the very center of the Sun is about 15,000,000 K with a density of about 150 g/cm³—about ten times the density of gold or lead. At this temperature, all the hydrogen and helium nuclei are stripped bare of their electrons. Heavy ions like iron are almost always fully stripped of their electrons.

Eddington, in his vision of the core, wrote:

Crowded together within a cubic centimeter, there are more than 1 trillion trillion atoms, about twice as many free electrons and 20 billion trillion x-rays. The x-rays are traveling with the speed of light and electrons 10,000 miles per second. Most of the atoms are … Simply protons traveling at 300 miles a second. Here and there will be heavy atoms, such as iron, lumbering around at 40 miles a second. I told you the speeds and the state of congestion of the road; now imagine the collisions.

A. Eddington, S. (1927). *Stars and Atoms*. New Haven, Yale University.

It is under these conditions that fusion occurs, providing the power of the Sun. It should be noted that the core contains nearly 50% of the Sun's total mass, but only occupies about 2% of the Sun's volume. The outer bounds for the core at about 0.26 solar radii are loosely defined by the point where the temperature and density are too low to support the proton-proton fusion chain.

In this region, the densities are high enough that not only do the nuclei and electrons

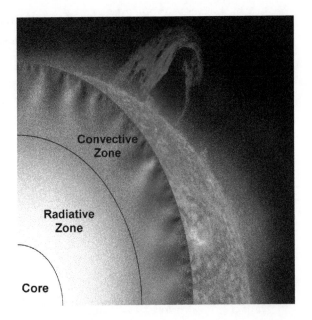

FIGURE 3.2.1. THE SOLAR INTERIOR SHOWING THE MAIN REGIONS INCLUDING (1) THE CORE; (2) THE RADIATIVE ZONE; AND (3) THE CONVECTION ZONE TO SCALE, RELATIVE TO THE RADIUS OF THE SUN.

undergo frequent collisions, but the gamma rays produced during the fusion process are also colliding with nuclei and electrons. With each collision, the photon loses a little bit of energy, so that as it undertakes this path, through the core and beyond, the frequency of the emission is slowly converted from a gamma ray to an X-ray, and eventually as it escapes the core, to UV and to visible light.

3.4. The Radiative Zone

Beyond the core, fusion ceases, and energy is able to move out through the propagation of electromagnetic radiation; hence the term radiative zone[7]. This region extends from about 0.26 solar radii to 0.7 solar radii. The total mass of the Sun contained within the radiative zone is approximately 48% and contains about 32% of the Sun's total volume.

---

6   http://solar-heliospheric.engin.umich.edu/hjenning/Core.html

7   http://solar-heliospheric.engin.umich.edu/hjenning/RadiativeZone.html

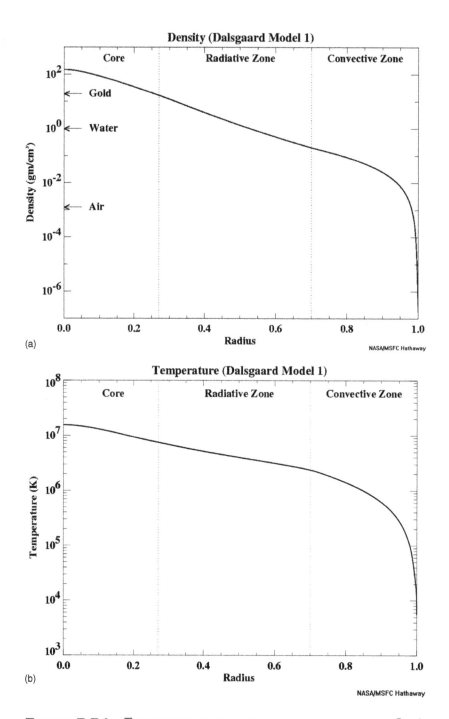

FIGURE 3.3.1. THE DENSITY AND TEMPERATURE PROFILES OF THE SUN'S
INTERIOR AS A FUNCTION OF RADIAL DISTANCE. THE DIFFERENT REGIONS ARE
IDENTIFIED BY CHANGES IN THESE PROFILES.

As we noted in the discussion of the proton-proton chain, the bulk of the radiation created by the Sun is in the form of gamma rays. However, the stopping length of gamma rays in lead is about 10 cm, which is close to the density at the bottom of the radiative zone.

In other words, every ten centimeters the gamma ray has a collision with a proton, and it has to travel close to a total of 350,000 km to escape. Most of the energy of the gamma ray going into a collision remains, but in an arbitrary direction so that the gamma ray, in fact, executes a very torturous path as it propagates through the radiative zone. The analogy is of a person weaving their way through a dense crowd of people bumping and being bumped from side to side, causing the person to continually have to change directions to get through the crowd. The only difference here is that the person is moving at the speed of light and participating in literally millions of collisions per second. This zigzag path is called a random walk[8] and greatly increases the path that the gamma ray takes before escaping the core. Demonstration of a random walk path can be seen at VLAB[9]. Despite the fact that the gamma ray is traveling at the speed of light, it takes nearly one million years to escape the radiative zone.

As noted at the end of Section 3.3, with each collision, the gamma ray loses a small fraction of energy. This causes the frequency of electromagnetic radiation to decrease, such that the energy is primarily X-rays at the bottom of the radiative zone and ultraviolet radiation at the top of the radiative zone. As this downshift in frequency is occurring, the temperature is falling from about 7,000,000 K at the bottom of the radiative zone to about 2,000,000 K at its top.

photons) can be absorbed by atoms. At the same time, the density has declined so that gravitational effects are not as strong. This leads to the energy transport process to switch to convection. The energy is trapped within the plasma, causing hot elements to rise to the top of the convection zone. At the top, energy (in the form of UV and visible wavelength photons) is lost to space, causing the plasma to cool and, under gravity, fall back to the bottom, creating the well-known convection pattern shown in Figure 3.5.1. Hence, this region is known as the convection zone[10].

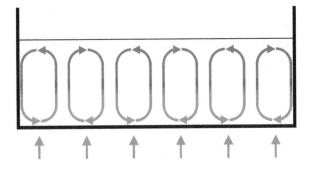

FIGURE 3.5.1. CONVECTION ZONE FLOW PATTERNS IN WHICH HOT (RED) MATERIAL AT THE BOTTOM RISES TO THE TOP OF THE CONVECTION ZONE, WHERE IT LOSES ENERGY, CAUSING IT TO COOL AND FALL BACK (REPRESENTED BY THE BLUE ARROWS) TO THE BOTTOM OF THE CONVECTION ZONE, WHERE THE PROCESS REPEATS.

3.5. The Convection Zone

The temperature change beyond the radiative zone is critical because it marks the demarcation line where the plasma is sufficiently cool enough that heavy ions (such as carbon, nitrogen, oxygen, calcium, and iron) are able to hold onto some of their electrons. This makes the material more opaque, as the electromagnetic radiation in the region (in the form of UV

The convection zone lies between 0.7–1.0 solar radii. It contains only 2% of the Sun's mass, but occupies 66% of the Sun's volume.

3.6. The Photosphere

The layer that sits on top of the convection zone is often referred to as the visible surface of the Sun. It is called the photosphere[11]. The

---

8 http://en.wikipedia.org/wiki/Random_walk
9 http://vlab.infotech.monash.edu.au/simulations/ swarms/random-walk/demo/

10 http://solar-heliospheric.engin.umich.edu/ hjenning/ConvectiveZone.html
11 http://solarscience.msfc.nasa.gov/surface.shtml

term is derived from Greek, *photos* meaning light and "sphere," denoting the spherical nature of the light source. The temperature for this region ranges from about 7000 K at the bottom to about 4000 K at the top. These temperatures are well below the 15,000,000 K of the core, and, in fact, some very interesting reactions take place in this temperature region. In particular, at 7000 K, we only have a partially ionized plasma present, meaning that there is a mixture of hydrogen atoms, protons, and free electrons. At this temperature, a few of the free electrons can combine with the neutral atoms to produce negative hydrogen ions.

These negative hydrogen ions are important because they absorb all the electromagnetic radiation coming out of the convection zone. Once this region is passed, the bulk of material appears as hydrogen atoms or plasma, both of which are transparent to light. It is at this point that the light can then escape from the Sun without any further modifications and be observed at long distances from the Sun. As a result, the radiation is seen as coming from a layer of only a few hundred kilometers from an object that is 700,000 km in radius. It is for this reason that, despite the fact the Sun is made entirely of gas, the Sun appears as a sharp sphere in white light as in Figure 3.6.1, with a sharpness similar to any of the planets.

The temperature of the photosphere should be familiar—it is the same range as the Sun's 6000 K blackbody temperature. In fact, it is the photosphere that determines the blackbody temperature, as it is the region where most of the Sun's energy is emitted.

Looking at the Sun in white-light images, the center of the disk appears brightest. This is because we are looking straight at the Sun, and we see all the emissions across the full length of the photosphere. When we look at the limb, or edge, the light is slanted so that we have seen emissions primarily from cooler and dimmer regions. This effect is known as "limb darkening"[12] in white-light images.

Note also that in the white-light images, there are no huge arches present that typify science fiction images of the Sun. To see these additional structures, one must look at specific wavelengths or frequencies of the electromagnetic emissions coming from the Sun. This process is very similar to how we used the Fraunhofer fringes to identify specific elements, but here we look at even smaller changes in wavelength to see motions within the Sun.

3.7. Helioseismology

One particular technique is to look at shifts in the line emissions from hydrogen and other atoms. As we saw in the previous chapter, each element has very discrete line emissions. If the source of the emissions is now moving, then this motion can produce a slight shift in the frequency of the line emissions. This effect is called the Doppler effect[13], most commonly experienced by humans through modification of sound waves associated with traveling vehicles. Higher frequencies are heard as the vehicle approaches the observer, with lower frequencies being heard as the vehicle drives away.

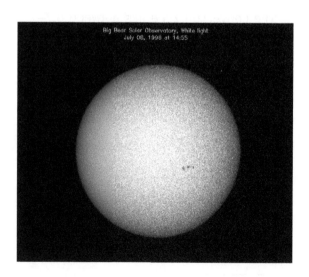

FIGURE 3.6.1. PHOTOSPHERE AS SEEN IN WHITE LIGHT FROM THE BIG BEAR SOLAR OBSERVATORY.

12   http://en.wikipedia.org/wiki/Limb_darkening
13   http://en.wikipedia.org/wiki/Doppler_effect

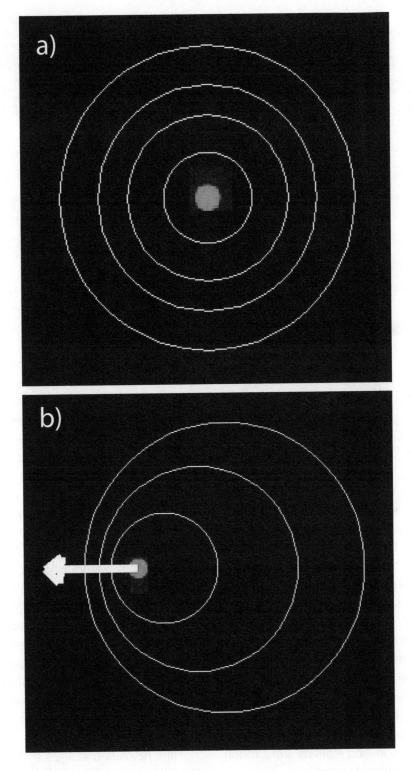

FIGURE 3.7.1. SCHEMATIC FOR THE DEVELOPMENT OF THE DOPPLER EFFECT.

The Doppler effect is illustrated in Figure 3.7.1. For a stationary source (top panel), the wave emitted by a source will travel away from the source uniformly in all directions. Now, suppose that the source starts to move to the right, as in the bottom panel. Because of its motion, the source will be catching up to the waves moving to the right, thereby causing

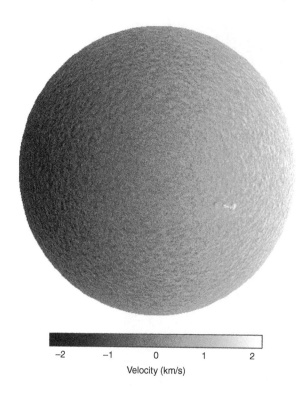

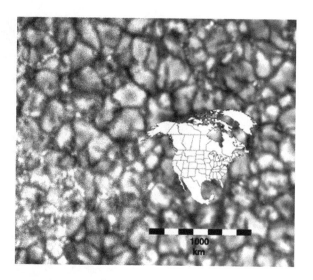

Velocity (km/s)

FIGURE 3.7.3. HIGH-RESOLUTION IMAGE OF SO-
LAR GRANULES WITH A MAP OF NORTH AMERICA FOR
SCALE[16].

FIGURE 3.7.2. DOPPLERGRAM OF THE SUN,
SHOWING A BUBBLING MOTION OF 1–2 KM/S ACROSS
THE ENTIRE FACE OF THE SUN. IMAGE COURTESY OF
IMAGE CREDIT: SOHO/MDI CONSORTIUM. SOHO
IS A PROJECT OF INTERNATIONAL COOPERATION BE-
TWEEN ESA AND NASA.

the appearance of a shorter wavelength or higher frequency to an observer on the right. Conversely, for an observer on the left, the wavelength will be longer and the frequency lower as the source pulls away.

This process is true for many types of waves, including sound waves and electromagnetic waves. The exact value of the change in frequency or wavelength is directly proportional to the speed of the source. Since sound waves have a relatively low speed, we can detect Doppler shift with our ears. For shifts in the frequency of light, one must have very good frequency resolution and speeds very much faster than that of a moving car.

The way that this effect is used in observations of the Sun is to look at frequencies slightly off from the main emission lines of a particular element, most commonly hydrogen. If light is detected at this shifted frequency, then we know how fast the source is moving relative to

the observer. Thus, information on intensity as a function of frequency can be converted into a map of different velocity motions on the Sun's surface. This is called a Dopplergram[14].

This technique, first used by Robert Leighton[15] in 1962, shows that the surface was moving up and down directly at the speed of about 1000 miles an hour (or a few kilometers per second) for a period of about five minutes. A modern Dopplergram demonstrating these kinds of motions is shown in Figure 3.7.2. When we first introduced the concept of convection in this chapter, we used the example of boiling water. These Dopplergrams show that this analogy is highly applicable to the Sun's convection zone, where the rising elements are actually lifting up parts of the Sun, producing a blue shift toward us, the observer, and the cooler components produce sinking motions of the surface, which are seen as red shifts in the line emissions.

High-resolution images of the Sun's surface are able to resolve the individual bubbles called granules[16]. An example is shown in Figure 3.7.3.

14 http://sepwww.stanford.edu/public/docs/sep109/
paper_html/node9.html
15 http://en.wikipedia.org/wiki/Robert_B._Leighton
16 http://en.wikipedia.org/wiki/
Granule_(solar_physics)

It was originally thought that this bubbling motion was random and chaotic in nature. A video of these granules in motion can be seen through this link.[17] Subsequent examination of the patterns showed that there was some ordering to the bubbling and that there was, in fact, a definitive periodic oscillation embedded into the bubbling motion within a five-minute period.

The fact that there is a coherent period in the bubbling motion has led to the development of the field called helioseismology[18], and it is the information derived from this field that provides essentially all the information about the solar interior as described above.

This field is, in many ways, related to the seismology[19] of the Earth. At the Earth, seismic waves from an earthquake are observed by multiple stations around the world, and, through mathematical models, the sources of the seismic waves in their paths through the Earth can be identified. Identifying the wave path, we are actually able to identify and map out the structure of the Earth's interior. In the terrestrial case, individual seismic events are recorded and analyzed. In helioseismology, there is a continual source of waves produced by the bubbling of the granulations, and no single event is actually tracked. Instead, there is a handful of observing stations that provide 24-hour monitoring of the Sun; one then has to model the entire spectrum of waves that are observed. A mathematical model is then created to fit the full spectrum of waves to the structure of the Sun.

In a system that is continually driven, the waves interact with each other, creating feedback on the wave. Only those that are natural modes for the system grow to any significant amplitude. This growth of natural modes is called resonance[20] and is illustrated for the general case in Figure 3.7.4. Suppose that there are two waves present. If the two waves are

When waves are out of phase, amplitude decreases as a result.

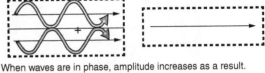

When waves are in phase, amplitude increases as a result.

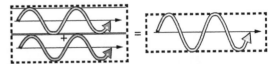

FIGURE 3.7.4. ILLUSTRATION OF HOW TWO WAVES WAVES NOT IN PHASE LEAD TO THE CANCELLATION OF THE WAVE (TOP PANEL), WHILE WAVES IN RESONANCE LEAD TO WAVE GROWTH (BOTTOM PANEL).

in phase, they add, leading to increasing the overall wave amplitude (top panel). However, if they are out of phase (bottom panel), they cancel, leading to essentially the cancellation of the wave power.

In the case of the Sun, we have a round sphere, so the wave can actually propagate around the entire length of the Sun—provided that the medium is not dissipative (i.e., little damping of wave power as it propagates, as is the case for seismic waves). The situation is shown in Figure 3.7.5. If the wave propagates around the Sun such that it is in phase when it gets back to the point of origin, then resonance occurs, and the wave intensity will grow. If it arrives out of phase, then the mode will cancel, and there won't be a strong mode observable.

The seismic waves can reflect on different boundaries. For example, they can't cross the photosphere, since there is no medium present in which they can propagate. They can also reflect off the bottom of the convection zone and the top of the radiation zone due to the differences in the properties of the material in these regions. The properties of the resonant modes are highly dependent on the density and temperature profiles for these different zones. Computer models are then used to fit the observed modes with their expected properties to determine the most likely internal structure of the Sun.

This analysis shows that the highest frequency waves of about three minutes are

17   http://apod.nasa.gov/apod/ap090405.html
18   http://en.wikipedia.org/wiki/Helioseismology
19   http://en.wikipedia.org/wiki/Seismology
20   http://en.wikipedia.org/wiki/Resonance

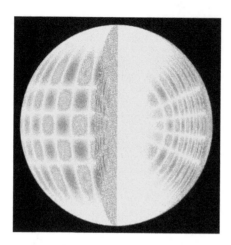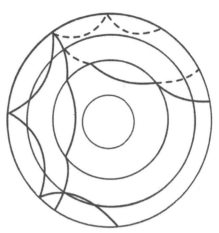

FIGURE 3.7.5. SCHEMATIC OF THE DEVELOPMENT OF RESONANT MODES WITHIN THE SUN SHOWING (A) THE DOPPLER SHIFTS PRODUCED BY THE WAVE MODE; AND (B) THE PATH OF THE WAVES THAT CREATE THE DOPPLER PATTERNS.

associated with waves that simply move along the surface. Waves with periods as long as an hour are associated with waves that reflect off the core. The period is longer because of the extra distance that is traveled by the wave. Through the study of these wave features, Douglas Gough[21] was able to demonstrate in 1977 that the bottom of the convection zone had to be at 0.7 solar radii, which was about twice the depth of previous estimates.

The field of helioseismology is still very young, and refinements continue to be made. One important area is that the wave structure is not only sensitive to the density structure, but also sensitive to the rotation structure within the Sun. The analysis shows that the Sun does

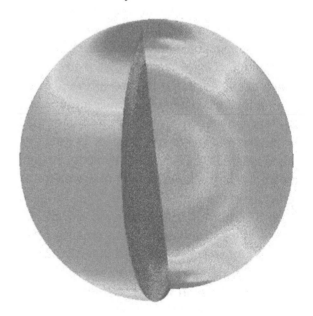

FIGURE 3.7.6. SOLAR ROTATION RATE AS A FUNCTION OF RADIUS AND LATITUDE. (AFTER KOSOVICHEV ET AL., 1997 *SOLAR PHYSICS*, V. 170, ISSUE 1, PP. 43–61.) REFINEMENTS OF THE ROTATION RATE CAN BE SEEN AT NSO/GONG. IMAGE CREDIT: SOHO/MDI CONSORTIUM. SOHO IS A PROJECT OF INTERNATIONAL COOPERATION BETWEEN ESA AND NASA.

FIGURE 3.7.7. A 3-D REPRESENTATION OF THE ROTATION OF THE SOLAR INTERIOR AS A FUNCTION OF DEPTH AND LATITUDE. RED = FASTER ROTATION, BLUE = SLOWER ROTATION. THE DATA USED TO GENERATE THE MODEL CAME FROM THE MICHELSON DOPPLER IMAGER (MDI) ONBOARD THE SOHO SPACECRAFT.

21   http://jila.colorado.edu/content/douglas-gough-0

not rotate as a rigid object (Figure 3.7.6): the core and the radiative zone rotate at the same rate of about 27 days, but the convection zone has a rotation rate that varies with latitude, with the high latitude regions having the slowest rotation rate of 35 days and the equator rotating slightly faster at 25 days. This differential rotation has an important effect on the solar atmosphere described in the next chapter.

Assignment Problem 3.1: *A watched pot never boils.* Find a regular pot with a lid. Pour one liter of water into the pot and measure the time it takes to boil. When it first starts to boil, where are the first bubbles most likely seen? Does the pot show any evidence of oscillations? Allow both the stove and pot to cool, and repeat the experiment, but now have the lid on. What is the time difference for the water to boil? Does the pot exhibit any oscillations? Explain the difference in light of the above discussion.

Helioseismology also allows scientists to develop complex three-dimensional models of the solar interior. One such model can be seen in Figure 3.7.7. The figure shows a model of the speed of the plasma flow not only as a function of latitude (while the surface of the Sun at the equator rotates faster than near the poles, they both rotate in the same direction), but also as a function of depth, and is a graphical way of representing the information in Figure 3.7.6. Besides using this information to understand the structure of the Sun, scientists can also use it to make predictions regarding the intensity of the next solar maximum (a time of maximum solar activity). The predictions take the form of when the peak in sunspot numbers will occur and what the peak number will be. The prediction for sunspot cycle 24 can be found at http://www.swpc.noaa.gov/SolarCycle/SC24/, while the predictions versus observations for the current and past solar cycle can be found at http://solarscience.msfc.nasa.gov/predict.shtml. The current solar cycle observations can be found at http://www.swpc.noaa.gov/SolarCycle/ In the next two chapters, we will talk in depth about why we care about the intensity of solar

maxima, both for living on Earth and for traveling in space.

Image Credits

Chapter 3 Opening Image: NASA/ESA/Allison Loll/Jeff Hester, "Most detailed image of the Crab Nebula," http://www.spacetelescope.org/images/heic0515a/. Copyright in the Public Domain.

Figure 3.1.1: Adapted from: Copyright © 2012 Depositphotos/blueringmedia.

Figure 3.2.1: "Sun Zones," http://solarscience.msfc.nasa.gov/images/cutaway.jpg. Copyright in the Public Domain.

Figure 3.3.1a: NASA/MSFC Hathaway, "Density (Dalagaard Model 1)," http://solarscience.msfc.nasa.gov/images/Dalsgaard1_density_vs_r.jpg. Copyright in the Public Domain.

Figure 3.3.1b: NASA/MSFC Hathaway, "Temperature (Dalsgaard Model 1)," http://solarscience.msfc.nasa.gov/images/Dalsgaard1_T_vs_r.jpg. Copyright in the Public Domain.

Figure 3.5.1: Copyright © McSush (CC BY-SA 3.0) at https://commons.wikimedia.org/wiki/File:Convection_cells.svg

Figure 3.6.1: Big Bear Solar Observatory/New Jersey Institute of Technology, "White Light," http://hesperia.gsfc.nasa.gov/~knisely/bbso_white_fd_19960708_1455.gif. Copyright © 1996 by Big Bear Solar Observatory. Reprinted with permission.

Figure 3.7.1a: Copyright © Saks (CC by 3.0) at https://commons.wikimedia.org/wiki/File:Particula_quieta.jpg.

Figure 3.7.1b: Copyright © Saks (CC by 3.0) at https://commons.wikimedia.org/wiki/File:Particula_subsonica.jpg.

Figure 3.7.2: Adapted from: SOHO/MDI Consortium, "Single Dopplergram," http://sohowww.nascom.nasa.gov/gallery/Helioseismology/mdi001.html. Copyright in the Public Domain.

Figure 3.7.3: NASA, "Granules2-Cropped-Photospheric-Granulation-G.Scharmer-Swedish-Vacuum-Solar-Telescope-10-July-1997," http://commons.wikimedia.org/wiki/File:Granules2-Cropped-Photospheric-Granulation-G.Scharmer-Swedish-Vacuum-Solar-Telescope-10-July-1997.jpg. Copyright in the Public Domain.

Figure 3.7.5a: "Helioseismology pmode1," http://en.wikipedia.org/wiki/File:Helioseismology_pmode1.png. Copyright in the Public Domain.

Figure 3.7.5b: Adapted from: USGS, "Earthquake wave paths," http://en.wikipedia.org/wiki/File:Earthquake_wave_paths.svg. Copyright in the Public Domain.

Figure 3.7.6: SOHO/MDI Consortiuum, "Convection/Radiation graph," http://sohowww.nascom.nasa.gov/gallery/Helioseismology/mdi013.html. Copyright in the Public Domain.

Figure 3.7.7: SOHO/MDI Consortium, "Solar Interior Rotation," http://www.opencourse.info/astronomy/introduction/12.sun_interior/mdi.html. Copyright in the Public Domain.

The Solar Atmosphere and Space Weather

4.1. A Magnetized Star

As noted in the previous chapter, the top of the photosphere is only a balmy 4000 K, well below the 15,000,000 K core of the Sun. At 4000 K, the hydrogen is only weakly ionized, with only a small percentage of free protons and electrons. The energies of these particles is so low they would not provide any type of radiation hazard in space. If the temperature remained level, space would be actually a very benign environment that humans could move about in with little worry about the prevailing space weather conditions.

But this is not actually the case. Our star has a magnetic field, and motions within the convection zone ultimately lead to heating of the solar atmosphere, creating a plasma with temperatures as high as a few million degrees, albeit at very much lower densities than in the core. There are many manifestations of this heating, including solar flares, coronal mass ejections, the solar wind, and the development of space weather conditions around the planet. The power of these energetic particles is sufficient to create auroras on the majority of solar system objects that have magnetic fields. In addition, they provide a source for the development of the radiation belt around the Earth, which is a hazard for satellites and human exploration above low Earth orbit. In this chapter, we investigate these processes. For readers who are interested in a more comprehensive history of solar physics, a compilation of major discoveries can be seen at http://www.hao.ucar.edu/education/spTimeline.php.

4.2. Sunspots

A small hint that the Sun is not completely benign is seen in the photosphere image in Figure 3.6.1, where there is a small, dark spot present on the disk of the Sun, called a sunspot[1]. The meaning of sunspots has been argued for centuries. Under normal conditions, the Sun will blind anyone looking at it. However, when there is a fog or haze present so that visibility is significantly reduced (especially near sunrise or sunset), the disk of the Sun can be seen without any modern technology. The first written record[2] of sunspots appears in the Chinese *Book of Changes*, written around 800 BC. For Western civilization, the first mention of these appeared in the literature around 300 BC by the Greek scholar Theophrastus[3], who was a student of Aristotle[4].

Despite these observations, the prevailing thought, particularly in Western civilization as taught by Aristotle[5], was that the Sun was a perfect globe of fire without blemish. This philosophy reigns as the prevailing thought until the 1600s, when the telescope is invented. Four men using telescopes, including Johannes Fabricius[6] in Holland, Christopher Scheiner[7] in Germany, Galileo Galilei[8] in Italy, and Thomas Harriot[9] in England, reported spots on the Sun.

These observations were dismissed because Aristotle's viewpoint was well entrenched into the culture at this time. For other observations, Galileo was eventually tried and convicted of heresy, and spent the latter part of his life under house arrest. The interpretation remained that the Sun is unblemished, and that spots must be clouds floating over a perfect Sun.

Nevertheless, observations with telescopes continued, and the presence of sunspots remained a persistent feature. In the 1700s, some astronomers thought that the spots must be solid mountaintops protruding above an ocean of flowing lava, with tides allowing mountaintops to peek above the lava now and again. In 1774, Alexander Wilson observed that the spots had a saucer-shaped appearance and that we were looking into a dark, cooler interior. While his interpretation was not exactly correct, it is true that the sunspots are regions of cool material on the surface of the photosphere. Because they are relatively cool, they appear dark on the bright surface of the Sun. However, if we were able to pick up a sunspot and place it next to the Moon, the Moon would then become the dim object, providing only one-tenth of the emission of the sunspot.

Using just simple telescopes, a lot of information about the characteristics of the Sun was obtained from sunspots. In particular, in 1826, Heinrich Schwabe[10] began his observations of sunspots in an effort to discover a new planet that was thought to sit inside the orbit of Mercury, tentatively called "Vulcan" (which is now popularized in the Star Trek culture), and which was thought needed to explain perturbations in the orbit of Mercury. Schwabe did not find the proposed planet, but after 11 years of observation, he noted that there is a period to the number of sunspots, and after another six years of observations, he was able to confirm this periodicity. He published these results after 17 years of observations, but his work was initially ignored. It took another 11 years for him to prove that the phenomenon is real, which showed real dedication.

This phenomenon is known as the sunspot cycle[11], in which the number of sunspots on the photosphere follows an 11-year cycle of maximum and minimum variations as illustrated in Figure 4.2.1. Solar maximum (minimum) refers to the time when the sunspot number is at a maximum (minimum) during the cycle. This cycle is the first hint that our star is not constant, but instead has some dynamic processes that

---

1   http://en.wikipedia.org/wiki/Sunspot
2   http://www.hao.ucar.edu/education/TimelineA.php
3   http://en.wikipedia.org/wiki/Theophrastus
4   http://en.wikipedia.org/wiki/Aristotle
5   http://en.wikipedia.org/wiki/Aristotle
6   http://en.wikipedia.org/wiki/Johannes_Fabricius
7   http://en.wikipedia.org/wiki/Christopher_Scheiner
8   http://en.wikipedia.org/wiki/Galileo_Galilei
9   http://en.wikipedia.org/wiki/Thomas_Harriot

10   http://en.wikipedia.org/wiki/Heinrich_Schwabe
11   http://en.wikipedia.org/wiki/Sunspot_cycle

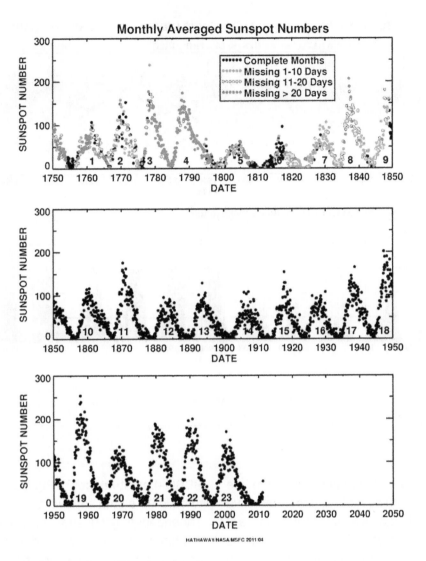

FIGURE 4.2.1. THE SUNSPOT CYCLE SINCE THE FIRST OBSERVATIONS WERE MADE IN THE MID-18TH CENTURY. CURRENT MEASUREMENTS CAN BE FOUND AT: HTTP://SOLARSCIENCE.MSFC.NASA.GOV/SUNSPOTCYCLE. SHTML

are modulating its behavior over time. We now know this sunspot cycle is directly related to solar activity, which can affect modern communications and the space environment, with the strongest effects associated during the period when the number of sunspots is at the maximum. Still unresolved is if there is another period present, one with about an 80–100-year cycle that leads to less intense or more intense sunspot maxima.

Richard Carrington[12] took up the investigation of sunspots in the 1860s and was able to demonstrate that the sunspots at the equator rotated at a period of about 27 days and at about 30 days halfway between the poles and the equator. Thus, the presence of differential rotation on the Sun, which was demonstrated in the previous chapter, is directly evident in the motion of sunspots across the face of the photosphere. So, just as we mark off the years on Earth, the rotation of the Sun is counted in terms of "Carrington rotation numbers."

The presence of sunspots starts to show that important processes are occurring on the Sun that are hidden by the simple white-light

---

12   http://en.wikipedia.org/wiki/Richard_Carrington

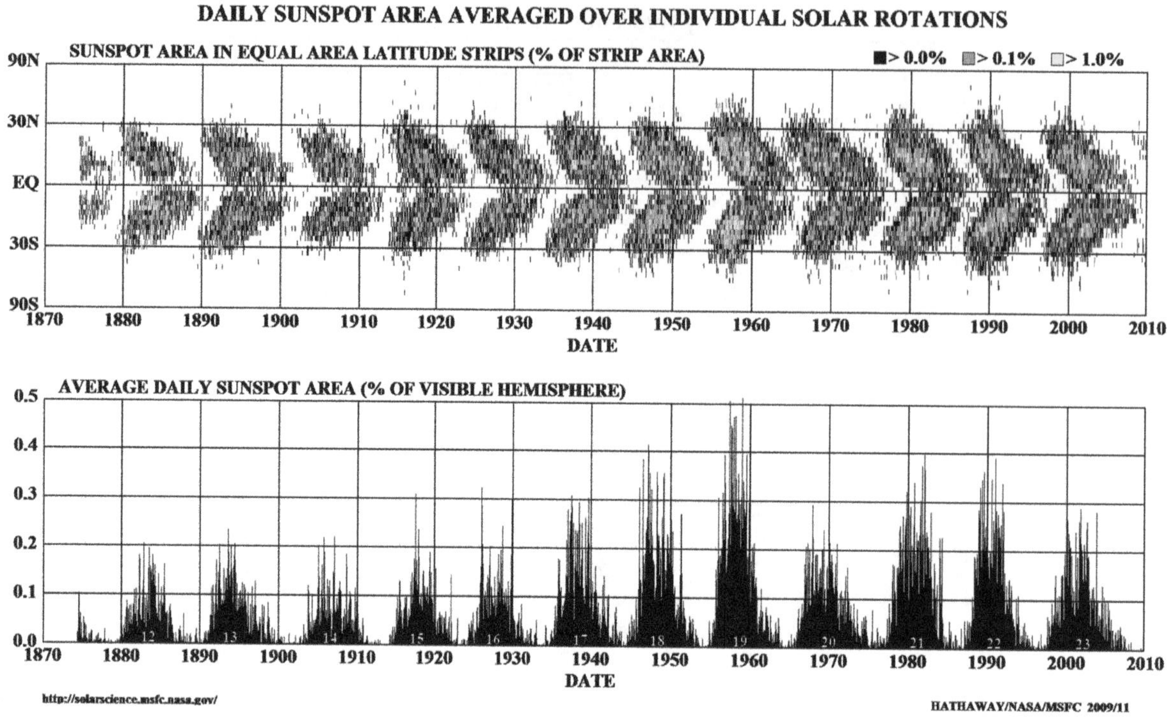

DAILY SUNSPOT AREA AVERAGED OVER INDIVIDUAL SOLAR ROTATIONS

FIGURE 4.2.2.   THE SUNSPOT BUTTERFLY DIAGRAM[13], SHOWING THE CHANGE IN POSITION OF THE SUNSPOTS DURING RECORDED HISTORY OF SUNSPOT CYCLES.

images of the Sun. Thus, beginning in the late 1890s and continuing today, comprehensive observations of particular line emissions are made on a routine basis. These observations not only enable us to see deeper into the dynamics of the Sun, but also reveal the very dynamic behavior of the Sun.

Not only is the number of sunspots seen to vary, but their position and total coverage of the Sun are seen to vary with the solar cycle as shown in Figure 4.2.2. As one moves from a sunspot minimum, the sunspots appear about +/−30° latitude. As the cycle continues toward sunspot maximum, the sunspots appear closer to the equator until they eventually fade away. This change in characteristics gives a hint to the source of the sunspots, which is described in the following sections.

Assignment Question 4.1. *Sunspots*. Use the solar intensity daily images available from the

BBSO–Latest Images[14]–Big Bear Observatory to build up a data set over the next two weeks. Try and identify sunspots in at least two different latitudes (this may be dependent on how active the Sun is). Describe how the sunspots evolve in the two-week period—do new spots appear, do old ones disappear, or do existing ones stay the same? How do they evolve in size and shape? How fast are they rotating?

4.3. The Chromosphere and the Magnetic Sun

So, these white-light observations of sunspots give the earliest hint that the Sun is not the perfect sphere that Aristotle was a proponent of and which was the accepted doctrine for the next 2000 years. Rare events could also

---

13   http://solarscience.msfc.nasa.gov/SunspotCycle.shtml

14   http://www.bbso.njit.edu/cgi-bin/LatestImages

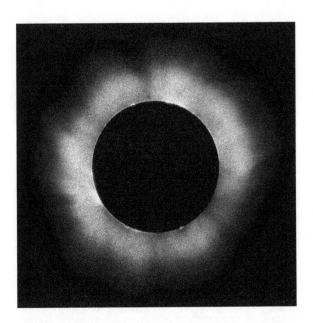

Figure 4.3.1. Optical emissions seen during the total eclipse of 1999, showing that the Sun has an atmosphere.

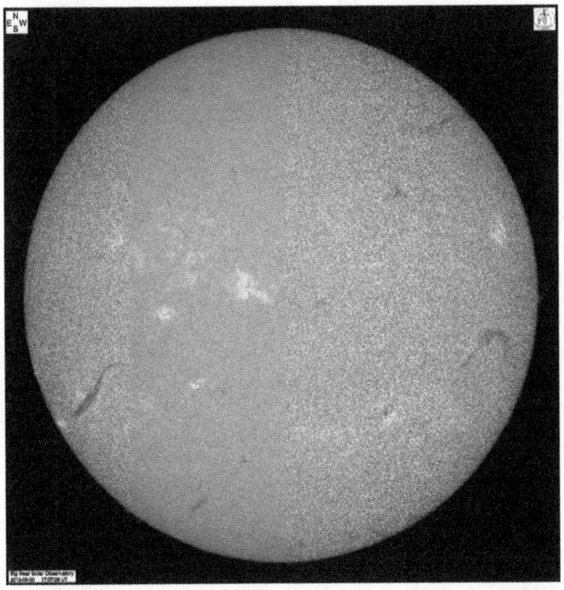

Figure 4.3.2. H-alpha image of the Sun, from Big Bear Solar Observatory[17] (8/30/2012). Daily images are available from this site.

give us a hint as to what happens above the photosphere. During total eclipses[15], where the bulk of the light from the disk is blocked by the moon, optical emissions are seen extending well above the photosphere as seen in Figure 4.3.1. These types of observations are the first to show that the Sun has an atmosphere! These observations raise the questions:

- How far does the solar atmosphere extend?
- What does the solar atmosphere consist of?
- What is producing the energy to support the atmosphere?

Very close to the lunar, occulting disk, a region of (red) color is seen extending just beyond the photosphere. This region is called the chromosphere[16], from *chromos*, the Greek word for color. Most of the color is coming from the red emission line of hydrogen atoms called H-alpha or H_α.

Starting in the 1890s, George Hale[18], through his development of special optical filters, was able to look just at these H-alpha emissions without the need of an eclipse. In so doing, he was able to look at the full disk of the Sun. His observations showed that the Sun has substantial structure over most of the surface. Since Hale's early observations, the Sun is routinely monitored in many different wavelengths, including H-alpha. Today's images can be seen from the Big Bear Solar Observatory[19]. A recent example is shown in Figure 4.3.2.

Sunspots in H-alpha appear black as in the white-light images, but the region surrounding the sunspots actually glows in H-alpha. These bright regions are called plages[20], from the French word meaning "beaches." These brighter regions indicate the presence of hot regions localized around the sunspots. Plages can be seen to appear before a sunspot is visible, giving a hint of a region where a sunspot may soon form.

15   http://en.wikipedia.org/wiki/Solar_eclipse
16   http://en.wikipedia.org/wiki/Chromosphere

17   http://www.bbso.njit.edu/cgi-bin/LatestImages
18   http://en.wikipedia.org/wiki/George_Hale
19   http://www.bbso.njit.edu/cgi-bin/LatestImages
20   http://en.wikipedia.org/wiki/Plage_(astronomy)

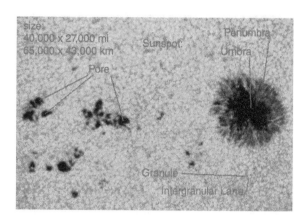

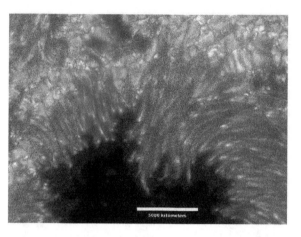

FIGURE 4.3.3. AT HIGH RESOLUTION, SUNSPOTS ARE SEEN TO HAVE STRUCTURE, INCLUDING A DARK CENTER CALLED THE UMBRA, AND A LIGHTER OUTER REGION CALLED THE PENUMBRA. SMALL SPOTS WITHOUT THIS STRUCTURE ARE CALLED PORES.

FIGURE 4.3.4. HIGH-RESOLUTION IMAGE OF A SUNSPOT IN H-ALPHA, OBSERVED BY THE SWEDISH INSTITUTE FOR SOLAR PHYSICS[23]. GEORGE HALE USED THE SPIRAL STRUCTURE AROUND THE SUNSPOT TO SUGGEST THAT OUR SUN HAS A MAGNETIC FIELD. A MOVIE VERSION OF THIS IMAGE CAN BE FOUND AT HTTP://WWW.YOUTUBE.COM/WATCH?V= 19T6U4-WSPQ.

There are additional features seen, including long, dark regions, which are called filaments[21]. Other structures, called prominences, seen during some eclipses, show features standing above the surface of the Sun. We now know that filaments and prominences are the same thing, just viewed from different angles, and that they have implications for other structures higher in the solar atmosphere.

At high resolution, one starts to see structure around the sunspot as shown in Figure 4.3.3, including:

- An umbra, which is the dark center of the sunspot, 2,000–20,000 km in diameter;
- A penumbra, lighter in color than the umbra, but still darker than the surrounding material, typically 20,000–60,000 km in size;
- Pores, which are small sunspots with no penumbra present.

George Hale, however, concentrated on the areas around the sunspots. A high-resolution image of a sunspot similar to what Hale might have seen is shown in Figure 4.3.4.

Hale noted that there is a spiral structure around the sunspots. This suggested to him that there is a whirling motion, as if the material is caught up in the eye of the hurricane or some other terrestrial-like storm. Recent observations and movies that show this can be found at http://www.solarphysics.kva.se/. Hale's observations were occurring at the same time as the discovery of the various subatomic particles, as outlined in Chapter 2. Thus, he surmised that this whirling motion is produced by electrons caught in a vortex produced by a magnetic field. He was not exactly correct, in that it is not just electrons, but he is correct in that we have a magnetized Sun![22]

Hale figured out a way to prove the hypothesis that there is a strong magnetic field on the Sun. It is known at this time that the trajectory of an electron is modified by the presence of the magnetic field. You could easily prove this in the good old days of cathode ray television sets, where the screen image would be modified by placing a magnet near the television.

The same effect occurs at atomic levels and is called the Zeeman effect[23], which earned the

21   http://www.hao.ucar.edu/education/slides/slide8. php

22   http://www.solarphysics.kva.se/
23   http://www.physlink.com/education/askexperts/ ae646.cfm

a) Splitting of orbits   b) Splitting of energy levels

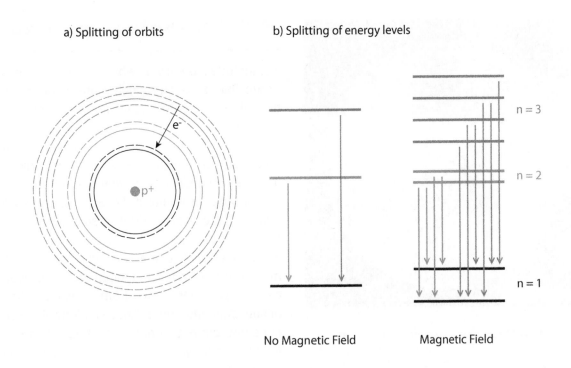

No Magnetic Field   Magnetic Field

FIGURE 4.3.5. ZEEMAN EFFECT: (A) THE PRESENCE OF A MAGNETIC FIELD SEPARATES ELEC-TRON ORBITS FROM A SINGLE ORBIT INTO MULTIPLE ONES AROUND A NUCLEUS. (B) THIS IS THEN SEEN AS AN INCREASE IN THE NUMBER OF SPECTRAL LINE EMISSIONS FROM THE ATOM.

discoverer, Pieter Zeeman[24], the Nobel Prize in 1902. (His initial work, like that of many others we have described so far, was impeded by his immediate supervisors, but he eventually prevailed.) This effect is illustrated in Figure 4.3.5. In the presence of a strong magnetic field, the electron orbits around the nucleus are modified. The shift in the orbits is proportional to the strength of the magnetic field, and the shift in direction is dependent on the polarity of the magnetic field. This, then, produces the splitting of the line emissions from the atom, with the shift dependent on the polarity and strength of the magnetic field.

Hale used the Zeeman effect to show that the Sun has magnetic fields as strong as 3000 Gauss (0.3 T). The scale of the Earth's magnetic field is only 0.3 Gauss at the magnetic equator. Rare-earth magnets can have field strengths comparable to that observed on the Sun, but you have to consider magnetic material with a size much greater than the Earth.

Hale was also able to show that the sunspots have the strongest magnetic fields around them, but they are, in fact, relatively calm regions. In essence, sunspots are regions that demarcate the flow of cold material back down to the bottom of the convection zone, and surrounding areas of the plages are associated with solar activity. This can be seen in the movie version of Figure 4.3.4. Plasma in the penumbra appears to be flowing toward the umbra, but is being inhibited (by an unseen magnetic field). The hotter plasma surrounding the sunspot is trying to flow from hot to cold to equalize the temperatures, but the strong magnetic field in the center of the sunspot is preventing the plasma from entering. (This connection between plasma flow and magnetic field is called the frozen-in-field effect. It is defined in the next section, and we will see this concept again when discussing the near-space region around planets and different in-space propulsion methods.)

Because of the importance of the solar magnetic field, routine monitoring continues

---

24   http://en.wikipedia.org/wiki/Pieter_Zeeman

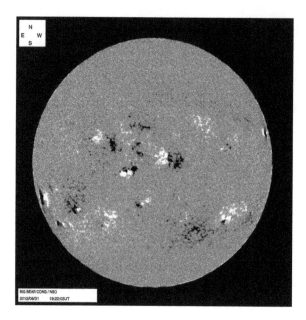

FIGURE 4.3.6. THE MAGNETOGRAM THAT CORRESPONDS TO THE H-ALPHA IMAGE IN FIGURE 4.3.2. SOURCE OF THE DATA IS FROM THE BIG BEAR SOLAR OBSERVATORY[26]. WHITE AREAS INDICATE NORTHWARD POLARITY, WHILE BLACK AREAS INDICATE SOUTHWARD POLARITY. AROUND EACH SUNSPOT, THERE TENDS TO BE A PAIR OF NORTH/SOUTH-ORIENTED MAGNETIC FIELD. ALSO NOTE THAT IN THE NORTHERN HEMISPHERE, ALL THE SUNSPOT REGIONS HAVE SOUTH TO THE LEFT AND NORTH TO THE RIGHT. THIS PATTERN REVERSES IN THE SOUTHERN HEMISPHERE.

today using the above methodology to produce what is called magnetograms[25] of the Sun's surface. An example of a magnetogram is shown in Figure 4.3.6. It is seen that the magnetic field is very much more complicated than the terrestrial magnetic field. In our case, there is a single north and south pole present. For the Sun, around each sunspot there is a north/south pair of magnetic field polarities. Moreover, the shape and distribution of the magnetic field varies quite strongly in time. The movie of such variations can be seen from recent observations from the Solar Dynamics Observatory[27] or at solar dynamo[28].

25   http://solar-center.stanford.edu/solar-images/magnetograms.html
26   http://www.bbso.njit.edu/cgi-bin/LatestImages
27   http://www.nasa.gov/mission_pages/sdo/news/magnetic-measuring.html
28   http://solarscience.msfc.nasa.gov/dynamo.shtml

4.4. The Solar Dynamo

So, the question now is why the magnetic field of the Sun is so very much more complicated than that of the terrestrial magnetic field. In particular, the magnetic field of the Earth has essentially the same shape as a simple bar magnet (seen in Figure 4.4.1), so why shouldn't the scaling continue up to that of the Sun?

The answer is that if the Sun rotated as a rigid body (i.e., if all latitudes rotated at the same speed, as they do on the Earth), then, in fact, the magnetic field of the Sun would indeed look much like the Earth's magnetic field. However, as we have seen above from an examination of sunspots and from helioseismology, the Sun does not rotate as a rigid body because it is a fluid that is subject to the forces of convection and rotation.

In order to understand what is happening, we first have to say a little something about how plasmas and magnetic fields interact. When both are present, they have a closely linked relationship. The charged particles that make up a plasma will feel the influence of any magnetic field, so if that magnetic field moves, the plasma will be dragged along with it. Similarly, a magnetic field will feel the influence of any plasma connected to it. If a plasma is moved around, the magnetic field will move with it. This concept is called the frozen-in-field theory.

A movie of the sunspot magnetic field associated with flare activity can be found at http://www.youtube.com/watch?v=2ifkdLpWYqA. Solar minimum is associated with a time when the Sun's magnetic field is very dipole-like (Part 1 of Figure 4.4.2). The differential rotation of the Sun means that any magnetic field laced throughout the plasma will move in a differential manner as well. We can see that in Part 2 of Figure 4.4.2, where the magnetic field lines near the equator lead the portion of the same magnetic field line closer to the poles. After many, many rotations, the effect accumulates, and the Sun's magnetic field becomes twisted up (Part 3 of Figure 4.4.2). This twisted magnetic field can produce kinks that pop up

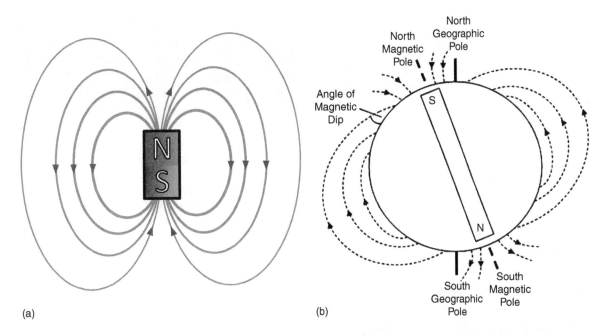

(a)   (b)

FIGURE 4.4.1. SCHEMATIC OF THE MAGNETIC FIELD LINES OF A BAR MAGNET (LEFT) AND THAT OF THE TERRESTRIAL MAGNETIC FIELD (RIGHT). THE LINES TRACE OUT THE DIRECTION OF THE MAGNETIC FIELD THAT WOULD, FOR EXAMPLE, BE DETECTED BY A COMPASS. BECAUSE THERE ARE TWO POLES (NORTH/SOUTH), THIS CONFIGURATION IS CALLED A DIPOLE.

above the photosphere, producing the features we see as sunspots. The time when the Sun's magnetic field is the most twisted up is sunspot maximum.

This process also explains why sunspots in the magnetogram (Figure 4.3.6) always have both a north polarity and a south polarity, why sunspots typically come in pairs, and why that polarity reverses when crossing the equator. Each polarity (sunspot) is associated with one part of the magnetic field pushing through the photosphere. Magnetic field lines can't end, so the magnetic field has to return below the surface at a region of opposite polarity. In some cases, the two paired sunspots can actually merge to form a single large sunspot, many times larger than the Earth.

This also explains a much more subtle feature in the magnetograms. If you look at Figure 4.3.6, you will see that in the upper portion, all of the sunspot groups have the south (black) polarity on the right (leading) side and the north (white) polarity on the left (trailing) side. This pattern switches when you look at the bottom half of the image. This is explained

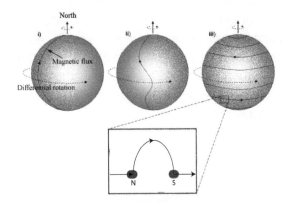

FIGURE 4.4.2. TWISTING OF THE SOLAR MAGNETIC FIELD DUE TO DIFFERENTIAL ROTATION LEADS TO THE DEFORMATION OF THE INITIAL MAGNETIC DIPOLE (1) INTO A DEFORMED MAGNETIC FIELD CONFIGURATION (2), WHICH EVENTUALLY BECOMES TWISTED, CREATING WITH MAGNETIC FIELD LINES, THEN POPPING OUT INTO THE SOLAR ATMOSPHERE (3). A MOVIE OF THIS PROCESS CAN BE SEEN AT HTTP://WWW.WINDOWS2UNIVERSE.ORG/SUN/ACTIVITY/SUN_MAG_FIELD_ROTATE_TANGLE.HTML

in Part 3 of Figure 4.4.2—as magnetic field lines can't end, the direction of the twisted-up magnetic field changes direction when crossing the equator.

So what happens after Part 3 of Figure 4.4.2? Dynamic processes that we will discuss in the next sections cause the twisted regions of magnetic field to annihilate or cancel out. After a few years, the Sun's magnetic field begins to return to a more dipole-like shape, albeit with the poles reversed.

As a side note, the Earth's magnetic field reverses, too, just not on an 11-year cycle like the Sun. There have been times when the Earth's magnetic field has reversed on a sort of 10,000-year cycle and times when it has been much more erratic. We do not fully understand why the Sun's magnetic field reversal period is so regular, while the Earth's is not.

Assignment Question 4.2: *Making your own magnet.* Find a large metal bolt (about 3/8" thick) and wrap 100 turns of wire over the bolt. Apply a 1.5-volt battery to the ends of the wire and see the number of paperclips that you can pick up. Repeat the experiment with a 9V battery. Is the strength of the magnetic field stronger or weaker in this case? Use a compass; taking photos, map out the direction of the magnetic field from your electromagnet. (Make sure you don't leave the wires connected too long!)

4.5. The Solar Corona: Views Using Coronagraphs

The presence of sunspots and associated magnetic field effects are not just interesting phenomena to debate about the perfection of the Sun of Aristotle. The presence of these magnetic fields' effects has dramatic consequences for the upper solar atmosphere, and, in fact, for the rest of the solar system. The upper atmosphere, which is called the corona, cannot be seen using simple white-light images like we used to see the photosphere.

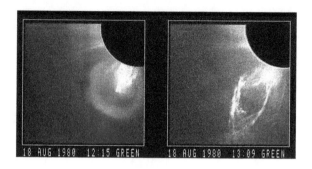

FIGURE 4.5.1. CORONAGRAPH IMAGES, WHERE THE INNER RADIUS IS BLOCKED OUT TO ABOUT 1.2 SOLAR RADII. THE SOLAR CORONA, WHICH IS SEEN OUT TO FOUR SOLAR RADII IN THIS VERSION OF THE CORONAGRAPH, CONTAINS MAGNETIC LOOP STRUCTURES THAT ARE LARGER THAN THE SUN ITSELF AND WHICH CAN CHANGE SHAPE AND SIZE WITHIN A PERIOD OF LESS THAN AN HOUR[29].

Special techniques must be used to see the solar corona. Images in science fiction movies that show a beautiful white-light image of a spacecraft surrounded by lots of structures around the Sun (such as in Chapter 1) are actually mixing wavelengths and techniques to create a more aesthetically pleasing image.

One of the simplest techniques to view the corona is to actually block out the light from the disk of the Sun. This occurs during a full eclipse and provided the earliest means to observe the solar corona (see Figure 4.3.1). Since full solar eclipses are rare, what is normally done is to place a disk in front of the telescope to block the light from the solar disk. Such a device is called a coronagraph[30], and by blocking out the bright emissions from the disk, the less intense emissions from scattered light in the upper atmosphere can be more easily seen.

The size of the occulting, or blocking, disk can be changed to enable different heights of the solar corona to be seen. The High Altitude Observatory Coronagraph[31] provides daily images using an occulting disk of about1.2 solar radii. With this type of occulting disk, magnetic loop structures are seen extending to at least

29 http://mlso.hao.ucar.edu/smm/smmcp_events/1980aug18.html
30 http://en.wikipedia.org/wiki/Coronagraph
31 http://mlso.hao.ucar.edu/

2014/04/02 14:48

(a)

2014/04/02 15:06

(b)

FIGURE 4.5.2. CORONAGRAPH IMAGES FROM SOHO, WITH THE WHITE CIRCLE INDICATING THE SOLAR DISK AND THE BLANKED-OUT REGION INDICATING THE SIZE OF THE OCCULTING DISK. THESE IMAGES SHOW THAT THE SOLAR CORONA IS VERY MUCH LARGER THAN THE SUN ITSELF. THE LARGE WHITE DOT IN THE FIGURE ON THE RIGHT IS A PLANET MOVING THROUGH THE FIELD OF VIEW[32].

four solar radii as they evolve on a timescale of less than an hour.

The Solar and Heliospheric Observatory[33] (SOHO), in orbit between the Earth and the Sun, carries two coronagraphs with occulting disks at 2 and 3.7 solar radii. Examples from these two coronagraphs are shown in Figure 4.5.2 and demonstrate that there are structures all the way out to the edge of the field of view, which is at 6 and 32 solar radii, respectively.

The Solar Terrestrial Relations Observatory[34] (STEREO) is continuing such coronagraph observations, but with the usage of two spacecraft, a full three-dimensional image of the solar atmosphere can be constructed.

Coronagraphs with very large occulting disks (relative to the size of the star) are now being used to image extrasolar planets[35]. An image from the Palomar Observatory Hale Telescope from a star known as HR8799, 120 light-years away, shows the presence of three planets around the star. Most extrasolar planets are not discovered in this manner, but are rather discovered by periodic variations in the light emissions of the star. This ability to image these stars using the coronagraph technique shows how developments in one field can be used to make new discoveries in a different field; the ability to provide imaging gives a much greater grasp of the significance of these extrasolar planets. The list of these planets continues to grow on an almost weekly basis, with over 800 planets associated with over 600 planetary systems. A full listing can be seen at http://exoplanets.org.

32   http://soho.nascom.nasa.gov/data/realtime/ c2/1024/latest.html

33   http://soho.nascom.nasa.gov/data/realtime-images.html

34   http://stereo.gsfc.nasa.gov/beacon/

35   http://en.wikipedia.org/wiki/Extrasolar_planet

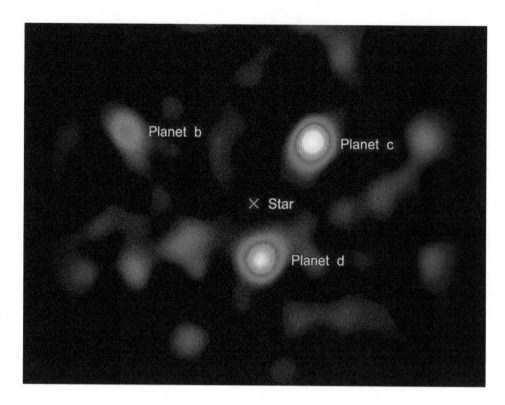

FIGURE 4.5.3. CORONAGRAPH IMAGES OF PLANETS AROUND A STAR 120 LIGHT-YEARS AWAY, CALLED HR8799. THE X MARKS THE POSITION OF THE STAR, WHICH HAS BEEN MASKED BY THE OCCULTING DISK[36]. SOURCE: NASA

4.6. The Corona: Views Using High-Temperature Lines

The fact that the corona is so much bigger than the Sun itself is indicative that it is much hotter than the surface of the Sun—otherwise, gravitational forces would keep the atmosphere bound to low altitudes. Thus, the other way that the solar corona is imaged is by looking at specific line emissions in the ultraviolet and X-rays that originate from very hot material. As noted in Chapter 1, UV and X-rays have a higher energy than any of the visible light emissions, so this part of the spectrum provides insight into more energetic phenomena. Emissions in this energy range do not come from neutral atoms. Instead, they come from atoms other than hydrogen that have been stripped of a significant

fraction of their electrons. SOHO used iron lines where more than eight electrons have been stripped of the atom, as well as helium that has been stripped of one electron. Recent images from SOHO are shown in Figure 4.6.1. Emissions at these wavelengths are coming from plasmas that have temperatures of 1,000,000 to 2,000,000 K, which represents a significant increase in temperature from the photosphere.

These images show the same kind of loop structures as in the coronagraphs, except they allow the ability to link them directly to the surface of the Sun. Indeed, the He II (helium missing one electron) image has the closest resemblance to the Hollywood image of Figure 1.4.1, where loops on a bubbling surface of the Sun can be seen. These images are very striking and also very important in understanding solar activity. One of the easiest things to observe in these images is that the magnetic loops are localized at mid-latitudes,

---

36   http://www.nasa.gov/topics/universe/features/exoplanet20100414-a.html

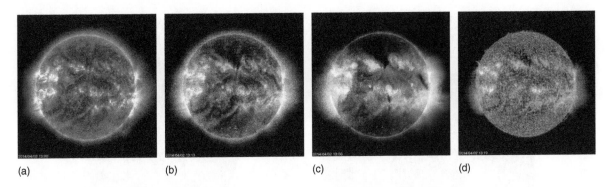

(a)　　　　　　(b)　　　　　　(c)　　　　　　(d)

FIGURE 4.6.1. UV IMAGES OF THE SUN ON 2012/09/14 TAKEN BY SOHO IN FE IX/X, FE XII, FE XV, AND HE II. THE NUMBER FOLLOWING THE ELEMENT DESIGNATION INDICATES THE NUMBER OF ELECTRONS PLUS ONE THAT HAVE BEEN STRIPPED FROM THE ATOM. FOR EXAMPLE, HE I WOULD INDICATE NEUTRAL HELIUM, WHILE HE II REPRESENTS HE THAT HAS BEEN STRIPPED OF ONE ELECTRON. SOURCE OF DATA: HTTP://UMBRA.NASCOM. NASA.GOV/EIT/EIT_FULL_RES.HTML

around which we have previously noted that the sunspots tend to be focused.

The fact that the emissions are associated with magnetic structures provides a clue as to why the solar atmosphere is so much hotter than the solar surface. The solar atmosphere is being heated by electrical and magnetic processes that drive currents in the plasma. These processes, in general, do not involve fusion, but are able to produce a host of phenomena; these phenomena produce energetic particles that fill the solar system and control the space weather environment around the planets. The next few sections detail these processes. We will also highlight the frozen-in-field concept. We can see these structures because there is plasma tied to the magnetic field, and the plasma is emitting radiation.

4.7. Helmet Streamers

The most prominent feature of the coronagraphs is the helmet streamer[37], which is a large loop-like structure that sits over an active region. The name originates from the fact that they have a shape similar to the World War I German officer's helmet, as shown in Figure 4.7.1. The distinct shape comes from the pressure of the embedded plasma being able to expand outward and thereby stretch the magnetic field, so that the original loops now have pointy ends. The structures are relatively stable, and while they are associated with particles moving out into space, these particles are typically of relatively low energy. Helmet streamers are not typically associated with significant solar activity.

The reason they are not associated with solar activity is that the magnetic field is diffusive—spread over many solar radii so that, like fusion, there is insufficient critical mass to produce strong particle acceleration. Any particles that are accelerated tend to be confined within the magnetic loops, so the escape of particles into space is highly inhibited.

37   http://en.wikipedia.org/wiki/Helmet_streamer

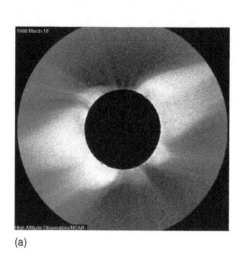
(a)

(b)

FIGURE 4.7.1. HELMET STREAMERS SEEN IN CORONAGRAPHS AND THE HELMET SHAPE AFTER WHICH IT IS NAMED.

4.8. Solar Flares

Underlying helmet streamers is a host of magnetic structures associated with sunspots and active regions. Small-scale sizes of isolated magnetic structures refer to sizes of the order of tens and hundreds of thousands of kilometers—that is, field structures that are the size of Jupiter. Medium-size structures refer to those several hundred thousand to a few million km. The intensity of the magnetic field is typically 100 to 1000 times stronger than the terrestrial magnetic field (i.e., between about 30 to 300 G). These magnetic fields are supported by currents in the coronal plasma, but both have to close into the lower atmosphere, including the chromosphere and photosphere.

Because the lower atmosphere is under constant motion due to convective processes below it, these magnetic field structures are unstable. An analogy can be made when there are many magnets on the table and if you bump and bang the table, eventually some magnets will enter the field of influence of the others.

This will cause them to be attractive to each other, with the release of energy occurring when magnets become attached to each other. On the Sun, the energy in the magnetic loops can be dissipated in a similar process called magnetic reconnection (or annihilation), which results in the phenomenon called solar flare[38]. Solar flares are associated with the generation of energetic particles and emissions across a significant part of the electromagnetic spectrum, including radio waves, ultraviolet and X-rays, and sometimes low levels of gamma rays, indicating that these can be very energetic phenomena.

In the ultraviolet part of the spectrum, solar flares are seen with very rapidly changing magnetic field structures. A couple of examples are at solar flare movie 1[39] and solar flare movie 2[40]. Solar flares can have durations of minutes to hours, with a frequency of tens of events per day during solar maximum.

---

38   http://en.wikipedia.org/wiki/Solar_flare
39   http://www.nasa.gov/mission_pages/sunearth/news/News070312-M5.6flare.html
40   http://www.nasa.gov/mission_pages/sunearth/news/News030512-2M-X1.html

Table 4.8.1. Solar flare classification.

Class	Peak Intensity (W/m²) between 0.1 and 0.8 nm	Effect on Earth
A	$< 10^{-7}$	
B	$10^{-7} - 10^{-6}$	
C	$10^{-6} - 10^{-5}$	Minor events—few noticeable consequences
M	$10^{-5} - 10^{-4}$	Medium events—brief radio blackouts near poles
X	$\geq 10^{-4}$	Major events—planetwide radio blackouts

The strength of a solar flare is classified by its power that is observed at Earth as in Table 4.8.1.

The smaller flares (classes A–C) are typically associated with the single or small loop structures going unstable. They have little impact on the terrestrial environment.

4.9. Coronal Mass Ejections and Space Hazards

The M and X classes are associated with a long series of magnetic loops and have the potential to modify the space environment around the Earth. These events are typically associated with magnetic field structures called filaments[41] when they are viewed on the disk of the sun (they appear as extended dark regions in H-alpha images) and prominences[42] when they are viewed on the limb of the Sun as they protrude beyond the limb. Initially, these structures may be low lying as in the first panel of Figure 4.9.1. If plasma within this magnetic field structure is heated by, for example, waves generated in the lower atmosphere, both the plasma and the magnetic field embedded in the plasma will rise (similar to the steam rising from a pot of boiling water) as in the second and third panels of Figure 4.9.1. This change in the magnetic field configuration is associated with the development of plasma currents. If this extended magnetic field is pinched off, for instance, through two motions of the foot points in the chromosphere (remember, the foot points are not rotating around the Sun at the same speed), the current in the plasma experiences a short circuit, and the magnetic field holds it to the surface to annihilate. This causes some of the magnetic field to rise even further and at the same time accelerating both the electrons and protons of the plasma. These energetic particles then produce enhanced electromagnetic emissions associated with the solar flare.

This release of the energy in the currents causes the magnetic field and the embedded energetic particles to continue to rise and eventually propagate out into space. An actual photo of such an event with the Earth and Jupiter for scale is shown in Figure 4.9.2. At the earliest stages of the energy release, magnetic field structures become a fraction of the solar radius. After a few hours, the structures can actually exceed the size of the Sun. Because of the huge size of these events, they have a special name called coronal mass ejection[43], or CME. A coronal mass ejection movie[44] of such an event, using a coronagraph, emphasizes the acute nature of the structures. The total

---

41 http://spaceweather.com/glossary/filaments.html
42 http://en.wikipedia.org/wiki/Solar_prominence
43 http://en.wikipedia.org/wiki/Coronal_mass_ejection
44 http://www.youtube.com/watch?v=GCjBgfOMaTs

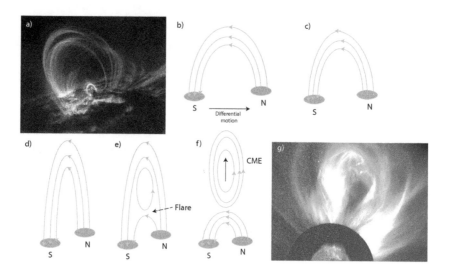

FIGURE 4.9.1. THE SEQUENCE OF THE MAGNETIC FIELD RECONFIGURATION THAT LEADS TO CMEs AND FLARES. THE MAGNETIC FIELD BEGINS IN A LOOPING STRUCTURE AS SEEN IN (A) BY THE TRACE SATELLITE. WE CAN SEE THE MAGNETIC FIELD BECAUSE HOT PLASMA IS MOVING ALONG THE MAGNETIC FIELD EMITTING RADIATION. (B) AT THE BASE OF THE LOOPS ARE OPPOSITE POLARITY SUNSPOTS. (C) - (D) MOTION OF THE PLASMA EITHER AT THE BASE OF THE LOOP OR WITHIN THE CORONA LEADS TO THE LOOP BECOMING ELONGATED. (E) AT SOME POINT, THE OPPOSITELY DIRECTED MAGNETIC FIELD CAN MERGE AND ANHILATE (CALLED "MAGNETIC RECONNECTION"). THE LOCATION OF THE MERGING OF THE MAGNETIC FIELD IS WHERE THE FLARE IS GENERATED. (F) THE MAGNETIC FIELD LOOP BECOMES COMPLETELY DISCONNECTED FROM THE MAGNETIC FIELD AT THE SURFACE AND CAN FLY OFF INTO SPACE TAKING THE HOT PLASMA CONNECTED TO THE MAGNETIC FIELD WITH IT. (G) THE RESULT IS A CME LIKE THIS ONE SEEN BY THE SOHO SPACECRAFT.[46]

mass of coronal mass ejection[45] can exceed 1,000,000,000 tons (10^{12} kg), reaching speeds of several million miles per hour (hundreds of kilometers per second).

It is important to note at this point that flares and CMEs, while related, are not the same thing. A CME is the plasma and magnetic field ejected from the Sun (the bubble in the upper portion of Part 6 in Figure 4.9.1). A flare is the intense radiation burst that typically precedes a CME. The flare is produced at the magnetic field annihilation point (the region where the arrows are pointed inward in Part 6 of Figure 4.9.1).

During sunspot maximum, CMEs can happen every few days. For the most part, we are not too concerned about this on Earth. One type of CME we are typically concerned about

is referred to as a halo event. It is given this name as it appears in SOHO movies as a halo of material appearing around the coronagraph that gets steadily bigger with time. What it actually means is that a CME is directed straight at the Earth. What we are seeing in the SOHO images/movies is a bubble of plasma expanding away from the Sun and toward the Earth.

Assignment 4.3. *Coronal Mass Ejections.* Take one of the last frames from the coronal mass ejection movie[47] where it is near full development. Make a sketch of this frame, and estimate the size of the CME. Assuming an average density of about 10^8 protons/cm^{-3} and the object is approximately symmetric, how many kg of the Sun is ejected with this event?

Flare activity (both large and small) tracks the solar cycle. In particular, during solar

45   http://pwg.gsfc.nasa.gov/istp/nicky/cme-chase. html

46   http://cse.ssl.berkeley.edu/segwayed/lessons/ exploring_magnetism/in_Solar_Flares/s4.html

47   http://www.youtube.com/watch?v=GCjBgfOMaTs

maximum, CMEs can occur as often as three per day, while during solar minimum, a CME only occurs about once every five days.

Examples of the variations of solar activity over the last few solar cycles is shown in Figure 4.9.3. One important feature for our topic at hand is the flux of galactic cosmic rays[48] (GCR). GCRs are very-high-energy charged particles that originate outside of our solar system and are produced in the shocks from supernovas within the galaxy. The flux of GCRs at Earth is anti-correlated with the solar cycle. This is because the CMEs that explode off the Sun regularly during solar maximum scatter GCRs away from the inner solar system, producing radiation shielding for the Earth from the galactic cosmic rays. GCRs constitute a significant radiation source for humans in space, both in terms of the fact they are always present and given their very high energies. When traveling for extended time periods—such as to other planets or in colonizing the Moon—we will have to figure out a way to shield astronauts from GCRs. But it is interesting to note that during solar maximum, the hazards for astronauts from the Sun increase, while the hazards from outside our solar system decrease.

The X-ray flux at the Earth is seen to vary by several orders of magnitude across the solar cycle. This is also true for ultraviolet emissions. Because they represent the energetic part of the electromagnetic spectrum, these emissions can lead to significant modifications of our upper atmosphere. This modification can have a variety of effects—from modifying radio emissions to modifying GPS signals, which now play a significant role in almost everyone's life in today's mobile society. It is for this reason that the GPS signals utilize two frequencies, so that differences due to the changes in the upper atmosphere can be taken into account. Also note that the increase in X-ray flux happens very quickly. This creates a hazard for humans in space, as our first indication of a solar flare is nearly coincident with the maximum flux of

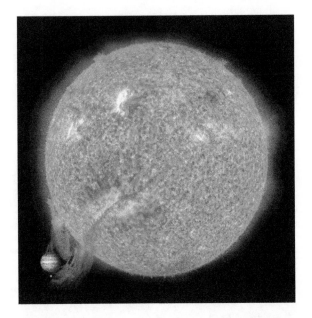

FIGURE 4.9.2. SCALE SIZE OF AN ERUPTING PROMINENCE.

X-rays, providing us with very little warning. If we want to keep astronauts safe for extended missions, particularly when they are outside their living quarters, we will either need to figure out how to create space suits that can protect against X-ray flux or figure out how to predict when solar flares will occur.

The presence of energetic particles associated with coronal mass ejections is seen in the fourth panel in Figure 4.9.3. These particles are called solar energetic particles/proton (SEPs)[49]. The fluxes are very spiky, as they are associated with individual CME events; and they provide an additional hazard for space travel, since these energetic charged particles can lead to the modification or destruction of DNA. SEPs are accelerated in the shock waves associated with CMEs and have energies just less than GCRs. So, while solar activity reduces the threat from galactic cosmic rays, it increases the flux of energetic particles from the solar flares. Fluxes of galactic cosmic rays tend to be much lower than the solar flares, but they are very much more energetic, so that galactic cosmic rays are the biggest threat

48   http://en.wikipedia.org/wiki/Galactic_cosmic_rays

49   http://en.wikipedia.org/wiki/
Solar_energetic_particles

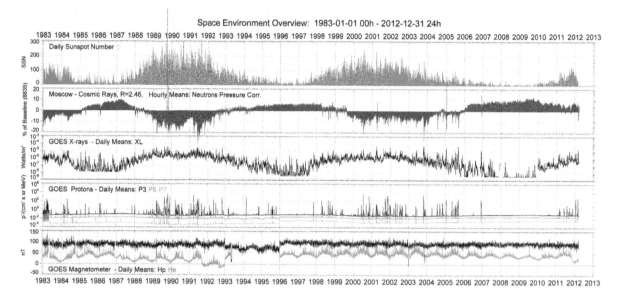

FIGURE 4.9.3. TOP PANEL SHOWS THE SUNSPOT NUMBER SINCE 1983. THE MIDDLE PANEL SHOWS THE COSMIC RAY FLUX, WHICH IS ANTI-CORRELATED WITH THE SOLAR CYCLE. THE MIDDLE PANEL SHOWS THE X-RAY FLUX ASSOCIATED WITH SOLAR FLARES, WHICH CLOSELY TRACKS THE SOLAR CYCLE. THE SECOND PANEL ON THE BOTTOM SHOWS THE FLUX OF ENERGETIC PROTONS, TYPICALLY ASSOCIATED WITH CORONAL MASS EJECTIONS. THE BOTTOM PANEL SHOWS MODIFICATIONS TO THE TERRESTRIAL MAGNETIC FIELD WITH THE SPIKES IN THE MAGNETIC FIELD ALSO ASSOCIATED WITH CORONAL MASS EJECTION EVENTS.

for long-duration spaceflight and are almost impossible to shield against.

The flux of energetic particles from solar flares can be many orders of magnitude higher than galactic cosmic rays (GCR), and while their energy is still very high, they are on average lower than galactic cosmic rays. Therefore, it is easier to shield a spacecraft against solar energetic particle events (SEPs) than it is to shield against GCR. However, if an astronaut is outside the spacecraft in an unprotected environment, then SEPs represent a major health hazard. The high energy of SEPs means they travel at just sub-light speed. Thus, the problem with this type of exposure is that the ability to predict solar flare activity is presently very limited, and there is typically only a few minutes' time space between when the flare is observed and the arrival of the first energetic particles.

4.10. Solar Wind

The last form of solar activity is in a form of bulk plasma moving out into space. This outflowing plasma is called the solar wind.[50] The origin of the solar wind is analogous to the boiling pot of water, which began our discussion of the structure of the Sun. The steam within the boiling pot is not only hotter, but it is at a higher pressure than its surroundings and therefore wishes to escape from the pot. This steam can easily escape if there is no lid on the pot, but if one places a loose lid on the pot, some of the steam will condense on the pot, and the amount of steam and temperature of the escaping steam that is able to escape is reduced.

For the Sun, the fluid that is trying to escape in the coronal plasma and the amount of boil-off is quite significant, representing close to four to six billion tons per hour. This represents a massive loss equal to the Earth approximately every 100 and 150 million years. The "lid" that can slow the escape of the solar wind is the

---

50   http://en.wikipedia.org/wiki/Solar_wind

coronal magnetic field that is associated with active regions and helmet streamers. Because the lid doesn't cover the entire surface of the Sun, there are two components of the solar wind: the fast (unimpeded) solar wind and the slow (partially confined) solar wind.

Assignment Question 4.4: Using the current mass of the Sun and a mass loss rate of 6 billion tons per hour, calculate how long it would take for the Sun to lose all its mass from the solar wind blowing off into space. How does the number compare to the age of the solar system? How does it compare to the estimated age of the universe (14 billion years)?

The solar wind is always present, but its characteristics change with solar cycle and solar activity. In yet another case of a scientist challenging the conventional wisdom, Sydney Chapman first proposed that a wind of particles would stream off the Sun and interact with the Earth's magnetic field (more on that in the next chapter). His ideas were soundly dismissed, as most solar scientists at the time believed that the mass of the Sun meant everything but the most energetic particles would be gravitationally bound. It wasn't until the first satellites were launched, confirming the presence of the solar wind, that his ideas were accepted. (As a side note, one of the tails emanating from comets, which have been observed for many centuries, actually prove the existence of the solar wind, if you understand what you are seeing.)

The situation is shown schematically in Figure 4.10.1. As we have already seen, active regions, which typically sit under helmet streamers, are associated with a relatively strong magnetic field. Spacecraft measurements have shown that solar wind particles emanating from these regions are relatively slow, hence the term slow solar wind. "Slow" here means speeds of 200–600 km/s.

Away from active regions, there are dark regions in the UV/X-ray images, which are called coronal holes[51] for no better reason than

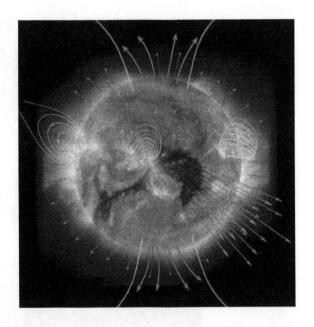

FIGURE 4.10.1. UV IMAGE OF THE SUN SHOWING ACTIVE REGIONS, WHICH ARE BRIGHT IN UV. REGIONS THAT APPEAR DARK IN UV ARE CALLED CORONAL HOLES. SCHEMATICS OF THE OVERLYING MAGNETIC FIELD STRUCTURE ARE SHOWN IN YELLOW, WHILE THE SPEED OF THE EMANATING SOLAR WIND IS SHOWN BY THE RED ARROWS, WITH THE SIZE OF THE ARROWS PROPORTIONAL TO THE SPEED OF THE SOLAR WIND. THE FAST SOLAR WIND IS ASSOCIATED WITH CORONAL HOLES, WHILE THE SLOW SOLAR WIND IS ASSOCIATED WITH THE MAGNETIC LOOP STRUCTURES THAT UNDERLIE HELMET STREAMERS[52].

there is a hole in the brightness in these types of images. Coronal holes are typically seen at the poles of the Sun as well as between active regions. The fast solar wind is seen to originate from these regions and reach speeds between 600–1000 km/s, though the density of the fast solar wind is typically only a fraction of the slow solar wind.

The average speed distribution of the solar wind as a function of latitude is shown in Figure 4.10.2. Since the active regions and sunspots tend to be localized near mid-latitudes when they first appear at the beginning of a sunspot cycle, the slow solar wind tends to be most commonly observed near mid-latitudes extending down to the equator. The fast solar wind generally is seen at higher latitudes or in coronal holes at low latitudes during solar maximum.

51   http://en.wikipedia.org/wiki/Coronal_hole

52   http://sohowww.nascom.nasa.gov/
hotshots/2005_05_20/

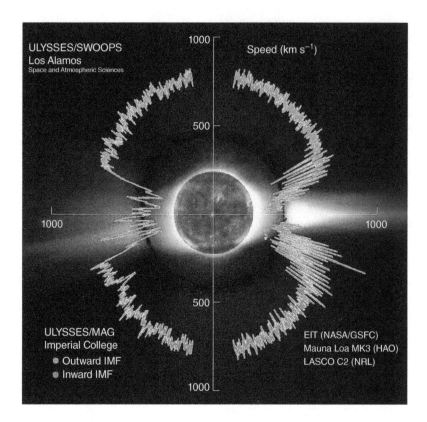

FIGURE 4.10.2. DATA FROM THE *ULYSSES*[53] SPACECRAFT, WHICH
WAS THE FIRST TO TRAVEL OVER THE POLES OF THE SUN. THE SPACE-
CRAFT PROVIDED THE FIRST DISTRIBUTION OF THE SLOW AND FAST SOLAR
WIND COMPONENTS. THE IMAGE SHOWS A UV IMAGE (INDICATING ACTIVE
REGIONS AND CORONAL HOLE) SUPERIMPOSED OVER CORONAGRAPHS
(SHOWING THE POSITION OF HELMET STREAMERS). THE GRAPH SHOWS
THE MEASURED SOLAR WIND SPEED, WITH THE SLOW SOLAR WIND BEING
OBSERVED AT EQUATORIAL TO MID-LATITUDES[54].

The average speeds shown in Figure 4.10.2 aren't just at the location of *Ulysses*. Once a packet of the solar wind is accelerated up to these hundreds of km/s speeds (which occurs well inside the orbit of Mercury), that blob of solar wind plasma will continue to travel at that same speed as it flows through the solar system. It will only slow down if it runs into a planet or when it impacts the termination shock for the heliosphere (discussed in the next chapter).

While Figure 4.10.2 shows the average solar wind speeds, the actual speed can vary quite a bit, especially at low latitudes, as that is where active features form. Around Halloween 2003, a series of halo events occurred. Over a

time period of several minutes, the solar wind speed at Earth increased from 600 km/s to in excess of 2000 km/s [1].

Assignment Question 4.5: If you assume that a packet of solar wind is accelerated up to 400 km/s at 700,000 km above the photosphere, how long will it take for it to arrive at the Earth? Repeat the calculation with a speed of 2000 km/s.

While the speed of a packet of solar wind plasma will remain relatively constant as it flows away from the Sun and toward the edge

53   http://en.wikipedia.org/wiki/Ulysses_(spacecraft)

54   http://solarscience.msfc.nasa.gov/SolarWind.
shtml

of our solar system, the density of that blob of plasma and magnetic field within it will change. The density of the plasma in the solar wind decreases with distance from the Sun, falling off at approximately $1/r^2$, just like the intensity of light. Average solar wind densities at the Earth are ~ 5 particles/cm^3 during solar minimum. During solar maximum, the density will vary from ~ 1 particle/cm^3 (associated with fast solar wind streams) to ~ 10 particles/cm^3 (associated with CME clouds passing the Earth).

Assignment Question 4.6: If you assume a solar wind density of 5 particles/cm^3 at the Earth, what will the density of that packet of plasma be at Mars? At Saturn? At Neptune?

The magnetic field within the solar wind (aka the interplanetary magnetic field, or IMF) not only decreases with distance from the Sun, it changes direction. Figure 4.10.3 shows how the IMF changes not only with distance from the Sun within the ecliptic plane (upper panel of Figure 4.10.3), but also how the IMF varies with distance above the ecliptic plane (lower panel of Figure 4.10.3). The IMF is not only bound to the solar wind plasma flowing away from the Sun (the frozen-in-field concept), it also remains connected to the rotating Sun (because magnetic field lines cannot simply end). This leads to a spiral shape to the IMF also leads to a change in direction in the IMF. As the quiet solar wind flows past the Earth, the IMF is typically pointed at an angle of 45° away from the flow vector. At the outer planets, the angle is closer to 90°. At boundaries between regions of oppositely directed IMF, a current must form. This is referred to as a current sheet. The three-dimensional structure of the current sheet can be seen in the lower panel of Figure 4.10.3. This picture is only true for the quiet solar wind. CMEs and coronal holes that occur during solar maximum will have their own magnetic field structure contained within them. The magnetic field associated with CMEs is

(a)

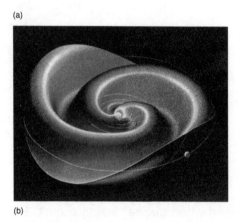

(b)

FIGURE 4.10.3. THE SPIRAL PATTERN OF THE INTERPLANETARY MAGNETIC FIELD (IMF) IN THE ECLIPTIC PLANE. THE SOLAR ROTATION IS IN THE COUNTER-CLOCKWISE DIRECTION (UPPER PANEL) AND THE 3D RIPPLED CURRENT SHEET THAT SEPARATES DIFFERENT SECTORS OF THE IMF (LOWER PANEL).

particularly complex, and usually no two are the same.

4.10. Summary of the Structure of the Sun

If one puts all the pieces together from this chapter and Chapter 3, then our view of the Sun is summarized as in Figure 4.11.1. There is a core where the density is ten times that of

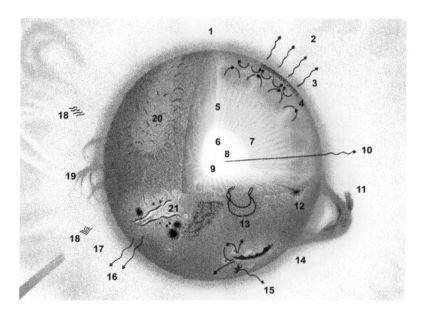

FIGURE 4.11.1. THE MANY STRUCTURES OF THE SUN, FROM ITS INTERIOR TO THE UPPER REACHES OF THE ATMOSPHERE.

lead and when nuclear fusion occurs. Energy in the form of gamma radiation escapes the core, and the energy is transported within the radiative zone. This energy of the gamma radiation is slowly degraded through the many collisions it participates in, and all electromagnetic radiation is fully absorbed at the bottom of the convection zone. The heated plasma in this region rises to the surface of the Sun and then sinks back to produce the convection zone. Light (in the UV or visible portion of the electromagnetic spectrum) is only able to escape at the surface, which is called the photosphere. Because of the high temperatures, much of the material is ionized, and currents can be generated to produce magnetic fields, which vary over the sunspot cycle. The most intense regions of the magnetic field are associated with sunspots, which appear as cooler, dark regions on the solar surface. Magnetic loops of all different sizes preside over the sunspot regions. The largest structures are helmet streamers that obtain sizes larger than the Sun itself. Underneath the helmet streamers are smaller magnetic loops that can be subject to

solar flares. Large arrays of these loops, which are known as filaments (if they are on the disk of the Sun) and prominences (if they are on the limb of the Sun), can also be unstable, leading to coronal mass ejections. In addition to flares and coronal mass ejections, the Sun also emits a continuous stream of particles on the surface called the solar wind: the fast solar wind coming from coronal holes and the slow solar wind coming from the more strongly magnetized regions of the Sun.

References

[1] Skoug, R. M., Gosling, J. T., Steinberg, D. J., McComas, C. W., Smith, N. F., Ness, Q. H., & Burlaga, L. F. (2004). Extremely high speed solar wind: 29–30 October 2003, *J. Geophys. Res.*, 109, A09102, doi:10.1029/2004JA010494.

Image Credits

Chapter 4 Opening Image: NASA/ESA/M. Livio/Hubble 20th Anniversary Team, "Hubble captures view of 'Mystic Mountain'," http://www.spacetelescope.org/images/heic1007a/. Copyright in the Public Domain.

Figure 4.2.1: HATHAWAY/NASA/MSFC, "Zurich sunspot number since 1750," http://en.wikipedia.org/wiki/File:Zurich_sunspot_number_since_1750.png. Copyright in the Public Domain.

Figure 4.2.2: HATHAWAY/NASA/MSFC, "Sunspot butterfly with graph," https://commons.wikimedia.org/wiki/File:Sunspot_butterfly_with_graph.gif. Copyright in the Public Domain.

Figure 4.3.1: Copyright © Luc Viatour (CC BY-SA 3.0) at http://en.wikipedia.org/wiki/File:Solar_eclipse_1999_4_NR.jpg

Figure 4.3.2: "BBSO Image," ftp://ftp.bbso.njit.edu/pub/archive/2012/08/30/bbso_halph_fl_20120830_170726.jpg. Copyright © by Big Bear Solar Observatory. Reprinted with permission.

Figure 4.3.3: NASA, "Star Child," http://starchild.gsfc.nasa.gov/Images/StarChild/questions/sunspot_dia.gif. Copyright in the Public Domain.

Figure 4.3.4: NASA/Robert Nemiroff/Jerry Bonnell, "Sunspot swedish label1," https://commons.wikimedia.org/wiki/File:Sunspot_swedish_label1.jpg. Copyright in the Public Domain.

Figure 4.3.5: Adapted from: Copyright © Evgeny (CC BY-SA 3.0) at http://en.wikipedia.org/wiki/File:Zeeman_p_s_doublet.svg

Figure 4.3.6: National Solar Observatory/AURA/NSF, "GONG/NSO Image," ftp://ftp.bbso.njit.edu/pub/archive/2012/08/31/gong_magxx_fd_20120831_192203.jpg. Copyright © 2012 by Big Bear Solar Observatory. Reprinted with permission.

Figure 4.4.1a: Copyright © JrPol (CC BY-SA 3.0) at https://commons.wikimedia.org/wiki/File:Dipolaire-magneet-schema.svg

Figure 4.4.1b: Copyright © Alexjoy (CC BY-SA 3.0) at https://commons.wikimedia.org/wiki/File:Earth%27s_Magnetism.jpg

Figure 4.4.2: Adapted from: Ian O'Neill, "Twistedflux," http://commons.wikimedia.org/wiki/File:Twistedflux.png. Copyright in the Public Domain.

Figure 4.5.1: NASA, "Coronal Mass Ejections (CMEs)," http://genesismission.jpl.nasa.gov/science/mod3_SunlightSolarHeat/SolarStructure/index.html. Copyright in the Public Domain.

Figure 4.5.2: NASA, "SOHO Images," http://soho.nascom.nasa.gov/data/realtime/. Copyright in the Public Domain.

Figure 4.5.3: NASA/JPL-Caltech/Palomar Observatory, "444226main exoplanet20100414-a-full," http://en.wikipedia.org/wiki/File:444226main_exoplanet20100414-a-full.jpg. Copyright in the Public Domain.

Figure 4.6.1: NASA, "SOHO Images," http://soho.nascom.nasa.gov/data/realtime/. Copyright in the Public Domain.

Figure 4.7.1a: NASA, "Helmet streamers at min," http://en.wikipedia.org/wiki/File:Helmet_streamers_at_min.jpg. Copyright in the Public Domain.

Figure 4.7.1b: Copyright © G. Garitan (CC BY-SA 3.0) at https://commons.wikimedia.org/wiki/File:Prusse_casque_de_dragon_de_ligne_mod_1860_4014.jpg?fastcci_from=6179180

Figure 4.9.1a: NASA, "Traceimage," http://commons.wikimedia.org/wiki/File:Traceimage.jpg. Copyright in the Public Domain.

Figure 4.9.1b-f: Adapted from: "Solar Flares," http://cse.ssl.berkeley.edu/segwayed/lessons/exploring_magnetism/in_Solar_Flares/in_Solar_Flares_images/fig_4p4.jpg.

Figure 4.9.1g: NASA, "Coronal Mass Ejection," http://soho.nascom.nasa.gov/gallery/images/20031202c2eit304.html. Copyright in the Public Domain.

Figure 4.9.2: Solar Dynamics Observatory, "Sun earth jupiter whole 600," http://en.wikipedia.org/wiki/File:Sun_earth_jupiter_whole_600.jpg. Copyright in the Public Domain.

Figure 4.9.3: Copyright © Daniel Wilkinson (CC BY-SA 3.0) at http://en.wikipedia.org/wiki/File:SpaceEnvironmentOverview_From_19830101.jpg

Figure 4.10.1: NASA, "Hot Shots," http://sohowww.nascom.nasa.gov/hotshots/2005_05_20/figure_2.jpg. Copyright in the Public Domain.

Figure 4.10.2: NASA, "Dial Plot," http://solarscience.msfc.nasa.gov/images/DialPlot.jpg. Copyright in the Public Domain.

Figure 4.10.3a: Adapted from: "CambEncySun," http://ase.tufts.edu/cosmos/pictures/CambEncySun/Sun_ency_figs_3/Fig8_12.jpg.

Figure 4.10.3b: NASA, "Heliospheric-current-sheet," http://en.wikipedia.org/wiki/File:Heliospheric-current-sheet.gif. Copyright in the Public Domain.

Figure 4.11.1: NASA, "Sun parts," https://commons.wikimedia.org/wiki/File:Sun_parts.jpg. Copyright in the Public Domain.

Chapter 5

Space Plasma Environments

Magnetospheres

We learned in the previous chapter that once accelerated, the solar wind streams away from the Sun at a speed that remains constant with distance (which happens to be supersonic speeds). But is that true for infinite distances from the Sun? No. Should the solar wind run into something, it will slow down. What can the solar wind run into? Two types of things, either a planet within the solar system, or it can run into things outside the solar system.

5.1. The Heliosphere

The Sun and the planets do not just float along in an empty vacuum of space. We are part of a galaxy that is made of up other stars, other planets around those stars, and gas and dust in between the different star systems. Figure 5.1.1 shows what we believe is the most likely structure for the galaxy and conditions in our local neighborhood. As we cannot take a picture of our galaxy from afar and have yet to send a probe outside of our solar system (more on that later), these are estimates from what we can observe. Our solar system is about two thirds of the way from the center of the galaxy in a spiral arm (Figure 5.1.1a). We are moving around the center of the galaxy at a speed of about 220 km/s, meaning we complete one orbit every 225 to 250 million years. Thus,

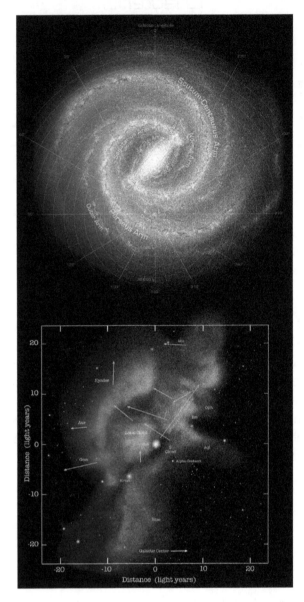

FIGURE 5.1.1. (A) OUR SOLAR SYSTEM IN A CARTOON OF THE BELIEVED STRUCTURE OF OUR GALAXY. (B) A ZOOMED-IN VIEW OF THEORIZED CONDITIONS IN OUR CURRENT LOCAL NEIGHBORHOOD (R. CASALEGNO, C. CONSELICE ET AL., WIYN, NOAO[1]).

we have made approximately 20 orbits around the galaxy since the solar system was formed, 4.5 billion years ago. It is also believed that we are currently in a local interstellar dust cloud (Figure 5.1.1b). It is difficult to assess the exact nature of the local interstellar medium (LISM)[2],

as we cannot measure magnetic field strengths or gas/plasma densities remotely.

As the solar wind streams away from the Sun, eventually it will begin to feel the effects of the gas and magnetic pressure exerted by the LISM and slow down. Where the solar wind slows down to subsonic speeds, a structure known as the termination shock[3] forms. Past the termination shock, the solar wind will continue to flow away from the Sun, albeit at subsonic speeds. Eventually, though, it will reach a region in which the gas and magnetic pressure from the LISM balances the gas and magnetic pressure from the solar wind. That boundary is called the heliopause[4]. Inside the heliopause, nearly all the plasma and magnetic field are of solar system origin. Outside of the heliopause, all the plasma and magnetic field will be of galactic origin. It is possible that there is one more boundary outside of the heliopause—specifically, a bow shock[5]. If our solar system is traveling through the LISM at a relative speed faster than the intrinsic sound speed of the LISM, a shock wave will form around the solar system, just like a sonic boom forms around an airplane traveling at supersonic speeds at Earth. We can't tell if a bow shock forms or not because we don't know what the conditions of the LISM are; it is not a type of structure that can be observed directly with remote-sensing techniques.

This bubble of plasma and magnetic field emanating from the Sun and being buffered by the LISM is called the heliosphere[6] (meaning the Sun's (*helio*) sphere of influence; the object itself is not really spherical). Figure 5.1.2 shows our best estimates for the locations of each boundary within the heliosphere. Where do we get those estimates? In part from models that compute the plasma flow, but also from

---

1   http://www.ibex.swri.edu/multimedia/

2   http://en.wikipedia.org/wiki/Interstellar_medium

3   http://en.wikipedia.org/wiki/
Heliopause_(astronomy)

4   http://en.wikipedia.org/wiki/
Heliopause_(astronomy)

5   http://en.wikipedia.org/wiki/
Heliopause_(astronomy)

6   http://en.wikipedia.org/wiki/
Heliosphere_(astronomy)

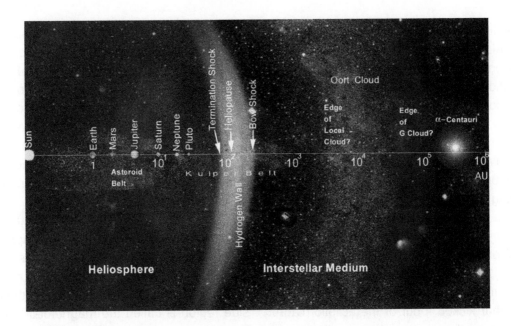

FIGURE 5.1.2. OUR BEST ESTIMATES OF THE LOCATIONS OF THE BOUNDARIES AT THE EDGE OF THE HELIOSPHERE RELATIVE TO THE LOCATION OF THE PLANETS. NOTE THAT DISTANCES ARE A LOG SCALE IN UNITS OF AU[7].

observations made by the *Voyager* spacecraft. *Voyager* 1 and 2, both launched in 1977, are heading out of the solar system. As they use a type of nuclear power source called radio-thermal generators (see Chapter 2), they don't depend on receiving power from the Sun to run their instruments. Not all the instruments are still working (they weren't designed to last for over 40 years), but enough are that we can receive information about the nature of the space they are traveling through. It is believed that *Voyager* 1 crossed the termination shock in 2004, while *Voyager* 2 crossed it five times in 2007. At the end of 2012, *Voyager* 1 was 123 AU from the Sun, while *Voyager* 2 was 100 AU from the Sun (for current locations, go to http://voyager.jpl. nasa.gov/where/index.html). Will we see data from the *Voyagers* when they finally cross into the LISM? It is hard to say. The power sources will last until 2020, and scientists believe they may enter the LISM in 2013–2015, but scientists also initially predicted that the termination

shock was closer than it actually turned out to be, so only time will tell. Even if we do not continue to hear from them when they cross into the LISM, they will still remain our first human-made objects to leave the solar system and begin an interstellar journey among the stars.

How did *Voyager* 2 cross the termination shock five times? Well, what really happened was the termination shock swept back and forth past *Voyager* 2 five times. Why would this have happened? As we saw in Chapter 4, the solar wind is not constant. Sometimes there are regions of slow solar wind, sometimes regions of fast solar wind, and sometimes there are coronal mass ejections thrown off the Sun. It is believed that during solar maximum, when CMEs happen in rapid succession, as the material from the CMEs flows away from the Sun and past the planets, the shocks from multiple CMEs can coalesce into larger shocks as material from one CME overtakes a CME ahead of it. When these larger shocks hit the termination shock, they push the termination shock out briefly in that region. So really, the termination shock is most likely not a smooth spherical

7   http://www.odec.ca/projects/2008/wang8c2/ regions/kulper.htm

surface like that shown in Figure 5.1.2, but rather a lumpy surface. *Voyager* 2 most likely witnessed the effects of CME shocks hitting the termination shock in the region, pushing the termination shock out briefly as the CME hit the boundary, sweeping out past *Voyager* 2. Once the material from the CME dissipated through the termination shock, the termination shock then returned back in to a closer distance, sweeping past *Voyager* 2 again, in the reverse direction. This highlights that the distance of the termination shock from the Sun will actually depend on the location and activity of the Sun. *Voyager* 1 did not experience multiple crossings as it underwent an orbital maneuver at Jupiter that kicked it out of the ecliptic plane. As we saw in the previous chapter, CMEs are ejected from the equatorial region of the Sun, and as such will travel mostly in the ecliptic plane.

Assignment Question 5.1. Calculate the average speed of both *Voyager* 1 and 2. Can you explain the difference in speed between the two spacecraft? (Hint: Consider their orbit trajectories.)

5.2. The Terrestrial Magnetosphere

The solar wind will also slow down when it runs into an obstacle within the solar system—usually a planet. The actual obstacle will be either the planet's magnetic field or, in the case of unmagnetized planets, the planetary atmosphere. In both cases, a magnetosphere forms around the planet—a "bubble" that separates the space plasma environment from the planetary environment (surface or neutral atmosphere). Magnetic fields play an important role because the trajectories of the charged particles that make up the solar wind are strongly modified by their presence.

Because of the influence of the magnetic field, this "bubble" is called a magnetosphere[8]. Similar to the solar corona, a host of plasma interactions occurs within magnetospheres that leads to the creation of energetic particle environments around the planets. That energy can be deposited into the topside atmosphere, or if the planet/moon has no atmosphere, directly on its surface, leading to the modification of planetary processes.

Figure 5.2.1 shows a schematic of the structure that forms when the solar wind impacts the Earth. The terrestrial magnetic field is pushed on in the dayside and elongated out on the nightside. Because of the stretching, the nightside region is called the magnetotail[9], (similar to a cometary tail), and can extend over 100 R_E from the Earth. This creates a teardrop-shaped, three-dimensional structure.

5.3. The Outer Magnetosphere and Magnetospheric Activity

The first boundary that forms as the solar wind encounters the Earth is a bow shock[10]. This is the boundary where the supersonic solar wind slows to just subsonic speeds. On the dayside, at the equator, the bow shock typically forms between a distance of 13 R_E and 15 R_E (where 1 R_E = 1 Earth radius = 6371 km) from the Earth. Just inside the bow shock is the magnetosheath[11]. In this region, the kinetic energy of the solar wind is converted into thermal energy, producing a hot, subsonic plasma of solar wind origin. This region is fairly hot by terrestrial standards with a temperature of nearly 1 million K (100 eV). This should come

---

8   http://en.wikipedia.org/wiki/Magnetosphere
9   http://en.wikipedia.org/wiki/Magnetosphere
10   http://en.wikipedia.org/wiki/Magnetosphere
11   http://en.wikipedia.org/wiki/Magnetosheath

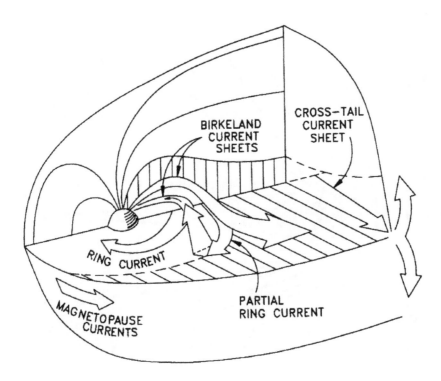

FIGURE 5.2.1. A 3-D CUTAWAY REPRESENTATION OF THE TERRESTRIAL MAGNETOSPHERE, SHOWING THE DIFFERENT REGIONS, INCLUDING THE BOW SHOCK, MAGNETOPAUSE, AURORAL OVAL, RADIATION BELT (TRAPPED PARTICLES), LOBES, AND PLASMA SHEET.

as no surprise, since the source of the plasma here is the solar corona. The density, though, is about 20 cm^{-3}.

The next boundary is the magnetopause[12], which demarcates where the plasma and magnetic field change from being of solar wind origin (on the outside) and where the plasma and magnetic field are primarily of terrestrial origin (on the inside). The magnetopause is typically found to be at a distance of about 10 R$_E$ on the dayside, at the equator.

Inside the magnetopause, the plasma densities vary greatly. Just inside the magnetopause in the magnetotail lies the plasma mantle, which is a region of tailward-flowing solar wind plasma. This plasma is unable to easily penetrate the magnetosphere due to the presence of the stretched terrestrial magnetic field. Inside, this region lines the lobes[13] (one in the northern hemisphere and one in the southern hemi-

sphere). In each lobe, one end of the magnetic field line is connected to the Earth's poles on one end, while at the other end, the magnetic field is connected to the solar wind, far downstream. There is very little entry of solar wind plasma in the lobes, so the plasma density is only 0.01 to 0.001 particles cm^{-3}, with a temperature of less than 1 eV. The plasma here typically originates from the topside of the atmosphere. The lobes of any magnetosphere are probably the best vacuums anywhere in space.

Between the two lobes is the plasma sheet.[14] This region consists of a layer of a weaker magnetic field and denser plasma, centered on the equator. This region is important because it carries the bulk of the current required to support the extended magnetic field of the magnetotail. Typically, it is 2–6 Earth radii thick during quiet solar wind conditions, when the terrestrial magnetosphere is not highly stressed. During this period, both ends of the

---

12 http://en.wikipedia.org/wiki/Magnetopause
13 http://www-spof.gsfc.nasa.gov/Education/wtail.html

14 http://www-spof.gsfc.nasa.gov/Education/wtail.html

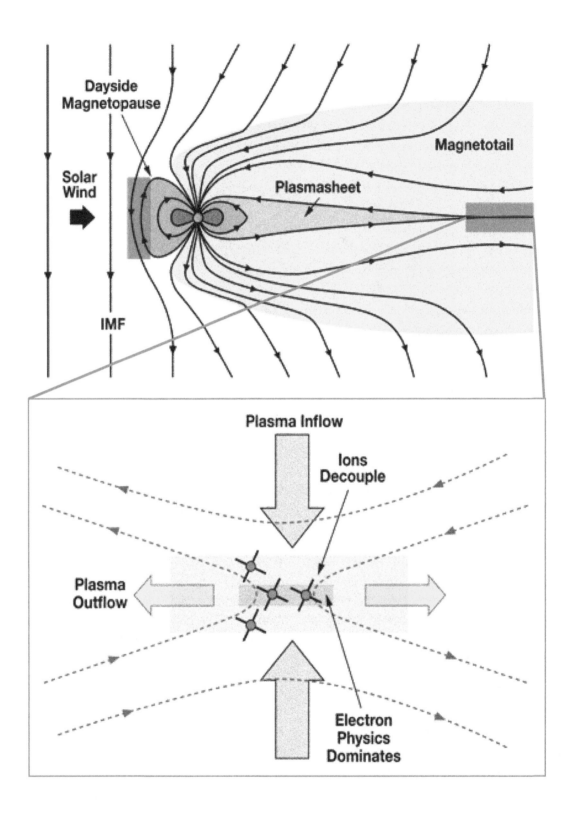

FIGURE 5.3.1. DURING TIMES OF BOTH QUIET AND ENHANCED SOLAR ACTIVITY, THE OPPOSITELY DIRECTED MAGNETIC FIELD IN THE EARTH'S MAGNETOTAIL CAN MERGE. THIS ANHILATION OF MAGNETIC FIELD (CALLED RECONNECTION) CAN ACCELERATE PLASMA TOWARD THE EARTH, ALONG THE REMAINING MAGNETIC FIELD. THAT PLASMA IMPACTS THE EARTH'S ATMOSPHERE NEAR THE POLES AND IS RESPONSIBLE FOR THE GENERATING THE AURORA. DURING TIMES OF ENHANCED SOLAR ACTIVITY, THIS CAN HAPPEN MORE FREQUENTLY AND LEAD TO AURORA BEING SEEN CLOSER TO THE EQUATOR FOR BRIEF (~ AN HOUR OR TWO) PERIODS. IMAGES CREATED FOR THE NASA MMS MISSION.

FIGURE 5.3.2. IMAGES OF THE AURORA BOREALIS AND AURORA AUSTRALIS, SHOWING THE DIFFERENT COLORS AND FEATURES THAT CAN DEVELOP.

field lines are connected to the Earth, and there is plasma primarily of terrestrial origin with a little bit of solar origin. However, when the solar conditions are such that they produce strong compression of the magnetosphere (such as high-speed streams or CMEs), the thickness of the plasma sheet can be less than 1600 km.

During such active periods, the temperature of the plasma can reach 1–10 keV (more energetic than the solar wind) and can become unstable to a variety of current/plasma instabilities. These instabilities can lead to the pinching up of the current in a process called magnetic reconnection[15], leading to the formation of magnetic loops or plasmoids (meaning a plasma/magnetic bubble) as shown in Figure 5.3.1. As a result, there is a reconfiguration of the entire terrestrial magnetic field, which can be measured on the ground. This process is similar to the one that creates CMEs and flares in the solar corona; it is just that the magnetic fields are weaker, and the plasma temperatures are lower at the Earth.

Assignment 5.2. Using the instructions at http://image.gsfc.nasa.gov/poetry/workbook/page9.html to make a homemade magnetometer, take observations over the next month and identify periods of time when the terrestrial magnetic field appears to change and by how much. The results will differ with geographic location.

The processes associated with the above reconfiguration are collectively known as a substorm[16]. This is associated with the venting of some of the energetic plasma sheet particles down the tail and eventually into the solar wind. Thus, the solar wind contains contributions from not just the Sun, but also from the planets.

In addition to this ejected plasma, some of the energetic particles are injected toward the Earth. Energetic electrons and some protons are able to reach the topside atmosphere to produce the aurora borealis (aka the northern lights) in the northern hemisphere and aurora australis in the southern hemisphere. One of the most familiar features of how the Earth's magnetosphere responds to enhanced solar activity is in the form of a bright aurora[17].

The light that is seen is produced by the energetic particles (usually electrons, but sometimes protons) impacting the atmosphere, exciting the electrons in neutral atoms via collisions. When the electrons relax back down to their ground state, the atoms emit the characteristic colors we associate with the aurora—red, green, pink, and a bluish-purple. Each color is characteristic of the element producing the light similar to the line emissions form the Sun as discussed in Chapter 1. Neutral oxygen emits both the red (557.7 nm) and green (630.0 nm) lights, albeit at different altitudes. These are the exact same wavelengths emitted by oxygen during the airglow process on the daylight atmosphere. Oxygen emits green light between 100 and 200 km and red light between 200 and 400 km (middle right panel in Figure 5.3.2). As the altitude of the emissions increases, they change from a light green to red. The other colors of the aurora come from nitrogen emissions. Neutral molecular nitrogen (N_2) emits pink light, while the bluish-purple light comes from ionized molecular nitrogen. A video of the development of an aurora can be seen at http://vimeo.com/38653299

From a local point of view, the auroras appear as sheets of light. With the advent of satellites, the development of the aurora could be seen as a global phenomenon that can extend from the nightside all the way around to the dayside, creating a structure centered around both magnetic poles called the auroral oval (Figure 5.3.3). The most intense emissions are most likely when the local time is a little before midnight. The auroral oval typically sits around 70° magnetic latitude (both north and south), but when solar wind conditions are very disturbed and substorms are occurring, the auroral oval can expand down to lower magnetic latitudes. A video of a global view of an auroral substorm can be seen at http://www.youtube.com/watch?v=8DeQfiokSkg&list=PL6D6A4A25F6C714C7. An important aspect is that the auroras are NOT generated by the direct entry of solar wind particles. If they were, the brightness features would be on the dayside. Instead, because the auroras occur near midnight, their sources are derived from particles accelerated within the magnetotail.

Note that above we have been using the term "substorm," with the "sub" referring to the fact that these processes last from 30–60 minutes. There are larger events that are called

15   http://en.wikipedia.org/wiki/Magnetic_reconnection
16   http://en.wikipedia.org/wiki/Substorm
17   http://en.wikipedia.org/wiki/Aurora_borealis

FIGURE 5.3.3.   LOCAL AND GLOBAL VIEWS OF AURORA BRIGHTENINGS ASSOCIATED WITH A SUB-STORM (I.E., AN INTENSIFICATION OF THE AURORA DUE TO CHANGES IN THE SOLAR WIND CONDITIONS).

geomagnetic (or magnetic) storms[18] which last longer (several hours to days). A storm is associated with an enhancement in the plasma density within a few Earth radii of the surface and is seen as a change in the magnetic field measured on the surface of the Earth.

This process of accelerating particles from the magnetotail toward the Earth's atmosphere to generate aurora is the same during both solar quiet and solar storm times. What changes during solar storms is that the process can become more dynamic. This has two consequences. First, the process can generate more energetic particles being directed toward the Earth, leading to much brighter auroras over a larger region, while during solar quiet times, the auroral oval is typically at 70° magnetic latitude. During magnetic storms, it can drop to 40° magnetic latitude. During the Carrington Event (discussed in the next chapter), auroras were seen at magnetic latitudes of 30°. This explains why people near the Great Lakes in the United States (say, those in Michigan) are more likely to see the aurora than those people living in Washington State, and it's not because it is always cloudy in Washington (although that may have a little to do with it). While Washington is closer to the geographic north pole than Michigan, it is further away from the

magnetic pole. This also means that it is also just as likely to see the aurora in California as it is in the Aleutian Islands of Alaska.

5.4. The Inner Magnetosphere

The inner magnetosphere consists of three main components: (a) the plasmasphere; (b) the ring current; and (c) the radiation belts. The plasmasphere[19] (Figure 5.4.1a) is the most benign of the regions. It consists of a high-density (1000 cm^{-3}), low-energy (< 1 eV) plasma that originates from the topside atmosphere. Because of the low energy of this plasma, it is tightly bound to the terrestrial magnetic field and therefore is in corotation with the planet.

The next region is the ring current[20] (Figure 5.4.1b), which geographically lies between the plasmasphere and the inner edge of the plasma sheet. Because of the plasma's higher energy (from 10s of keV to a few hundred 100 keV), it does not undergo corotation and instead undergoes what is called drift motion

18   http://en.wikipedia.org/wiki/Magnetic_storm

19   http://plasmasphere.nasa.gov/
20   http://en.wikipedia.org/wiki/Ring_current

a Inner Magnetosphere : Plasmasphere

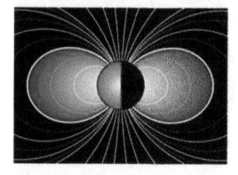

b Inner Magnetosphere : Ring Current

c Inner Magnetosphere : Radiation Belt

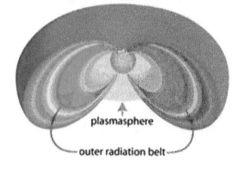

FIGURE 5.4.1. THE STRUCTURE OF THE INNER MAGNETOSPHERE.

around the planet, with the ions moving in a clockwise direction and the electrons moving in a counterclockwise direction. Some of the most energetic particles in the ring current can be O+, which has been accelerated out of the Earth's atmosphere, into the tail, and reinjected into the inner magnetosphere. On its journey, the O+ experiences several different acceleration processes to produce energies that are higher than the average coronal temperatures.

This difference in motion of the ring current particles produces a clockwise current around the Earth. The magnetic field from this current is in the opposite direction of the terrestrial magnetic field and is sufficient to produce significant currents in the Earth within pipelines (leading to enhanced corrosion) and transmission wires (which can lead to power failures). Periods of enhanced currents due to pumped-up ring currents are geomagnetic storms. The space environment can influence the terrestrial environment and will be discussed in detail in the next chapter.

The final region is the Earth's radiation belts[21] (Figure 5.4.1c). These were experimentally confirmed by James van Allen in 1958, using data from Geiger counters aboard the *Explorer* 1 and *Explorer* 3 satellites. Van Allen had argued that the Geiger counters should be included on the satellites in order to study particles in space, something not all scientists at the time believed to exist. He also discovered that there are two distinct radiation belts, dubbed the inner belt and the outer belt. The outer belt is located between 2 RE and 10 RE and consists of ions and electrons, with energies between 1 and 100 keV. The inner belt is located between 0.1 RE and 1.5 RE and is made up of protons and electrons, with energies between 10 and 50 MeV. The inner and outer belts are formed through two different processes. The source of the outer radiation belt is particles from further out in the magnetosphere. Through dynamic processes, they get injected in closer to the Earth and accelerated up to very high energies. We still don't completely understand the process that creates the outer radiation belt. We do understand the origin of the inner belt much better. The source of the inner belt is something called cosmic ray albedo neutron decay (or CRAND). The Earth is constantly bombarded by radiation from space (galactic cosmic rays). When that radiation interacts with the atoms in our atmosphere, it acts like nature's version of an atom smasher—lots of exotic particles (like muons and pions) are created, in addition to some not-so-exotic particles (like gamma rays and neutrons). Because they are neutral, the neutrons that are created can travel in all

21 http://en.wikipedia.org/wiki/Radiation_belt

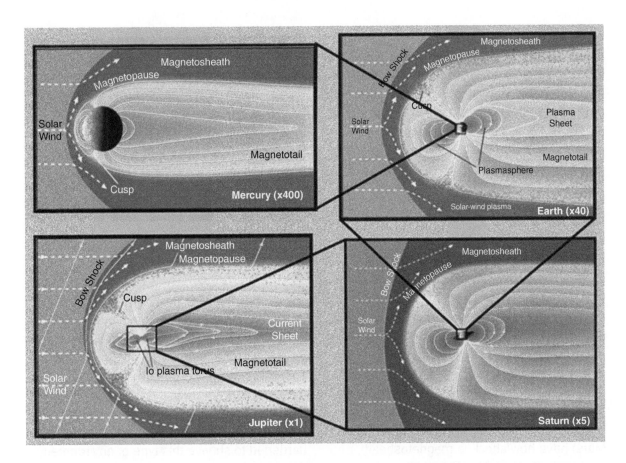

FIGURE 5.5.1. COMPARISON OF SIZE AND SHAPE OF SOME THE PLANETARY MAGNETOSPHERES WITHIN THE SOLAR SYSTEM. CREDIT: FRAN BAGENAL AND STEVE BARTLETT

directions, including back into space. But as we saw in Chapter 2, free neutrons are not stable, and they will decay into a proton, an electron, and a neutrino. The electron and protons, being charged, will suddenly feel any ambient magnetic field. If this happens in space, they will form a very-high-energy plasma. This is exactly the process that creates the inner radiation belt. Free neutrons have a characteristic lifetime, and in that time those heading back out to space decay at the exact location of the inner belt.

The outer radiation belt particles are strongly modulated by magnetic storm activity. Storms can lead to both a bleeding of particles out of the radiation belt (as the terrestrial magnetic field is distorted), as well as lead to the injection of new energetic particles created by magnetotail processes and the injection of these particles into the inner magnetosphere.

An important point to note is that the ring current and radiation belts are colocated—the difference is the energy of the plasma; radiation belt particles are much higher energy. These two different plasma populations can coexist in the same location; because the densities are so low, the particles never collide.

Because of their high energy, the radiation belt particles represent significant space hazards. This hazard is not just restricted to humans and the potential for causing life-threatening cancers, but also to electronics, which can experience false commands from what is called single-event (electronic upset) effects[22]. This happens when a high-energy

22   Present status and future challenges of modeling the Sun–Earth end-to-end system by D.N. Baker, M.J. Wiltbergerb, R.S. Weigela, S.R. Elkingtona, Journal of Atmospheric and Solar-Terrestrial Physics, Volume 69, Issues 1–2, February 2007, Pages 3–17

particle penetrates into electronics, producing a fake signal in digital electronics (which is based on a zero or one count). The particles are sufficiently energetic within the ring current and radiation belts that they can shred proposed solar sails within about ten days. A deeper discussion on space weather effects is given in the next chapter.

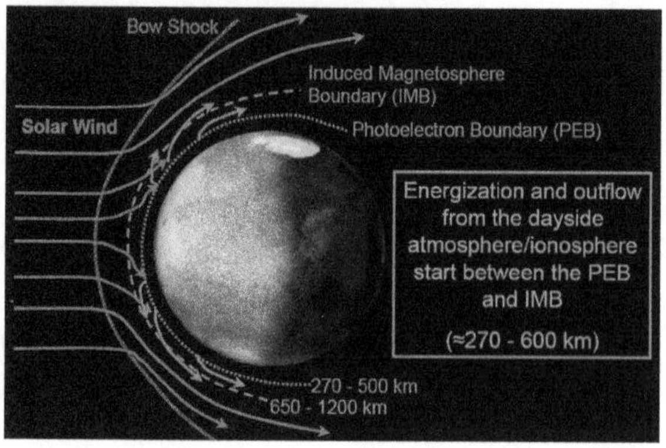

FIGURE 5.5.2. THE INDUCED MAGNETOSPHERE AROUND MARS.

5.5 Other Planets

Magnetospheres form around other planets in the solar system as well. While all planetary magnetospheres have certain features in common such as a bow shock and magnetosheath, each planetary magnetosphere also has characteristics unique to that system. All the planets with a global magnetic field (all but Venus and Mars) have bow shock, a magnetosheath, and a magnetopause. Where each forms relative to the size of the planet is dependent on the strength of the planetary magnetic field and sources of plasma internal to the magnetosphere. Figure 5.5.1 shows the relative sizes of the magnetospheres for the outer planets.

We can see that the Jovian magnetosphere is the Goliath of the solar system. Even though Jupiter is only one-tenth the size of the Sun, its magnetosphere dwarfs the Sun. The Jovian magnetosphere can also emit more radio emissions than the Sun during solar minimum. What causes the Jovian magnetosphere to be such a powerhouse? It's a combination of two things—Jupiter's rapid rotation and the presence of the volcanically active moon, Io (we will learn more about those in Chapter 10). It has many characteristics similar to Earth's magnetosphere. There is a bow shock where the solar wind is slowed to subsonic speeds when it runs into Jupiter's magnetic field. There

is a magnetosheath and magnetopause. The Jovian magnetosphere has a similar tear-drop shape to the terrestrial magnetosphere—pushed in on the dayside and elongated out on the nightside. Its radiation belts provide some of the harshest space environments within the solar system. Electronics have to be especially hardened to survive this type of environment.

But what happens if the planet doesn't posses a global magnetic field? Something called an induced magnetosphere forms around those planets as shown in Figure 5.5.2 for Mars. A bow shock still forms as the solar wind runs into the planetary atmosphere and slows. Here, though, the bow shock is very close to the planet. The upper atmospheres of the planets are ionized by solar UV and collisions with incident solar wind particles. That ionosphere is a conductor that can inhibit or prevent the interplanetary magnetic field (IMF) from penetrating deep into the ionosphere, and thus the IMF (and solar wind) flows around the planet. However, there is essentially no inner magnetosphere, in the sense that induced magnetospheres do not have a plasmasphere, ring current, or radiation belt. Thus, from an energetic particle perspective, the induced magnetosphere has a somewhat more benign nature.

Image Credits

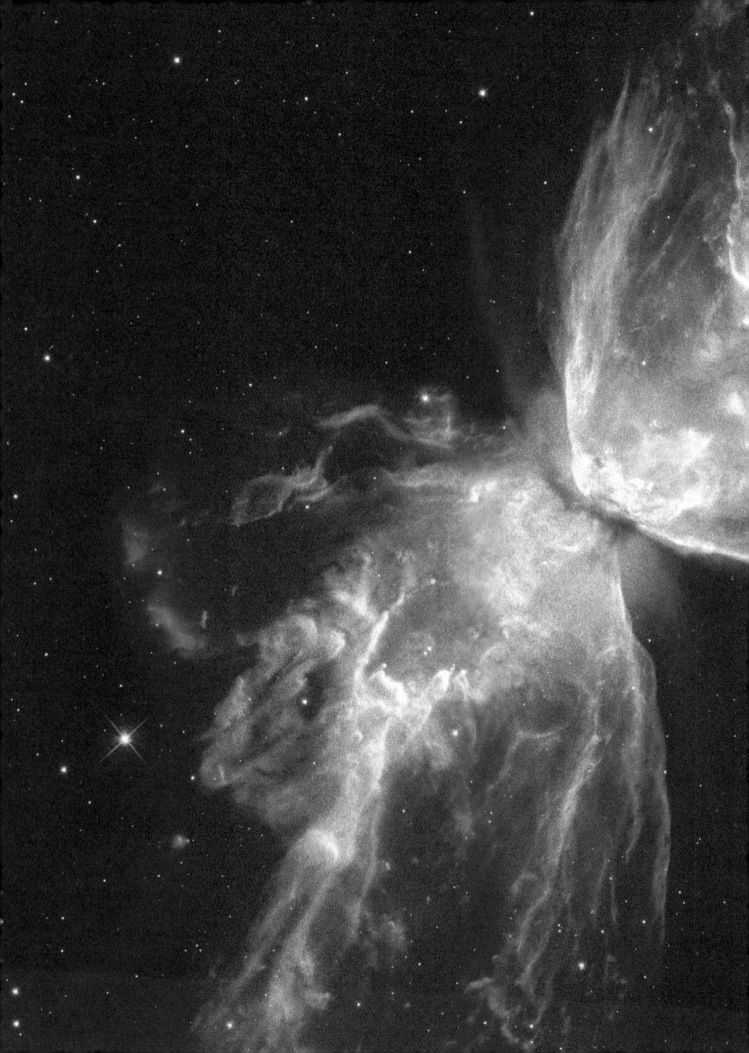

Space Weather

W hen we think of weather, most of us think of rain and wind or storms blowing in from the coast. There is weather in space also, but in the case of space weather, storms blow in from the Sun. These storms are caused by the different types of solar activity we saw in Chapter 4, ranging from solar flares to coronal mass ejections to high-speed solar wind streams. Once solar activity reaches the Earth (or any other planet, for that matter), it becomes space weather.

Figure 6.0.1 shows the variety of problems solar storms can create in both the near-Earth environment and on the surface of the Earth. It should be noted that solar storms have been buffering the Earth and other planets for billions of years. What makes them of concern now is that humans have become increasingly dependent on technology. We have also recently become a space-based society. It is our technology, both in space and on Earth, that is susceptible to the effects of solar storms and space weather.

6.1. Solar Flares and SEP Events

Solar storms can damage our space-based technology in several ways. Bursts of UV and X-ray radiation from solar flares can ionize the outside surface of a satellite,

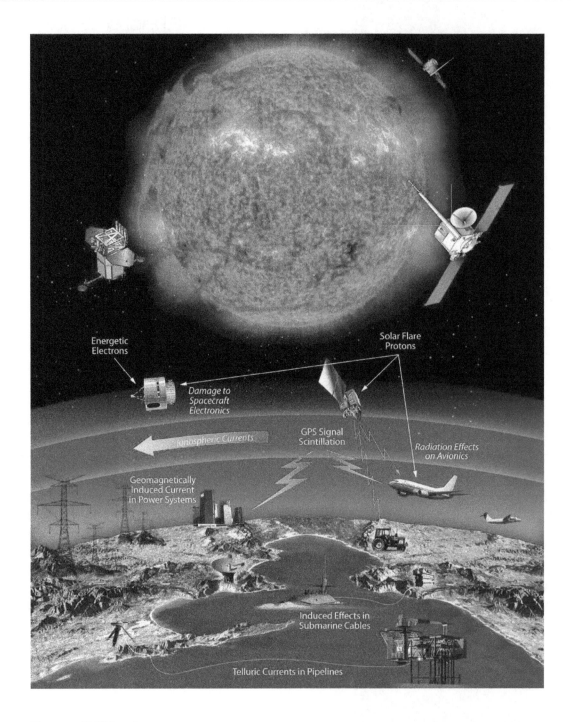

FIGURE 6.0.1. A SCHEMATIC SHOWING THE VARIETY OF EFFECTS SPACE WEATHER EVENTS CAN HAVE ON HUMAN TECHNOLOGY, BOTH IN SPACE AND ON THE SURFACE OF THE EARTH. IMAGE CREDIT: NASA

causing it to build up a charge relative to the rest of the satellite. If that charge rebalances itself in a rapid manner, similar to the spark we see when we touch a doorknob after scuffing our feet on a carpet, the results can be catastrophic for the satellite. If solar energetic particles (SEPs) impact crucial parts of a satellite—such as the memory for the onboard computers—the satellites can shut down and go into something called a safe-mode, where they wait for instructions from ground control stations. Worse, the memory on the satellite could be so damaged either by a single burst of SEPs or a static discharge that it ceases to function.

Those are ways that satellites can be killed quickly by space weather events. Satellites can also be slowly taken out of action by the cumulative effect of solar storms during an entire solar maximum. During solar maximum, the absorption of energy from repeated solar flares and SEP events by our atmosphere heats the atmosphere. This can cause the atmosphere to puff up and expand, so that the density of both neutral and charged particles at any given altitude (above the stratopause) increases. This means that satellites orbiting around the Earth in low Earth orbit (LEO) will be traveling through higher densities of atmosphere and will experience more atmospheric drag (i.e., resistance). Over the course of a solar maximum, this can slow down a satellite and cause it to slowly spiral into a lower orbit. If uncorrected, the satellite will eventually experience so much drag that it burns up in the atmosphere. The reduction in satellite altitude can be prevented by the use of station-keeping thrusters onboard the satellite. But these thrusters typically require a fuel source. Once the fuel source is depleted, there is no way to keep the satellite in place. If any given solar maximum is more intense than expected, the station-keeping thrusters will need to be used more than initially planned, further reducing the lifetime of a satellite.

The X-rays and SEPs generated in solar flares and coronal mass ejections can pose a significant health hazard to humans in space who are not well shielded from radiation. Solar-generated radiation is particularly difficult to deal with, as the flux of X-rays and energetic particles can increase by several orders of magnitude over mere minutes, and we have no way of predicting when it will happen. The risk of increased radiation exposure doesn't just increase for astronauts during space weather events, it can also increase for frequent airplane travelers. Energetic particles can be funneled toward the Earth magnetic poles during one of these events. Anyone flying in an airplane traveling via a polar route, such as people flying from North America to Asia, can receive an increased dose of radiation should the airplane fly near the magnetic pole. While the increased dose is small and of little concern for the casual traveler, repeated exposure could lead to an increased risk for cancer in frequent travelers, such as flight crews or businesspeople. It is partially for this reason that polar flights will be diverted away from the magnetic poles during times of increased solar activity. Unfortunately, this is not without consequences. Diverting polar flights away from their usual route means the flights will be longer, more fuel will be used by the airplane, and more pollution will be produced by the engines.

Another reason flights are diverted away from the polar regions during solar storm events is due to the possible risk of something called a radio blackout. The increased flux of X-rays and energetic particles to the Earth's atmosphere during a solar storm event leads to increased ionization of the atmosphere, changing the structure of the ionosphere and potentially creating something called plasma bubbles in the ionosphere. Radio waves that we use for communication on the surface of the Earth bounce off different altitudes of plasma in the ionosphere. If the nature of the ionosphere changes, the bouncing and propagation of radio waves through the ionosphere will change, potentially reducing our ability to communicate with radio waves (it can also improve our ability to communicate with people at great distances, too!). If the increased flux of radiation is particularly intense, it can actually completely shut down the ability to use radio waves to communicate, both between stations on Earth and with satellites in space. When that happens, a radio blackout has occurred. Radio blackouts are particularly dangerous for systems that rely on satellites such as GPS to function or communication with the ground such as air traffic control towers. Most modern navigation systems in airplanes rely on GPS. If those systems cannot communicate with the GPS satellites and the flight crews cannot use radio communication with flight control towers as a back-up, both due to a radio blackout, the situation can become very dangerous for those

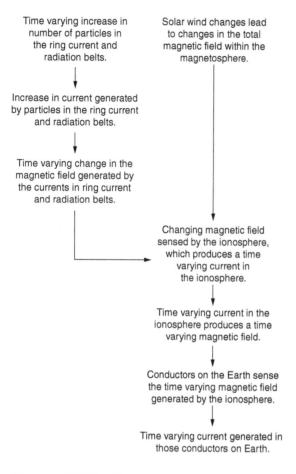

Time varying increase in
number of particles in
the ring current and
radiation belts.

Solar wind changes lead
to changes in the total
magnetic field within the
magnetosphere.

Increase in current generated
by particles in the ring current
and radiation belts.

Time varying change in the
magnetic field generated by
the currents in ring current
and radiation belts.

Changing magnetic field
sensed by the ionosphere,
which produces a time
varying current in
the ionosphere.

Time varying current in the
ionosphere produces a time
varying magnetic field.

Conductors on the Earth sense
the time varying magnetic field
generated by the ionosphere.

Time varying current generated in
those conductors on Earth.

FIGURE 6.2.1. THE TWO PATHWAYS IN WHICH
SPACE WEATHER EVENTS LEAD TO CURRENTS BEING
GENERATED IN CONDUCTORS ON THE SURFACE OF
THE EARTH.

aboard the airplane. As X-rays are electromagnetic radiation and not affected by the Earth's magnetic field, radio blackouts can occur anywhere, but the fact that solar storms can lead to an increased flux of energetic charged particles to the Earth's polar regions means that radio blackouts are more likely in the polar regions.

6.2. Geomagnetically Induced Currents

Solar storms don't just affect the ionosphere through increased ionization. As the material from a coronal mass ejection or high-speed solar wind stream travels past the Earth and buffers the Earth's magnetosphere, it will cause the magnetic field within the magnetosphere to change in multiple ways. One way is through the compression of the magnetosphere by the increased solar wind pressure. The changing solar wind conditions can also lead to an increase in particles in the radiation belts (Chapter 5). Both the changing magnetic field in space and the changes in the radiation belts (the currents generated by the moving particles in the radiation belts generate magnetic fields) can induce currents in the ionosphere. (Remember, changing magnetic fields can generate currents in conductors that sense that changing magnetic field.) Figure 6.2 shows a flow chart of how this then leads to currents flowing in conductors at Earth, be they power lines, oil pipelines, or telecommunication cables. These are referred to as geomagnetically induced currents (GICs).

Figure 6.2.2 depicts this process in cartoon form and also shows actual GICs measured in a natural gas pipeline in Finland. When currents flow in metal oil pipelines, they can lead to leaks in the pipeline. In order to move crude oil through a pipe, it must be heated up. The people who built the Alaska pipeline learned the hard way that when the chemicals in hot crude oil interact with a metal pipe that has a current running through it, a reaction occurs that greatly accelerates corrosion of the metal pipe, leading to leaks. As Alaska is in a region where currents frequently flow through the ionosphere directly overhead due to the frequent auroral displays, the metal pipe in the Alaska pipeline had to be replaced with a pipe made from a nonconducting material that cannot carry currents.

A more immediate problem is that increases in currents flowing in power lines can lead to power blackouts. One such event happened

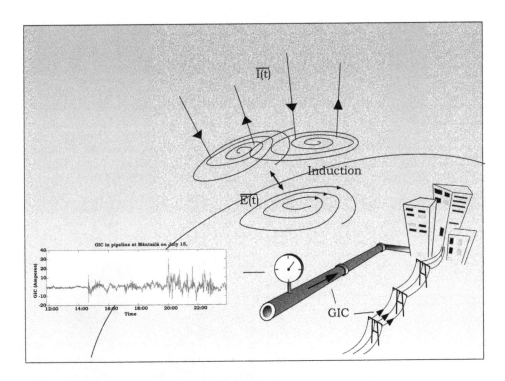

FIGURE 6.2.2. A CARTOON SHOWING THE PRODUCTION OF GEOMAGNETICALLY IN-
DUCED CURRENTS (GICs) AND AN EXAMPLE OF THE RESULTING CURRENTS IN A NATURAL
GAS PIPELINE.

on March 13, 1989, in the Canadian province of Quebec. GICs during a solar storm led to an increase in the currents running through a step-up transformer in the Quebec power grid. That current was more than the transformer could carry. That transformer failed, which in turn led to an increase in current load in surrounding transformers, as the current that was originally moving through the failed transformer was shifted to other transformers. The combination of the increased load from the failed transformer and GICs led to currents in the neighboring transformers to be too large, causing those transformers to fail, and so on, producing what is called a cascade failure. Like a stack of falling dominoes, a series of transformers within the Quebec power grid failed, leading to a blackout that lasted several hours and affected over nine million people.

One important note regarding GICs in power lines: It is not just the magnitude of the current that can cause problems; the frequency of the GIC is important, too. Power lines in the United States are designed to only carry currents with frequencies ranging between 59.95 Hz and 60.05 Hz. A small GIC with a frequency outside that range can do as much damage and has just as much probability of leading to a power failure as a large GIC within that range.

Why was the event in Quebec so damaging to the power grid? We don't know. Even though it happened during the modern space age, there were no satellites in place at the time to measure the preceding solar wind conditions. This is a case (See Section 6.3 for a more spectacular example) of a solar storm occurring, and our only information about it is the sunspot number.

One can also ask what a similar type of event would be like in the United States. Figure 6.2.3 shows the interconnection of the power grid within the United States. A cascade failure could potentially disrupt an entire interconnection. It is estimated that currently, 50% of the

North American Regional
Reliability Councils
and Interconnections

Western
Interconnection

Québec
Interconnection

Eastern
Interconnection

Texas
Interconnection

	NPCC		FRCC		TRE
	RFC		MRO		WECC
	SERC		SPP		ASCC

------ Interconnection

Source : North American Reliability Corporation

FIGURE 6.2.3A   THE THREE MAIN INTERCONNECTIONS OF THE U.S. POWER GRID.

high-voltage transformers in the United States are at or above capacity. A National Academies report [1] estimates that a Carrington Event–type (Section 6.3) event in the United States that led to the loss of a series of high-voltage transformers within an interconnect to cost $1 trillion–$2 trillion (2008 dollars) in the first year due to both equipment replacement cost and impact on the economy as a result of the lack of power and productivity. They also estimate that it could take four to ten years for the country to recover from such an event. That is only partially due to the time it takes to replace the failed equipment—it takes approximately one to three years to take delivery of a high-voltage transformer after an order is placed.

Figure 6.2.4 illustrates the basis for some of these estimates by showing the

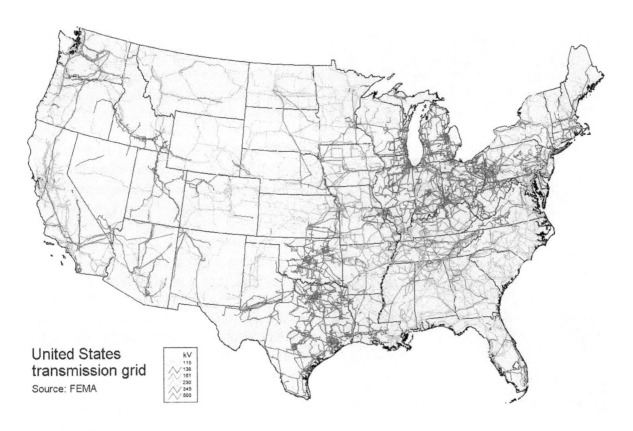

United States transmission grid

Source: FEMA

kV
115
138
161
230
345
500

FIGURE 6.2.3B THE THREE MAIN INTERCONNECTIONS OF THE U.S. POWER GRID.

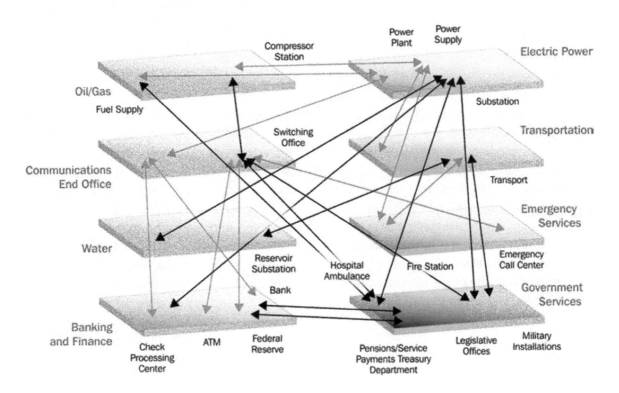

FIGURE 6.2.4. THE INTERDEPENDENCE OF SOCIETY. MODIFIED FROM AN ORIGINAL IMAGE BY THE DEPARTMENT OF HOMELAND SECURITY AND THE NATIONAL INFRASTRUCTURE PROTECTION PLAN.

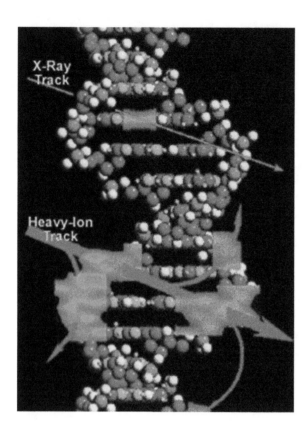

FIGURE 6.4.1. REPRESENTATION OF THE DAMAGE OF DNA FROM X-RAYS AND AN ENERGETIC HEAVY ION[1].

interdependence of our society. Even the failure of something like the GPS system can have a significant effect in unexpected areas. While it seems obvious that our transportation system depends on GPS, the use of GPS by the banking and power industry is not as clear. What most people do not realize is that GPS not only provides information for locating your position, it also provides high-precision timing information. Both the banking and power industry make heavy use of the timing information from GPS. Thus, even if GICs do not adversely affect a power grid, the power system could still suffer interruptions due to loss of communication with GPS satellites.

[1]6.3. The Carrington Event

Richard Carrington was a British amateur astronomer who made numerous observations of the Sun. On September 1, 1895, he was quite fortuitously making a map of one sunspot group, as during his observations he saw a white-light solar flare in the same region. As you saw in Chapter 4, it is very rare for solar flares to emit light in the visible portion of the electromagnetic spectrum. They primarily emit radiation in the extreme-UV and X-ray portion. But the event became even more unusual 18 hours later, when the effects of the solar flare were felt at the Earth, and would eventually become known as the Carrington Event. Auroral displays were observed all over the Earth, including in the Caribbean. In fact, there are reports of miners in the mountains of Colorado being woken up by a bright red light in the sky. It was only after they began fixing breakfast that they realized it was still the middle of the night, and what they were seeing was not the sunrise. In 1859, technology was not as prevalent as it is today, but one thing was prevalent throughout Europe and North America—telegraph lines. These were the precursor to telephone wires and not very-well-shielded conductors; thus, they were highly susceptible to the effects of geomagnetically induced currents (GICs). Telegraph machines failed throughout Europe and North America, in many case spectacularly sending sparks flying from the machines and telegraph poles, and shocking the telegraph operators. There are reports of telegraph paper catching fire from the sparks, and in some cases, telegraph machines continued to send and receive signals even after being unplugged from power outlets!

As we learn more about the effects that solar storms can have on human technology and as we become more dependent on

---

[1] http://www.sciencedirect.com/science/article/pii/S1364682606002264

that technology, scientists, engineers, and policy makers have become worried about the ramifications of a Carrington Event–type solar storm happening now. In 2008, the National Academies of Science in the United States issued a report regarding the possible effects of a severe space weather event occurring now. One of the biggest problems with regard to preparing ourselves for an event like the one in 1859 is the fact that we don't know why it was so damaging. There were no satellites in space, and thus no solar wind monitors during the Carrington Event. All we have regarding the conditions on the Sun is sunspot number.

6.4. Human Exploration

Space radiation[2] consists primarily of ionizing radiation, which exists in the form of high-energy charged particles. There are three naturally occurring sources of space radiation: trapped radiation (that is, from the radiation belt particles described in this chapter), solar energetic particle events[3] (SEPs) from coronal mass ejections, and galactic cosmic radiation[4] (GCR) associated with particle acceleration processes from other stars and solar systems. The radiation belt particles present a continuous hazard to anything moving from low Earth orbit to geosynchronous orbit. SEPs can produce significant increases in energetic particle fluxes up to energies of about 1 GeV, but their presence is very sporadic; they have the highest occurrence rate during solar maximum. GCRs are the most energetic and penetrating radiation form, with energies in excess of 10 GeV, but ironically, their flux within our

solar system is reduced by about half during solar maximum due to the extension of the solar magnetic field by the solar wind during this period. Because of the high energies, GCRs are the most difficult to protect astronauts against.

Radiation hazards range from mild and recoverable effects such as nausea and vomiting to central nervous system damage and even death. Long-term risks include development of cataracts and an increase in the probability of the development of cancer. Radiation produces these effects through two mechanisms:

- The water in the organism (e.g., a person's body) absorbs a large portion of the radiation and becomes ionized to form highly reactive, water-derived radicals. The free radicals then react with DNA molecules, causing the breaking of chemical bonds or oxidation.
- Radiation directly collides with the DNA molecule again, causing the breaking of chemical bonds forming the DNA. Measurements indicate that the heavy ion nuclei of GCR are much more damaging than X-rays.

We calculate radiation exposure based on an estimate of the radiation absorbed by the body. The metric/SI unit for this is a Gray (Gy). One Gray is defined as one Joule of energy absorbed per kilogram of material. An older unit that measures the same feature is the rad: 1 rad = 0.01 Gy. But just measuring the amount of energy deposited doesn't tell the whole story regarding radiation hazard for living organisms. Different parts of a living system will respond differently to radiation exposure. For example, radiation deposited onto human skin will have different effects from the same amount of radiation directed at a blood-forming organ. The quantity Sievert (Sv) (and the older unit rem) describes the biological equivalent radiation dosage and takes into account the type of radiation and the biological damage it can cause.

---

2 http://srag-nt.jsc.nasa.gov/SpaceRadiation/What/What.cfm
3 http://en.wikipedia.org/wiki/Solar_energetic_particles
4 http://en.wikipedia.org/wiki/Galactic_cosmic_rays

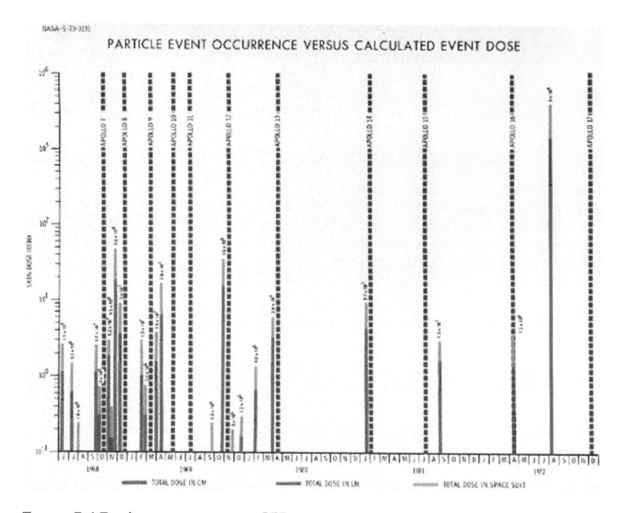

FIGURE 6.4.2. A PLOT OF MAJOR SOLAR SEP EVENTS AND OCCURRENCE OF *APOLLO* MISSIONS.

During an average six-month stay aboard the International Space Station, an astronaut will receive 80 mSv of radiation during solar maximum and 160 mSv during solar minimum. For comparison, one mSv is approximately equivalent to three chest X-rays, although the type of radiation is different from that astronauts receive aboard the ISS. NASA limits radiation exposure for astronauts to 200 mSv/yr, and the National Council on Radiation Protection (NCRP) limits the exposure for airline flight crews to 500 mSv/yr. The typical background radiation dose on Earth is about 2 mSv/yr, although this will vary with local geology (such as the presence of radon gas), altitude, and other factors.

On Earth, the exposure rate to radiation is about 2.4 milliSieverts[5] (mSv) annually and is sufficiently small that damaged cells can repair the broken DNA or die off and are replaced without significantly impairing bodily functions. The main concern comes from damaged cells reproducing, which results in cancers. The higher the exposure rate, the higher the probability of this occurring. The present exposure limits for astronauts is about 100 times this value for a 30-day period.

Except for the *Apollo* missions, NASA's manned spaceflight missions have stayed well below the altitude of the Van Allen belts. However, a part of the inner Van Allen belt dips down to about 200 km into the upper region of the atmosphere over the southern Atlantic

_____
5   http://en.wikipedia.org/wiki/Sievert

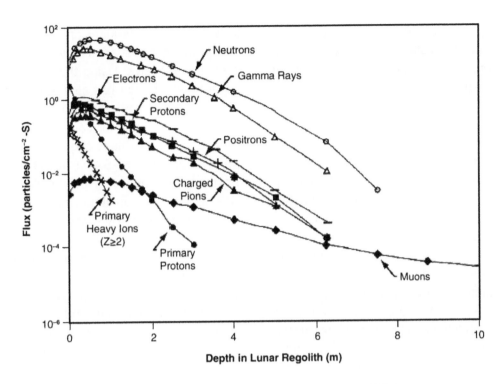

FIGURE 6.4.3. SIMULATED PARTICLE FLUX WITH DEPTH AT THE MOON.

Ocean off the coast of Brazil. This region is known as the South Atlantic Anomaly. The dip results from the fact that the magnetic axis of the Earth is tilted approximately 11 degrees from the spin axis, and the center of the magnetic field is offset from the geographical center of the Earth by 280 miles. The largest fraction of the radiation exposure received during spaceflight missions has resulted from passage through the South Atlantic Anomaly. Low-inclination flights typically traverse a portion of the South Atlantic Anomaly six or seven times a day. As a result, astronaut dosage[6] on the International Space Station receives about 150 mSv per year. Estimates are that unshielded humans in interplanetary space would receive annually roughly 400 to 900 mSv (compared to 2.4 mSv on Earth), and that a Mars mission (12 months in flight and 18 months on Mars) might expose shielded astronauts to ~500 to 1000 mSv. These doses approach the one to four Sv career limits.

The above estimates are for average conditions. During SEPs, there can be substantial spikes in energetic particle fluxes that can be significant health threats. These issues came up during the *Apollo* missions. The SEP flux for this period is shown in Figure 6.4.2.

Between the *Apollo* 16 and 17 missions, one of the largest solar proton events ever recorded occurred. It produced radiation levels of sufficient energy for the astronauts outside of the Earth's magnetosphere to absorb lethal doses within ten hours after the start of the event. It is indeed fortunate that the timing of this event did not coincide with one of the *Apollo* missions. As NASA ponders the feasibility of sending manned spaceflight missions back to the Moon or to other planets, radiation protection for crew members remains one of the key technological issues which must be resolved.

The space environment needs to be fully taken into account when considering missions beyond low Earth orbit. Either one has to provide shielding (which adds mass and mission

6   http://en.wikipedia.org/wiki/Health_threat_
from_cosmic_rays

cost), or one has to develop new propulsion systems to get astronauts quickly to their destination, which again adds cost to the missions. These issues are discussed in the next chapters.

If we want to send people past low Earth orbit for any length of time, we have to figure out ways to protect them from these types of radiation. Even landing on another planet may not be much help. It is our atmosphere that protects us on Earth from most incoming radiation, but the Moon completely lacks an atmosphere, and Mars possesses only a thin atmosphere. One idea is to use other types of in-situ materials as radiation shielding—namely, the geology. This has the advantage that the explorers don't have to bring the materials with them, reducing the cost of the mission both in terms of price and fuel/energy needed. People analyzing images of the surface of Mars have been hunting for signatures for caves. Caves would provide a location with natural radiation shielding, in which we could build future human settlements. Figure 6.4.3 shows simulation results for the penetration depth of different types of radiation into the lunar regolith. The results indicate that for most types of radiation, building the human habitation under approximately six meters of regolith would result in at least a one-hundred-times reduction in incident radiation. The figure also illustrates the concept of too little shielding being worse than none at all. Note the particle flux initially increases before decreasing. This is the result of shower products being produced within the regolith.

Using in-situ materials only works once astronauts actually get to their destination. First, they have to get there. So, what do we do to protect them while they are traveling in space? There are multiple options being explored. On Earth, lead is commonly used to block radiation. The problem with using lead for space missions is it is very heavy, and not taking enough of it puts the astronauts at even greater danger. Hydrogen reserves could be used for both fuel and radiation protection, but to store hydrogen requires cryogenics, which is both problematic as far as preventing leaks and is energy intensive. Using the water and food supplies as a barrier has also been discussed, but that opens the question of what is the impact on the safety for consumption of those supplies after they have absorbed a mission's worth of radiation. NASA has also been exploring the effectiveness of polyethylene $(C_2H_4)_n$ for stopping radiation. It has many advantages, including the fact that it is made up of light-mass elements so they have few neutrons that could be liberated, and subsequently make other radioactive elements. Also, a carbon nucleus typically breaks apart or decays into helium nuclei, which are both inert and non-radioactive. Another advantage of polyethylene is that it is both pliable, so it can be used in space suits to provide protection during exploration of a surface, and can be made stiff (called RXF1) for usage in spacecraft hulls and habitation structures.

Researchers are also investigating using electromagnetic fields for radiation protection. Pure electric fields could deflect charged particles (but not X-rays or gamma rays) away from human settlements on the Moon, but the method has one fatal flaw (literally). In order to deflect the high-energy particles that are so dangerous, very large voltages would be required on the sources of the electric fields. That produces a high risk for arcing, even at the Moon with its nearly nonexistent atmosphere. It would not do much good to try to protect lunar explorers with large electric fields, only to electrocute them with human-made lunar lightning bolts. Magnetic fields do not have a similar risk, and nature has provided us with an example of such a type of radiation protection in the form of a magnetosphere. Usage of pure magnetic fields is not feasible, as the magnetic field strengths required to deflect GCRs are very large (the Earth's magnetic field does not deflect GCRs). This would necessitate the use of superconducting magnets, which require both cryogenic cooling and large amounts of power. This limitation can be overcome if we make use of the full example nature provides us with. As we have seen in this chapter, the Earth's magnetosphere is not just a magnetic bubble—it is also a collection of currents supported by plasma flow. A magnetic shield that employs both magnetic fields and plasma to support currents could provide shielding with much lower magnetic field strengths (the plasma currents amplify the magnetic field generated by the spacecraft), thus using non-superconducting magnets. An example of one method to produce such a type of shielding is called mini-magnetospheric plasma propulsion (M2P2). As the name implies, the M2P2 would not only provide radiation shielding, it could also be used as an in-space propulsion system as we will see featured in Chapter 8.

While radiation is one of the major hazards for humans traveling in space, it is not the only one. There are also several health hazards associated with living in a low- or no-gravity environment. Some of these health problems are temporary and easily recovered from, while others have more long-term consequences. One of the temporary health impacts on humans in a low- or no-gravity environment is something called puffy face syndrome. On Earth, the human heart and body have to work against gravity to deliver blood to the head, while not working at all to pump blood to the legs. Upon arriving in space, an excess of blood will be delivered to the head and a deficit delivered to the legs. An astronaut will develop a puffy face due to excess fluid in the head, and with that typically come nasal congestion, headaches, swollen eyes, dizziness, and nausea. But these effects are only temporary. In a process that takes about two or three days, the heart will begin pumping more blood. The kidneys respond by producing more urine, and the pituitary gland produces more anti-diuretic hormones, which make an astronaut less thirsty. The combination of all of these responses by the body means that the excess fluid in the head and chest are eliminated. Upon returning to Earth, the body quickly readapts to regular gravity (at least after the six-month or shorter

stays aboard the ISS). In a related response, the kidneys also decrease the production of a hormone called erythropoietin, which stimulates red blood cell production. As a result, both the number of red blood cells and volume of blood fluid decreases. This, too, returns to normal soon upon return to Earth.

Muscle atrophy is a more long-term health hazard associated with reduced gravity. When floating, the human body adopts a more fetal-like position. The person also typically makes use of their arms. This leads to a loss of muscle mass and tone, primarily to the lower body, but all muscles, including the heart, will be affected. Astronauts try to mitigate this by exercising frequently using equipment that provides resistance. One such piece of exercise equipment is a treadmill that has a harness on it. The harness acts like large rubber bands pulling the astronaut toward the treadmill.

Another long-term risk associated with spaceflight is a reduction in bone mass. The human body has two types of bone cells: osteoblasts and osteoclasts. Osteoblasts lay down new minerals on bones. Osteoclasts chew up some of those mineral layers. On Earth, the two processes are usually finely balanced. For reasons we do not understand, in space, the osteoblasts slow down, while the osteoclasts continue to work at a normal rate. The net effect is that astronauts can lose up to 10% of bone mass and become weaker at a rate of 1% per month due to the lack of bone-forming minerals. After a two-to-three-month mission in space, it will take two to three *years* for an astronaut's bones to return to normal density. A side effect of this is that the imbalance between production of bone-forming minerals and the removal of bone mineral leads to an increase in calcium in the bloodstream. This puts astronauts at a higher risk for developing kidney stones. NASA is currently trying to develop drugs that will mitigate the problem. Those drugs could also help people on Earth who have brittle bones due to either a genetic syndrome or osteoporosis.

Astronauts also have to deal with quality-of-life issues. While in reduced gravity, the human spine elongates, and the vertebrae separate slightly. While this makes astronauts taller, it also leads to back pain. Nausea and dizziness are also a potential problem for astronauts. Our brain uses a combination of signals from both the eyes and ears to orient the human body and determine which way is up or down. When one is floating, those signals can become confused. This is not helped by the typical design of space vehicles. Space onboard the ISS is at a premium. This, combined with the fact that astronauts do not need to walk around, means that there is no floor on the ISS, and all the walls have instruments and sensors on them. This can further enhance the disorientation to the brain, not able to distinguish up or down.

Another issue astronauts currently must deal with is associated with space suit design. One of the results of the *Apollo* 1 fire was the switch away from pure oxygen atmospheres onboard spacecraft. The problem with that, though, is that our current space suit design requires the breathing of pure oxygen by an astronaut in a space suit. If they did not breathe pure oxygen, the air pressure within the suit required to provide sufficient oxygen for the human body to function would be so high that the astronauts would not be able to bend their arms, elbows, or legs. The transition from regular air onboard the ISS (or, in the past, on the Space Shuttle) means an astronaut must slowly purge the nitrogen from their body before a spacewalk. Failure to do so will lead to nitrogen bubbles forming in the blood, causing damage to tissue and possible death. One of the goals of better space suit designs in the future is to eliminate this issue.

When we talk about astronauts experiencing weightlessness, we are often referring to those astronauts aboard the ISS, in which case we are being sloppy. We see those astronauts floating, but really they are in free fall. Objects in orbit around the Earth are falling toward the Earth, but the curved surface of the Earth means the objects never actually hit the surface and instead circle around the Earth. The astronauts are still experiencing gravity, albeit reduced gravity relative to that on the surface of the Earth, but they appear to be weightless because both they and the ISS are falling at the same rate; thus, the astronaut never hits the floor. Astronauts in low Earth orbit, either on the ISS or Space Shuttle, experienced gravity that is about 3% less than that on the surface and thus were actually in a "microgravity" environment. What this means for astronauts experiencing true, long-term weightlessness is not known.

Image Credits

Chapter 6 Opening Image: NASA, ESA and the Hubble SM4 ERO Team, "Butterfly emerges from stellar demise in planetary negula NGC 6302," http://www.spacetelescope.org/images/heic0910h/. Copyright in the Public Domain.

Figure 6.0.1: NASA, http://www.nasa.gov/images/content/607989main_FAQ13-orig_full.jpg. Copyright in the Public Domain.

Figure 6.2.2: Axpulkki, "GIC generation," http://en.wikipedia.org/wiki/File:GIC_generation.jpg. Copyright in the Public Domain.

Figure 6.2.3a: Copyright © Bouchecl (CC BY-SA 3.0) at https://commons.wikimedia.org/wiki/File:NERC-map-en.svg

Figure 6.2.3b: Rolypolyman, "UnitedStatesPowerGrid," https://en.wikipedia.org/wiki/File:UnitedStatesPowerGrid.jpg. Copyright in the Public Domain.

Figure 6.2.4: Department of Homeland Security, "Connections and interdependencies across the economy," http://science.nasa.gov/media/medialibrary/2009/01/21/21jan_severespaceweather_resources/interdependency.jpg. Copyright in the Public Domain.

Figure 6.4.1: NASA, "Space Radiation," http://srag.jsc.nasa.gov/SpaceRadiation/Why/DNA1.gif. Copyright in the Public Domain.

Figure 6.4.2: NASA, "Solar proton events during the Apollo Program," http://srag.jsc.nasa.gov/Publications/TM104782/solarpr.jpg. Copyright in the Public Domain.

Figure 6.4.3: NASA, "Simulated particle flux with depth at the moon," http://ntrs.nasa.gov/archive/nasa/casi.ntrs.nasa.gov/19940026920_1994026920.pdf. Copyright in the Public Domain.

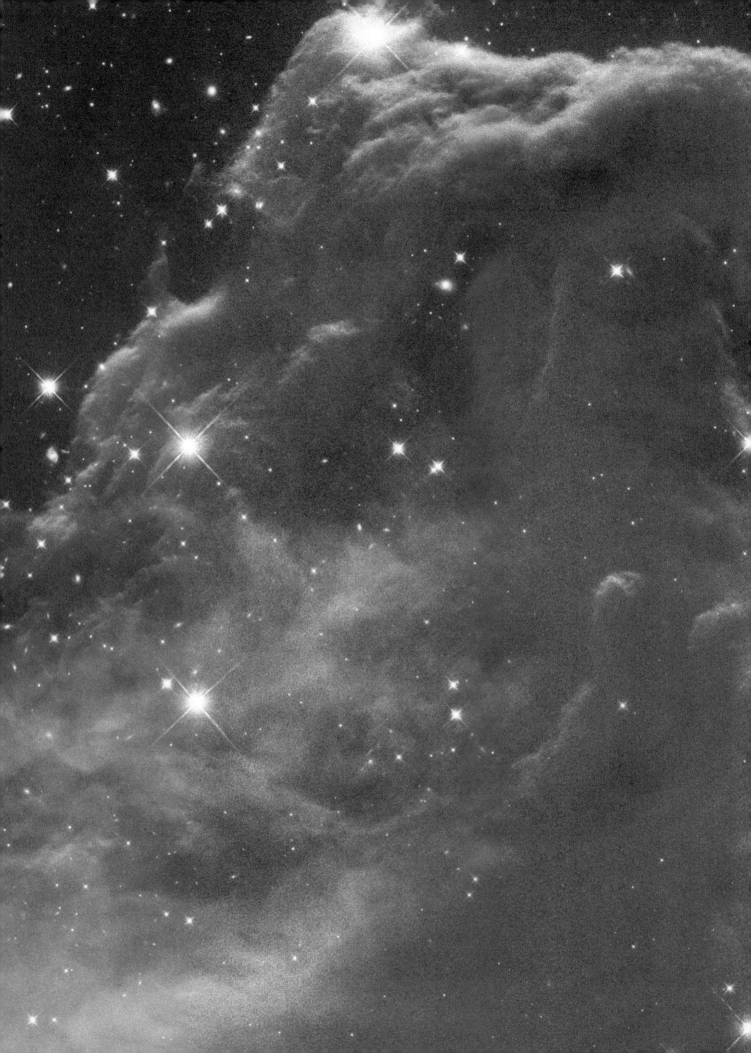

Chapter 7

Traveling to the Planets

In the previous chapters, we have established the space environment between the planets. We know that it is not actually empty, but filled with energetic particles that can be a hazard to space travel. We will see in the following sections some ideas on how to improve space travel. We have also emphasized the need to understand the scale lengths involved and fully describe all of the solar system. In planning a mission to the planets, we have to understand the speeds at which objects move in the solar system and our ability as humans to be able to produce spacecraft that can move at the appropriate speeds within required cost limitations. From our perspective as humans on Earth, we do not appear to be traveling very fast. The reality, though, is that the Earth and the other planets are actually moving at substantial speeds—beyond the typical speeds that we experience here on the Earth. One-way missions to the solar system objects are pretty easy to design if one is not too concerned about the flight time, which is typically on the order of years if one is going to the object beyond the Moon. Developing return missions is much more difficult because in general, the Earth and the target solar system object move substantially around their orbit around the Sun for transit times presently available. This motion means that the traveler has to wait for planetary alignments to favor the return leg, which can take years, or to ask to undertake the flight path that is very much longer, which leads to other risks and costs to the mission.

In this chapter, we consider planetary motion within the context of space travel, with a particular emphasis on orbital speeds. We will first consider what is available with present-day technology, using conventional chemical propulsion systems, also known as rockets. We then consider opportunities that may become available with advanced propulsion systems that could eventually involve nuclear power—both fusion and fission—lasers, solar energy, and/or plasma systems.

7.1. Medieval Astronomy[1]

The motion of the planets and the speeds involved are actually hard to conceive, particularly from the human perspective. Sitting on our Earth, it looks like the universe revolves around the Earth. Indeed, the early models of the solar system proposed by the Greeks, including Eudoxus[2] (400–347 BC), were geocentric (earth-centered), with the heavenly bodies moving along concentric spheres. Ptolemy[3], a Greco-Roman astronomer (90–168 AD), modified the concept to one in which the planets move on a small circle (epicycle), which in turn moved on a larger circle (deferent) that was centered about the Earth.

However, this model always had problems accurately describing the motion of the planets, particularly something called a retrograde[4]—when a planet appears to move backward across the sky. Throughout the next few centuries, the geocentric model was questioned by others, including Martianus Capella[5] in the fifth century, when he suggested that the motion within the solar system would be more accurately described by a heliocentric[6] (sun-centered) system. The differences between the geocentric and heliocentric models are shown in Figure 7.1.1. In both models, the motion of the Sun and the Moon is well described by motion about a single circle. The motions of the other planets are significantly different between the two models. In order to distinguish these different models, detailed observations are required. While it is easy to dismiss the geocentric model in today's world, the point to emphasize here is that the difference required detailed observations to be made, and only when these observations are made can progress truly occur.

Such detailed observations were not forthcoming until the 16th century by Nicolaus Copernicus[7] (1473–1543). He was able to bring the heliocentric system to the forefront by developing detailed astronomical tables that could be used to compute past and future positions of the stars and planets. Moreover, detailed observations could show the presence of retrograde orbits, which could not be explained in a geocentric model. Copernicus's model was strongly debated, with one of the strongest critics being Tycho Brahe[8] (1546–1601). He took his own set of astronomical observations to disprove the heliocentric model. However, Brahe died at a relatively early age, and his successor, Johannes Kepler[9], was able to use his data to determine the laws governing the motion of the planets. These laws, known as Kepler's Laws of Planetary Motion[10], govern our present-day understanding of the solar system.

1   http://outreach.atnf.csiro.au/education/senior/cosmicengine/renaissanceastro.html
2   http://en.wikipedia.org/wiki/Eudoxus_of_Cnidus
3   http://en.wikipedia.org/wiki/Ptolemy
4   mailto:http://www.lasalle.edu/~smithsc/Astronomy/retrograd.html
5   http://en.wikipedia.org/wiki/Martianus_Capella

6   http://en.wikipedia.org/wiki/Heliocentrism
7   http://en.wikipedia.org/wiki/Nicolaus_Copernicus
8   http://en.wikipedia.org/wiki/Tycho_Brahe
9   http://en.wikipedia.org/wiki/Johannes_Kepler
10 http://en.wikipedia.org/wiki/Kepler's_laws_of_planetary_motion

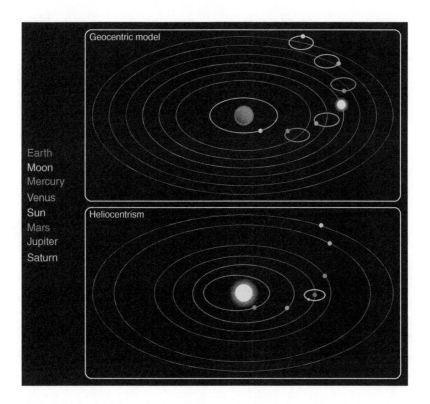

Earth
Moon
Mercury
Venus
Sun
Mars
Jupiter
Saturn

FIGURE 7.1.1. TOP PANEL SHOWS THE MOTION OF THE SOLAR SYSTEM IN THE GEOCENTRIC MODEL, WHERE THE EARTH IS AT THE CENTER OF THE MOTION. THE BOTTOM PANEL SHOWS THE HELIOCENTRIC MODEL WITH THE SUN AT THE CENTER OF THE SOLAR SYSTEM.

7.2. Kepler's Laws of Planetary Motion[11]

Kepler developed three laws for planetary motion. The first two were published in 1609 and the third in 1619. Kepler was able to fit Brahe's data to the Copernican model, but there were always small but significant errors in those fits. He realized that the perfect circles used in the Copernican model were not accurate, and that orbits of the planets were more accurately described by ellipses. Hence:

Kepler's First Law—The Law of Ellipses: All planets orbit the sun in elliptical orbits, with the Sun at one of the two foci of the ellipse. This law basically describes the influence of gravity on the orbits and the noncircular shape of an important comes from the initial velocity of the object when the solar system formed.

Figure 7.2.1 shows the orbit of a planet around the Sun, but it holds true for any object orbiting around another one, such as a moon orbiting around a planet. For the case of a planet orbiting around the Sun, the location of closest approach by the planet to the Sun is referred to as perihelion, while aphelion is the location at which the planet is furthest from the Sun. The first focus point is the location of the Sun, while the second focus point has no physical significance except that if the orbit were a perfect circle, the two focal points would lie on top of each other. The *semi-major axis* is defined as the average of the perihelion and aphelion distances, or half of the major axis length. Another way to characterize an ellipse is by eccentricity[12], which is equal to the distance between the foci divided by the length of the major axis. A circle has an eccentricity equal to zero. The closer the eccentricity is to one, the

11 http://en.wikipedia.org/wiki/
Kepler's_laws_of_planetary_motion

12 http://www.windows2universe.org/physical_
science/physics/mechanics/orbit/eccentricity.html

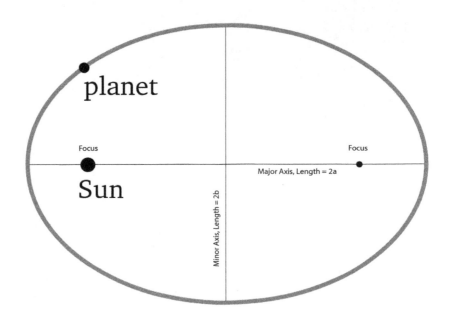

FIGURE 7.2.1.   ILLUSTRATION SHOWING KEPLER'S FIRST LAW. FOR ANY ORBIT, THE BODY BEING ORBITED IS AT ONE OF THE TWO FOCII.

more elongated an ellipse is. If we define the distance between the two foci, along the major axis, as 2c, then the eccentricity is equal to c/a (Figure 7.2.1).

Kepler's Second Law—The Law of Equal Areas: The line between a planet and the Sun sweeps out equal areas in equal periods of time as illustrated in Figure 7.2.2. This law is most easily seen in objects that have highly elliptical orbits, such as comets. When comets are seen far out in the solar system, they are moving relatively slowly, and therefore the sector they cross in a fixed part of time is relatively narrow. However, because the radius at this time is long, the area covered by the comet is relatively large. When the object is closer in, the comet is seen to move faster, and the width of the sector that it transects is correspondingly larger. However, the radius is smaller, so that the area that is swept out over the same time period is the equal to that when the object was further out. An animation of this can be found at http://upload.wikimedia.org/wikipedia/com-mons/9/94/Elliptic_orbit.gif. This law is another way of describing the conservation of angular

momentum. Another example of this effect is seen when an ice skater performs a spin—arms in, the skater goes faster; arms out, the skater slows.[13]

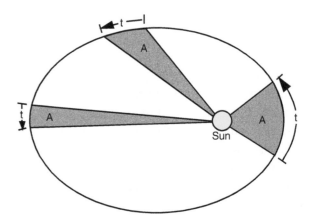

FIGURE 7.2.2.   ILLUSTRATION SHOWING KEPLER'S SECOND LAW. THE MOTION OF A PLANET IS SUCH THAT IT CUTS OUT THE SAME AREA IN THE SAME TIME ALONG ITS ORBIT. THIS MEANS THAT IT MOVES RELATIVELY SLOWLY WHEN IT IS FARTHER OUT AND MOVES FASTER WHEN IT IS CLOSER TO THE SUN[13].

13   http://outreach.atnf.csiro.au/education/senior/cosmicengine/renaissanceastro.html

Table 7.2.1. Key parameters of the planets closest to the Earth.

Planet	T (yr)	R (AU)	T²	R³	Speed (km/s)	Eccentricity
Mercury	0.24	0.39	0.06	0.06	61	0.206
Venus	0.62	0.72	0.39	0.37	38	0.007
Earth	1	1	1	1	30	0.017
Mars	1.88	1.52	3.53	3.51	24	0.093
Jupiter	11.9	5.2	142	141	13	0.049
Saturn	29.5	9.54	870	868	10	0.056

Kepler's Third Law—The Law of Periods: The amount of time a planet takes to orbit the Sun is related to its orbit's size, such that the period T squared is proportional to the semi-major axis a cubed, i.e.,

$$T^2 = k\, a^3 \qquad (7.3.1)$$

where k is a constant which is dependent on the mass of the star. However, since we know the period and distance of the Earth, we can substitute these values in to obtain

$$\left(\frac{T}{T_{Earth}}\right)^2 = \left(\frac{R}{R_{Earth}}\right)^3 \qquad (7.3.2)$$

where T_{Earth} = 1 year and R_{Earth} = 1 AU. So, once the radial distance of a planet is known, the period can automatically be determined. And once the period is known, the velocity of the planet can be determined. For example, if the planet or object is in a nearly circular orbit, then its speed is given by

$$V = 2\,\pi\, R\, /T. \qquad (7.3.3)$$

Using this information, we can construct a table of speeds for distances for the planets as in Table 7.2.1. The Earth is moving at 30 km/s around the Sun. Both Mars and Venus have speeds relatively close to that of the Earth, which we will see later means that they can be reasonably accessed for space travel using current technology. Going to any of the others planets requires double-digit changes in velocities. A spacecraft going into orbit around these systems not only has to travel larger distances, *but* they have to undergo substantial acceleration in order to match speeds with the planet (or risk crashing into it). So, there are costs arising from both distance to be traveled as well as speed to be obtained.

7.3. Kepler's Third Law Using Newton's Laws of Motion

Isaac Newton[14] (1642–1727) was able to show that the planetary motions described by Kepler's laws are due to the planets acting under the gravity of the Sun. Newton demonstrated that the acceleration that an object experiences under gravity is given by

$$\alpha = \frac{GM}{R^2} \qquad (7.3.4)$$

where M is the mass of the object influencing the path of the subject,

R is the distance between the object and the subject, and

G is the gravitational constant which is equal to 6.67×10^{-11} m³kg⁻¹s⁻².

---

14 http://en.wikipedia.org/wiki/Issac_Newton

Table 7.3.1. Escape velocities from the Moon and the planets.

Planet	Mass (kg)	Radius (m)	v_{escape} (km/s)
Mercury	3.3×10^{23}	2.4×10^6	4.4
Venus	4.9×10^{24}	6.0×10^6	10.4
Earth	6.0×10^{24}	6.4×10^6	11.2
Moon	7.36×10^{22}	1.7×10^6	2.6
Mars	6.4×10^{23}	3.4×10^6	5.0
Jupiter	1.9×10^{27}	7.1×10^7	59.7
Saturn	5.7×10^{26}	6.0×10^7	35.5
Uranus	8.7×10^{25}	2.6×10^7	21.3
Neptune	1.0×10^{26}	2.5×10^7	23.5

Form this equation, Kepler's Third law can be shown to reduce to

$$\left(\frac{T}{2\pi}\right)^2 = \frac{R^3}{GM} \qquad (7.3.5)$$

This equation can be used to determine parameters of orbits. For example, suppose we wanted to place a weather satellite in orbit around the Earth such that it always looks at the same piece of real estate. This type of orbit is called geosynchronous[15] and requires the satellite to have a period of 24 hours. Therefore, the orbital distance for the spacecraft must be such that

$$R = (GM)^{1/3} (T/2\pi)^{2/3} \quad (7.3.6)$$

$$= (6.67 \times 10^{-11} \text{ m}^3\text{kg}^{-1}\text{s}^{-2}) \times (6 \times 10^{12} \text{ kg})^{1/3}(24 \times 60 \times 60\text{s}/2\pi)^{2/3}$$

$$= 4.16 \times 10^7 \text{ m}$$

$$= 6.6 \text{ Earth Radii}$$

The speed of the spacecraft can be obtained by using 7.3.3 in the above equation to yield

$$R = (GM)^{1/3} (R/V)^{2/3} \qquad \rightarrow V^2 = R/GM$$

15 http://en.wikipedia.org/wiki/
Geosynchronous_orbit

$$V = \sqrt{\frac{GM}{R}} \qquad (7.3.7)$$

Assignment Question 1. Determine the speed and orbital period of a spacecraft in low Earth orbit at 400 km altitude (i.e., a radius of 6371 + 400 km). Now, repeat the calculation for the Moon's orbit around the Earth (you can assume a circular orbit).

Assignment Question 2. Using the orbital period of the Moon, calculate its orbital radius.

The escape velocity is the velocity required for anything to overcome the gravitational force attracting it. For a spacecraft to leave a planet, it is $\sqrt{2}$ faster than the low orbit speed, i.e.,

$$V_{Escape} = \sqrt{\frac{2GM}{R}}. \qquad (7.3.8)$$

Note that the escape velocity for an object is NOT a function of the mass trying to escape. Rather, it is dependent only on the mass of the planet that one is trying to escape from.

A summary of escape velocities for solar system objects is given in Table 7.3.1. It is seen that the escape velocity of the Moon, Mars, and Mercury are relatively low at less than about 5 km/s. For anything else, the speed is going to be a significant fraction or even exceeds

Frame of Reference: Moving with Planet

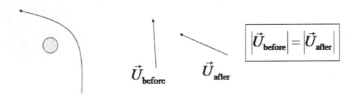

$$\left|\vec{U}_{before}\right| = \left|\vec{U}_{after}\right|$$

Frame of Reference: Planet Moving Left

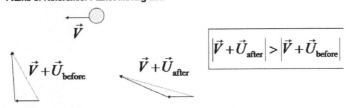

$$\left|\vec{V}+\vec{U}_{after}\right| > \left|\vec{V}+\vec{U}_{before}\right|$$

FIGURE 7.4.1. CHANGE IN VELOCITY OF A SPACECRAFT'S SPEED (U) AS IT INTERACTS WITH A SOLAR SYSTEM BODY MOVING SPEED V. DUE TO THE MOTION OF THE BODY THE SPACECRAFT CAN PICK UP A CHANGE IN SPEED OF A MAXIMUM OF TWICE THE SPEED OF THE PLANET.

the orbit speed of the object. As the speed increases, so does the energy budget. It is this cost that limits our ability to move freely about the solar system.

7.4. Orbital Assist

The velocities of the planets are sufficiently high that a spacecraft can gain a significant amount of speed as it flies by the planet. This process is known as an orbital or gravity assist[16] as is shown in Figure 7.4.1. Suppose a spacecraft is moving out in the solar system with speed V relative to the Sun and that it encounters a planet with an orbital speed of U. An observer on the planet will see the spacecraft moving toward the planet with a net velocity of -V-U, which we will call W. Within the reference frame of the planet, the spacecraft will interact with the gravity of the planet and alter its course. The gravity field of the planet is such that the spacecraft gains speed at closest approach, but loses speed as it pulls away, so that it leaves the planet at the same speed it entered, i.e., W. However, in the frame where the Sun is at rest, the spacecraft will be seen to be leaving with a total speed of W+U = V+2U.

Thus, in principle, the spacecraft can pick up a maximum speed of 2U from interacting with a planet. This is an extreme case, where the spacecraft does a full 180° turn. In general, spacecraft interactions tend to be more tangential, but the point is that even at a fraction of a planet's orbital speed, the gain can be significant. Examples of trajectories of some major NASA missions are shown in Figure 7.4.2. Not only do missions moving out of the solar system require orbital assists, even trying to get to Mercury and attain the correct orbital velocity requires several orbital assists.

---

16   http://www2.jpl.nasa.gov/basics/grav/primer.php

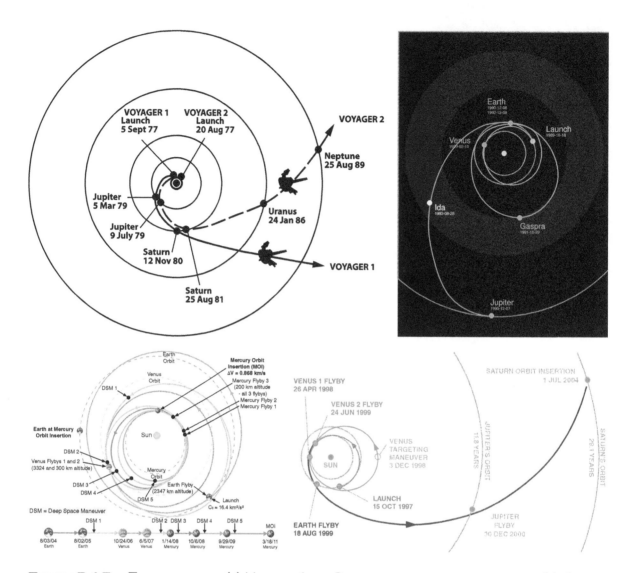

FIGURE.7.4.2. TRAJECTORIES OF (A) *VOYAGER* 1 AND 2 TO THE EDGE OF THE SOLAR SYSTEM; (B) *GALILEO* TO JUPITER; (C) *MESSENGER* TO MERCURY; AND (D) *CASSINI* TO SATURN. EACH MISSION REQUIRED SEVERAL ORBITAL ASSISTS TO GAIN ENOUGH VELOCITY TO REACH THEIR DESTINATION. TRIP TIMES ARE SEVERAL YEARS FOR ALL FOUR MISSIONS.

7.5. Rocket Equation

One might ask, why not just "put the pedal to the metal" and fly directly to the planet? It turns out the speeds we need to attain are much higher than our everyday experiences, and trying to attain them directly is a very hard problem to solve. Going down the highway at 100 miles per hour may seem extremely fast for a pedal-to-the-metal type, but it is nothing compared to

space-like requirements. The planetary orbital speeds listed in Table 7.2.1 require speeds typically at least a thousand times faster.

The limitation on how fast one can go is dependent on two key parameters: (a) how fast you can throw material out the back of your spacecraft; and (b) the mass that you are trying to push. These two quantities are related by the law of conservation of momentum[17], which requires that momentum (the product of mass

17   http://en.wikipedia.org/wiki/Momentum

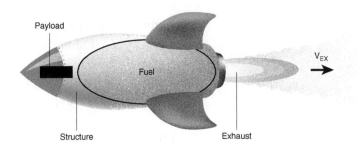

FIGURE 7.5.1. CONSERVATION OF MOMENTUM APPLIED TO A ROCKET SYSTEM.

times velocity) is constant for a closed system where there are no outside forces.

The configuration for a rocket is shown in Figure 7.5.1. Suppose that we are in a reference frame where the rocket is initially at rest. Thus, in this frame its initial momentum is zero, since V is zero. Now, suppose that it instantaneously ejects an amount of fuel (M_{fuel}) out the back with exhaust velocity V_{fuel}.

Conservation of momentum then requires that the final momentum, which is the sum of the momentum of the rocket and fuel, must still be zero, i.e.,

$$0 \text{ (rocket at rest)} = M_{craft}V_{craft} + M_{fuel}(-V_{fuel}) \quad (7.5.1)$$

with the minus sign indicating that the fuel is in the opposite direction that the spacecraft is moving. With manipulation of (7.5.1), we find that

$$M_{craft}V_{craft} = M_{fuel}V_{fuel} \quad (7.5.2)$$

or

$$V_{craft} = M_{fuel}V_{fuel}/M_{craft} \quad (7.5.3)$$

It is seen from (7.5.3) that to make the rocket go faster, one must

- Maximize fuel speed;
- Maximize fuel mass, and/or;
- Minimize the mass of the spacecraft.

Most importantly, if your fuel speed is so much smaller than your desired speed, then the ratio of fuel mass must be very much larger than the mass of the actual spacecraft. It is for this reason that when you watch a rocket launch, the launch vehicle tends to be much, much bigger than the payload being carried.

In the above example, we assumed that the fuel vented instantaneously. In general, this doesn't occur because the acceleration would be devastatingly large. Instead, we have a steady rocket burn, and then the conservation law for a small-time Δt becomes

$$\frac{\Delta\left(M_{craft}V_{craft}\right)}{\Delta t} = \frac{\Delta\left(M_{fuel}V_{fuel}\right)}{\Delta t} \quad (7.5.4)$$

Assuming that the mass of the spacecraft and the speed of the fuel are constant (7.5.4) reduces to

$$M_{craft}dV_{craft} = V_{fuel}dM_{fuel} \quad (7.5.5)$$

or

$$\Delta V = V_{fuel}\frac{dM}{M} \quad (7.5.6)$$

where we have dropped the spacecraft subscript and ΔV represents the change in the spacecraft velocity. Integrating this last equation, one obtains the ideal rocket equation[18]:

---

18   http://en.wikipedia.org/wiki/Tsiolkovsky_rocket_equation

$$\Delta V = V_{fuel} \ln\left(1 + \frac{M_{fuel}}{M_{craft}}\right) \qquad (7.5.7a)$$

or

$$\frac{M_{fuel}}{M_{craft}} = e^{\Delta V/V_{fuel}} - 1 \qquad (7.5.7b)$$

The term "ideal" refers to the fact that we have made some simplified assumptions, including constant fuel velocity (which does change as during an actual burn), and no losses due to processes like air resistance are included.

The derivation is not important for our discussion here. The important point is that for changes in velocity that are much smaller than the fuel velocity, the change in speed given by the ideal rocket equation reduces to the simplified derivation of (7.5.3), when only a small amount of mass (relative to the mass of the spacecraft) is expended. However, if the required ΔV is much larger than the V_{fuel}, then one has to carry exponentially more fuel than payload mass. One way to interpret this is that because the fuel is not burned instantaneously, one has to carry fuel to carry the fuel that is not burnt, and as a result, the mass requirements increase exponentially.

As described in the next section, typical chemical rocket motors have exhaust velocities between 2–5 km/s. The spacecraft speed for just low Earth orbit requires a speed of 9 km/s. Trying to do pedal to the metal to go to any

a.	Earth	Moon Earth (round-trip)	$\Delta V = 9.6$ km/sec
b.	Earth	Mercury (one-way)	$\Delta V = 16$ km/sec
c.	Earth	Mars Earth	$\Delta V = 14$ km/sec
d.	Earth	Jupiter	$\Delta V = 32$ km/sec
e.	Earth	Saturn	$\Delta V = 55$ km/sec
f.	Earth	Saturn Earth	$\Delta V = 110$ km/sec

of the planets with a chemical rocket basically means that your payload will be exponentially small relative to your fuel bill, which makes things highly uneconomical.

The value of ΔV will depend on the mission—specifically, where the rocket is going and how it will get there. For a simple rocket launch off the Earth with only the rocket burn at launch, the initial velocity of the rocket is zero, so ΔV is just equal to the final speed of the rocket. In reality, most missions involve multiple rocket burns associated with changing from one type of orbit to another.

Assignment Question 3. Assuming your launch vehicle is an ATLAS-V rocket ($M_{FUEL,MAX} = 8,000$kg), find the largest possible payload for the following missions for an efficient chemical rocket ($C_E = 5$ km/sec) (assume no gravity assists are used):

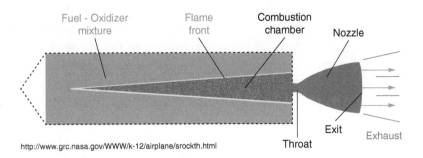

Fuel - Oxidizer mixture | Flame front | Combustion chamber | Nozzle | Exit | Throat | Exhaust

http://www.grc.nasa.gov/WWW/k-12/airplane/srockth.html

FIGURE 7.6.1. CONFIGURATION FOR A SOLID-PROPELLANT ROCKET.

A key concept when evaluating propulsion methods is thrust. Thrust is defined as the force generated by an engine or rocket and is equal to the exhaust speed of the rocket times the fuel mass flow rate. A technical term that is used to describe the efficiency of an engine is called the specific impulse[19], or *Isp*, which is the force regarding the amount of propellant used in the unit time. The higher the specific impulse, the lower the propellant flow rate required for a given thrust. It turns out mathematically that

$$Isp = V_{fuel}/g \text{ (units in s)} \qquad (7.4.8)$$

where g is the earth's gravity equal to 9.8 m/s². High *Isp* (or propellant speed) in general means higher efficiencies in terms of mass expended, but if the velocity of the propellant is much faster than the desired speed of the spacecraft, then you end up wasting energy. So, there is a need to match the speed of the propellant with the actual application. This also means that a rocket engine that has high thrust while using little fuel will have a high *Isp*.

Despite the cost, chemical rockets are the only proven means to date to get from the Earth's surface into space. As such, spacecraft systems must be extremely well optimized to minimize cost. Changes in efficiency of only a percent change still represent huge savings. In the following, we review the various systems available and what is being done to lower cost and increase spacecraft speeds in an affordable fashion.

7.6. Chemical Rocket Systems

There are several different types of chemical rocket motors[20]; each are tuned for their specific applications for optimal performance and cost. The main systems are (1) solid propellants; (2) monopropellants; (3) bipropellants; and (4) hybrid rocket motors.

7.6.1. Solid Propellants

Solid rocket motors are typically mixtures of solid oxidizer with some type of combustible material held together with some type of rubberized adhesive. One of the most common forms uses ammonium perchlorate (~70%) combined with about 16–20% fine aluminum powder held together with 11–14% hydroxyl-terminated polybutadiene (HTPB). This propellant is used for rockets as small as Estes rockets[21] to the large launch systems, including the solid boosters on the Space Shuttle[22] and the Delta IV Heavy[23]. A typical configuration of this system is shown in Figure 7.6.1.

Solid motors have the advantage of simple design, substantial flight heritage, high reliability, compact size, long storage times, high

---

19   http://en.wikipedia.org/wiki/Specific_impulse

20   http://en.wikipedia.org/wiki/Rocket_propellant
21   http://www.estesrockets.com/
22   http://en.wikipedia.org/wiki/Space_Shuttle
23   http://en.wikipedia.org/wiki/Delta_IV

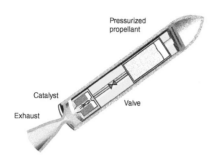

FIGURE 7.6.2. MONOPROPELLANT ROCKET MOTOR.

payload mass fraction, and low costs. Because the exhaust speed is relatively low at 2–3 km/s, they are used primarily in large rocket systems as boosters when the speed of the rocket is low during its first leg into space.

There are, however, several disadvantages to these rockets. They are impossible to run off once lit. Cracking or air bubbles in the fuel grain can cause them to explode or rupture. They also use rubber seals, which, if they fail, allow venting of hot gas. This failure mode was the cause of the Space Shuttle *Challenger* disaster[24] in 1986.

7.6.2. Monopropellant Engines

Monopropellant systems use only a single propellant, which passes through a catalyst and causes a reaction, creating heat and various by-products. The most common type of monopropellant is hydrazine (N_2H_4). Hydrazine is easily stored as a liquid requiring no cryogenics, and when passed over a catalyst such as iridium metal, it decomposes into ammonia, nitrogen gas, and hydrogen gas. These gases have an exhaust velocity of about 2.3 km/s. This reaction can be very tightly controlled by fast switching valves, making these types of systems ideal for altitude control.

These systems have also been extremely important as the terminal descent thrusters for *Viking* landers[25], as well as the *Phoenix* lander[26] and the *Curiosity* rover[27]. These applications are similar to altitude control, as they require the ability to have fine adjustments. Only small changes in velocity are required, which fits well with the low-exhaust velocities needed for final descent.

The main advantages of monopropellant rockets are that they provide simple, robust, and reliable performance. There is minimal plumbing that can fail during operation in space, and they have a substantial flight heritage.

The disadvantages of these systems are that they have a low-exhaust velocity and so are not efficient for usage as a main thrust engine. The fuel itself is also very toxic, and there are lifetime issues associated with the use of a catalyst.

7.6.3. Liquid Bipropellant Engines

Liquid bipropellant systems have the oxidizer (typically liquid oxygen) separated from the fuel (which is also a liquid) as shown in Figure 7.6.3. The fuel and oxidizer are then pumped into the combustion chamber, where the fuel is ignited and then vented through the exhaust nozzle. These systems have the highest speed of any of the chemical rocket systems. The fastest speeds are obtained through a mixture of liquid oxygen (LOX) and liquid hydrogen. Such systems are used for the Space Shuttle main engine, Saturn V upper stages, Delta IV, and the Ariane 5. One disadvantage of the systems is that the liquid hydrogen needs cryogenics to remain in its liquid form, which is required to maintain the highest possible mass

24   http://en.wikipedia.org/wiki/Challenger_accident

25   http://en.wikipedia.org/wiki/Viking_program
26   http://en.wikipedia.org/wiki/Phoenix_(spacecraft)
27   http://en.wikipedia.org/wiki/Curiosity_rover

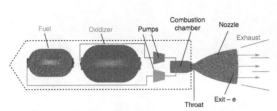

FIGURE 7.6.3. SCHEMATIC OF A LIQUID BI-PROPELLANT ROCKET MOTOR.

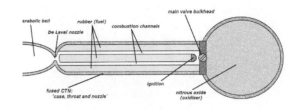

FIGURE 7.6.4. HYBRID ROCKET MOTOR IN WHICH THE OXIDIZER IS A LIQUID AND THE FUEL IS A SOLID. COMBUSTION IS CONTROLLED BY THE FLOW OF THE OXIDIZER INTO THE CHAMBER.

density. Another problem is from the cold temperatures involved. Falling ice from the cryogenically cooled main tank led to the damage of the heat tiles on the Space Shuttle *Columbia*[28] eventually led to its disintegration on reentry in 2003. This system also typically requires elaborate valve systems.

The combination of liquid oxygen and kerosene is used for the Falcon rocket family[29], presently being developed by Space Exploration Technologies (aka SpaceX). This method has slightly lower exhaust velocities, but it does not require the cryogenic cooling of the oxygen/hydrogen systems. It is well suited for operation at full atmospheric pressure.

For deep space missions in which one needs to minimize all cryogenic systems, a mixture of nitrogen tetroxide (N_2O_4) and hydrazine (N_2H_4) is used, since both oxidizer and fuel can be stored as liquids for long periods without cryogenics. This system is used on the Space Shuttle orbiter maneuvering system.

7.6.4. Hybrid Rocket Motors

A hybrid motor is one in which the fuel is a solid. During flight, the liquid oxidizer is pumped into the combustion chamber, where it is ignited and burns the solid fuel grains as shown in Figure 7.6.4. Unlike solid motors, these systems can be throttled by controlling the flow of the oxidizer into the chamber. The oxidizer tends to be either liquid oxygen or nitrous oxide. The fuel can be ABS plastic or synthetic rubber, which are both relatively inexpensive. Moreover, there the system is relatively inert should there be a failure in the motor. They can have a relatively high exhaust velocity of about 4 km/s, which is slightly less than the liquid bipropellant systems. This system was used on *SpaceShipOne*[30], which was the first private human spaceflight launched in 2004. This system is being used to power up a larger version called *SpaceShipTwo*[31] designed for private space tourism.

28 http://en.wikipedia.org/wiki/
Space_Shuttle_Columbia_disaster
29 http://en.wikipedia.org/wiki/
Falcon_(rocket_family)

30 http://en.wikipedia.org/wiki/SpaceShipOne
31 http://en.wikipedia.org/wiki/SpaceShipTwo

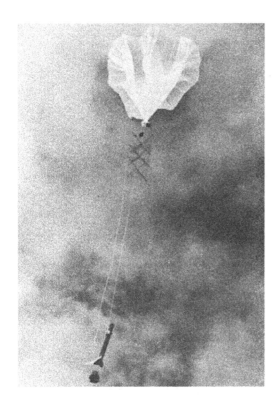

FIGURE 7.6.5. THE 1949 LAUNCH OF THE FIRST ROCKOON.

7.6.5. In-Air Launches

SpaceShipOne and *SpaceShipTwo* are also in the class where the rocket is first taken up to a higher altitude and then launched. This type of system provides fuel saving by not only increasing the altitude at which the rocket is launched, but also in reducing the atmospheric drag. The first variant of this was launched in 1949, when a high-altitude balloon was used to lift the rocket to 70,000 feet before launch. This system is known as a rockoon[32] (rocket + balloon). While they require much less fuel, they have the problem that accurate positioning and launching cannot be achieved with a free balloon.

The next up is to use a plane launch rocket. This was successfully used by the Pegasus rocket[33] (Figure 7.6.6), which was developed in the 1990s with payloads able to achieve low Earth orbit. This system produced cost savings by using the plane with its aerodynamic lift to

FIGURE 7.6.6. LAUNCH OF THE PEGASUS ROCKET FROM A LOCKHEED L-1011.

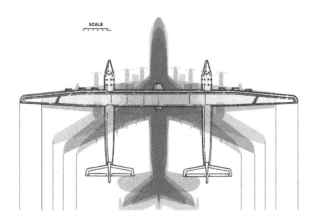

FIGURE 7.6.7. STRATOLAUNCH IS PROPOSED TO TAKE HUMANS TO LOW EARTH ORBIT, LAUNCHED FROM TWO COUPLED 747S.

get the payload up to 40,000 feet, where the atmosphere is only ~20% of that at sea level. So, cost savings come from (1) high altitude at launch; (2) less drag; and (3) higher speed at launch. A video of a launch can be seen at http://www.youtube.com/watch?v=0BK5753cjt0.

SpaceShipOne[34] and *SpaceShipTwo*[35], mentioned in the previous section, both use the same principle for suborbital launches (i.e., ones that reach space, but their trajectory is parabolic and doesn't complete a full revolution around the Earth). The full-sized version, known as *SpaceShipThree*[36], will utilize two coupled 747s to lift the rocket of approximately 500,000 lbs. The rocket will then have the

---

32   http://en.wikipedia.org/wiki/Rockoon

33   http://en.wikipedia.org/wiki/Pegasus_(rocket)

34   http://en.wikipedia.org/wiki/SpaceShipOne

35   http://en.wikipedia.org/wiki/SpaceShipTwo

36   http://en.wikipedia.org/wiki/SpaceShipTwo

capacity to take humans to low Earth orbit as opposed to suborbital. The X-prize launch of *SpaceShipOne* can be seen at http://www.youtube.com/watch?v=G68_dmC4BYI.

7.7. Cost of Chemical Systems

A tabulation of the size and cost of some of the more frequently used rockets is shown in Figure 7.7.1. (A listing of the major systems worldwide can be found at http://en.wikipedia.org/wiki/Comparison_of_orbital_launch_systems.) As the payload gets bigger, the costs increase faster because of all the additional infrastructure and atmospheric drag for the bigger systems. For small payloads, the lowest cost shown is

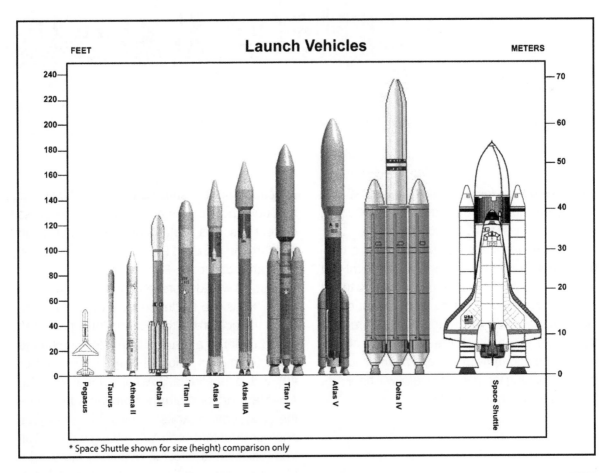

*Space Shuttle shown for size (height) comparison only

Launch Vehicle	Payload to LEO	Total Cost (million)	Cost/lb
Delta IV	56,800 lb	$294 (2008)	$5200
Titan IV	47,790 lb	$525(1999)	$11,000
AtlasV	27,000 lb	$294(2008)	$10,900
Ariane5	35,273 lb	$120 (2008)	$3400
Space Shuttle	53,600 lb	$450 (2008?)	$8400

FIGURE 7.7.1. DIFFERENT TYPES OF ROCKETS AND THEIR PAYLOAD CAPACITIES AND COSTS.

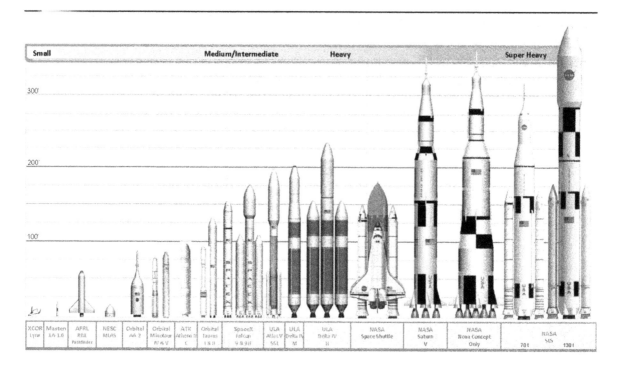

FIGURE 7.7.2. COMPARISON OF PRIVATE-FIRM LAUNCH VEHICLES WITH NASA HEAVY-LIFT VEHICLES.

about $3400/lbs. for payloads less than 30,000 lbs. Increasing to payloads of about 50,000 lbs., the cost is closer to $5000 to $10,000/lb.

To put these costs into perspective, a half-pound hamburger that costs $4 at the local fast food joint would cost a minimum of $1700 to put into space. So, we have to worry about every single pound that goes into space. Moreover, the bigger you make it, the greater the cost—there is no economy of scale in space endeavors, and putting the pedal to metal will bankrupt you faster than a rocket liftoff.

7.8 Mission to Mars

Now that we know about all the variables that go into planning a mission to another planet,

we can look at a specific example. A mission that does not employ a gravity assist (such as current missions to Mars) uses a method called a Hohmann transfer. Figure 7.8.1a shows how such an orbit works. For the case of a mission to Mars, O would represent the Sun. The green orbit (#1) is the Earth's orbit around the Sun. Upon launch from the Earth, the spacecraft would undergo a thruster burn (ΔV) to change the orbit into an elliptical one (yellow orbit or #2), with perihelion at 1 AU and aphelion at 1.5 AU (Mars' orbital distance from the Sun). Once the spacecraft is at its aphelion, it undergoes another thruster burn ($\Delta V'$), changing the orbit from elliptical to circular, matching Mars' orbit (the red orbit or #3). For a mission to Mars, a Hohmann transfer represents the path in which the minimum amount of thruster energy is used. It comes at a cost though, in terms of time. A Hohmann transfer is the slower way to get to Mars.

Assignment Question 4. Use equation 7.3.1 to calculate the time it takes for Part 2 of the orbits shown in Figure 7.8.1a. Put your answer in days. Does it match the time for the travel of the MAVEN mission given in Figure 7.8.1b?

Assignment Question 5. Use the same method as for question #4 to calculate the time it takes for a spacecraft to travel from the Earth to the Moon. Assume that the spacecraft begins in low Earth orbit (400 km above the Earth's surface).

Although there are faster options for going to Mars, they will typically cost you in terms of fuel. The faster option is particularly important if one wants to do a return mission involving humans. Figure 7.8.2 shows two options for a return mission to and from Mars. Figure 7.8.2a is a mission that uses the classic Hohmann transfer between the planets. This uses less fuel than a faster mission, but it also requires a much longer stay on Mars in order for the orbits of Earth and Mars to realign in the proper way to make use of a Hohmann transfer on the return. The mission shown in Figure 7.8.2b is faster because the spacecraft actually flies faster between the planets, and it travels past Venus on the return. This could only be done if you have some method for slowing down when you arrive at both Mars and Earth. If the spacecraft cannot slow down at either planet, it will either crash into the surface or fly right past. The gravity of each planet would be insufficient to capture the spacecraft. In order to slow down, the spacecraft could carry extra fuel, but remember the rocket equation. In order to carry more fuel, you need more fuel. The problem compounds. An alternative would be to use some other method to slow down. In the next chapter, we will discuss some advanced in-space propulsion technology—specifically, the beamed-energy technology is of particular interest for our topic here of a faster mission to

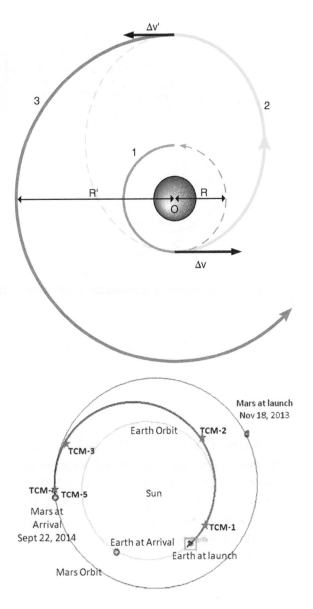

FIGURE 7.8.1. A HOHMANN TRANSFER ORBIT. ON THE TOP (A) IS A THEORETICAL ORBIT; ON THE BOTTOM (B) IS THE ORBIT FOR THE MAVEN MISSION.

Mars. If we could park space stations around both the Earth and Mars that can beam energy, say a beam of plasma (Figure 8.3.6 in the next chapter), to either accelerate or slow a spacecraft, we eliminate the need to carry extra fuel.

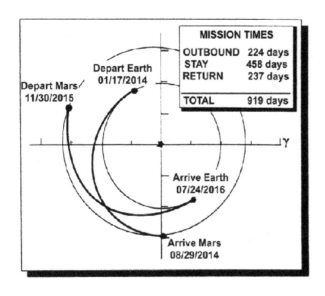

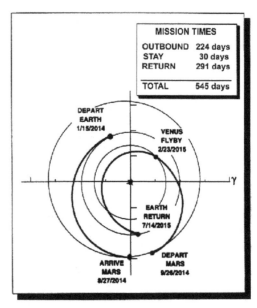

FIGURE 7.8.2. TWO TYPES OF RETURN MISSIONS TO MARS: (A) THE SLOW MISSION ON THE LEFT; AND (B) THE FAST MISSION ON THE RIGHT.

Discussion Question 1. What are the pros and cons of the two types of missions shown in Figure 7.8.2 for human exploration? Think in terms of energy usage (not just fuel, but also the energy and materials required to keep humans alive) and risks (radiation, human health, etc.).

Image Credits

Chapter 8

In-Space/ Advanced Propulsion

The previous chapter showed us that access to low Earth orbit is possible with chemical rocket systems and that advances are being made to allow space tourism. But as we also saw, going to Mars for the lowest cost requires mission durations of several months. Trips to the outer planets or to Mercury require trip times of several years, and even then, planetary assists are required to get sufficiently high speeds for the spacecraft. There are alternatives to using chemical rockets, and they have the potential to reduce trip times and cost.

These systems all seek to either increase the speed of the propellant or utilize other sources of energy to propel the spacecraft. They are all in their infancy, each with significant advances and disadvantages. Most of these applications require the spacecraft to actually be in space already, hence the term in-space propulsion[1]. As a result, there is no true front-runner at this time. An analogy can be made with man's initial attempts at powered flight. Despite all the great technology we presently have available, our attempts at space travel will by the end of the century (hopefully) look as primitive as the Wright Brothers' first flight now looks after nearly a century of aviation. In this chapter, we review the main contenders, and we will let the future decide which one eventually will lead the way for the future of space exploration.

---

1   http://www.inspacepropulsion.com/

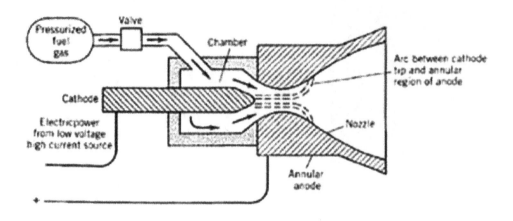

FIGURE 8.1.1. SCHEMATIC OF AN ARCJET THRUSTER.

8.1. Electric Propulsion

Electric propulsion uses onboard electrical power to generate an accelerated plasma. The exhaust speed (aka plasma speed) tends to be much higher than the exhaust speed for chemical rockets—thus, electric propulsion can generate much larger *Isp*s. This means that less (fuel) mass is required to reach a given velocity. Alternatively, the spacecraft can achieve higher speeds for the same amount of propellant mass. The main issues are the power requirements, additional mass to the system to generate that power, and low thrust, so the engines must remain on for a very long time. Also, only low-power (several kW) systems have been flown, although MW class systems have been proposed for flight. Because of the restrictions on available power, electric propulsion systems tend to have only low thrust and hence are only viable for in-space applications. However, as noted above, mission times tend to be very long, so that the application of low thrust over the very long periods can actually allow the spacecraft to reach higher speeds than chemical systems with a large thrust that is applied over a short time.

There are three main types of electric propulsion systems: (1) electrothermal; (2) electrostatic; and (3) electromagnetic thrusters.

8.1.1. Electrothermal: Resistojet and Arcjet

The simplest form of electrothermal propulsion is to run the propellant over a hot incandescent filament before it is expelled out the nozzle of the thruster. These systems are very simple and power efficient, but the *Isp* obtained is the smallest of all the electric propulsion systems. Nevertheless, they have been used for station keeping, including on the Iridium satellite constellation[2].

A schematic of an arcjet thruster is shown in Figure 8.1.1. Propellant (typically hydrazine or ammonia) flows between two electrodes which have a high voltage placed across them. The point on the center electrode causes the intensification of the electric field there and leads to the partial ionization of the propellant. Once there is partial ionization, the current, or arc, then flows between the two electrodes. The density is sufficiently high that both neutrals and charged particles have multiple collisions as they transit between the electrodes. These collisions produce heating of the propellant, which is converted into thrust as the hot gas exits the nozzles. The creation of the arc uses essentially the same principles involved in an

---

2   http://en.wikipedia.org/wiki/Iridium_satellite_constellation

arc welding system, except that instead of depositing the heated material on the surface, it is expelled out the nozzle to produce thrust.

Arcjet systems are able to produce nearly a doubling of the exhaust velocity to between 4–16 km/s, utilizing between about 400 W to 100 kW, with a power efficiency of 30% to 50%. Low-power arcjets have been used for station-keeping applications, while a high-power system is presently being considered as the main propulsion unit for a test satellite to the Moon.

8.1.2. Electrostatic: Gridded Ion Thruster

Electrostatic thrusters can produce higher propellant velocities or *Isp*s by utilizing a gas with lower densities, allowing the propellant to be fully ionized—unlike the arcjet system, in which the gas is only partially ionized. A schematic of a gridded ion thruster is shown in Figure 8.1.2. Propellant is injected between anode (positively charged) and cathode (negatively charged) grids. Any electrons present are accelerated toward the anode; as they do, they can have collisions with the propellant (i.e., gas) to produce its ionization. These ions are accelerated out of the thruster by the negative charge on the cathode. The voltage on the cathode can be set in a range of voltages from a few hundred volts to several kilovolts to produce the desired *Isp*. The ions that are accelerated away from the cathode into space must be neutralized by the addition of one electron beam—otherwise, the spacecraft can become negatively charged, and the ions would be accelerated back to the spacecraft and negate any thrust.

The propellant typically used is xenon for space applications. Xenon has the advantage that it can be easily stored in liquid form without

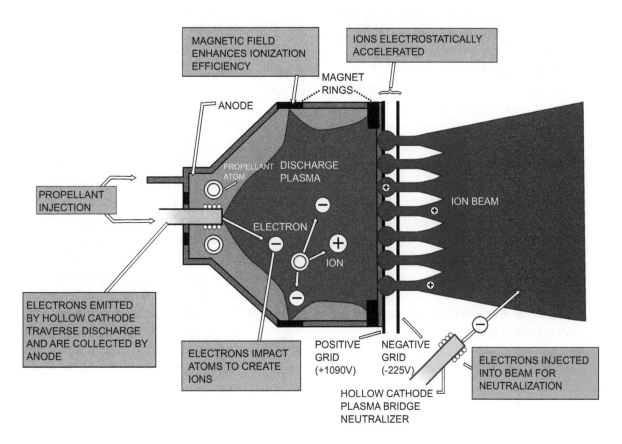

FIGURE 8.1.2 SCHEMATIC OF AN ELECTROSTATIC GRIDDED ION THRUSTER.

cryogenics. Testing in the laboratory typically uses argon or krypton, which are very much cheaper than the xenon ($50 per liter versus $700 per liter of xenon). Depending on the propellant and voltages applied, exhaust speeds can reach between 15 to 50 km/s, with efficiencies of 60% to 80%. Typical thrust levels obtained are about 40 mN/kW (the force of 1 mN being equivalent to that required to hold a piece of paper in the palm of your hand). Missions that have flown electrostatic thrusters as their primary propulsion unit include

- *Deep Space* 1[3], launched in 1998 with a mission to demonstrate several new technologies, including an electrostatic ion thruster, and to do a flyby of the asteroid 9969 Braille and an encounter with the comet Borrelly. The exhaust speed obtained by the thruster was 35 km/s (very much faster than possible with chemical propellants) and only utilized 74 kg of xenon fuel. The thruster increased the speed of the 373-kg satellite by ΔV of 4 km/s over a period of nearly 700 days, utilizing 2.5 kW from the new type of solar panels being tested.
- The *Dawn*[4] mission was launched in 2007 and is exploring the asteroids Vesta and Ceres. It has a larger mass at 1400 kg, with 10 kW of power available at 1 AU. Exhaust speeds of 31 km/s can be attained from its thruster.
- The *Hayabusa*[5] mission, which was launched in 2003, was able to rendezvous with the asteroid Itokawa, collect a small sample of surface material, and return it to Earth in 2010. This was the world's first sample return mission from an asteroid and used an 8mN thruster, requiring 350 W electrical power.

So these types of thrusters are having significant impact on opening up access to space.

8.1.3. Electromagnetic Thrusters

However, one of the problems with electrostatic thrusters is that if they are to be scaled to higher power, then the thruster has to become increasingly larger. This limitation arises because the densities allowed within electrostatic thrusters are fixed by plasma physics processes. Thus, the only way to increase thrust is to increase the area, and this is not necessarily a viable solution, as we try to keep spacecraft size down to the very minimum. Electromagnetic thrusters, which utilize interactions between induced currents and various magnetic field geometries, can produce higher densities in the exhaust (and thus more thrust) with engine geometries that are smaller than their electrostatic equivalents. The efficiencies gained to date, though, are not as high as the electrostatic thrusters, so there are definitely trade-offs between the different types of systems.

One of the simplest forms of an electromagnetic thruster is the pulsed plasma thruster[6] (PPT). The original design used noble gases similar to the electrostatic thrusters, but recent systems use a solid propellant such as Teflon, which removes the need for valves and the storage required for liquid propellants. A schematic of the system is shown in Figure 8.1.3. A spark plug is used to create some ablation and ionization of material of the surface of the Teflon. An arc is then created between the cathode and anode, similar to the arcjet. One difference, however, is that the plasma density is sufficiently low so that the current is not as strongly damped out; a significant magnetic field is also created. The interaction of the current and magnetic field produces electromagnetic acceleration of the plasma,

3   http://nssdc.gsfc.nasa.gov/nmc/spacecraftDisplay. do?id=1998-061A

4   http://dawn.jpl.nasa.gov/

5   http://www.jaxa.jp/projects/sat/muses_c/index_e. html

6   http://en.wikipedia.org/wiki/ Pulsed_plasma_thruster

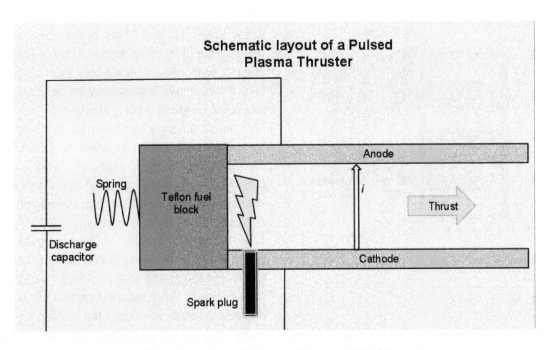

FIGURE 8.1.3. SCHEMATIC OF A PULSED PLASMA THRUSTER (PPT).

in much the same way that a current in a wire will experience a deflection from an externally applied magnetic field. This interaction leads to the generation of higher energies than can be attained in an arcjet.

Exhaust speeds obtained for the plasma can be between 6–20 km/s, while the non-ionized neutrals have substantially lower speeds. Because of the presence of both neutrals and plasma, the power efficiency is relatively low at about 10%. The pulsed nature comes from the fact that the currents and production of neutrals cannot be sustained. To produce significant thrust, the system must be repeatedly pulsed.

PPTs have been used for station keeping. In addition, the small size of these systems makes them candidates for propulsion units on small spacecraft such as a Cubesat[7], which has a volume of only about a liter—i.e., 10-cm cube, weighing no more than 1.3 kg. Such miniaturized satellites have some advantages if distributed observing is required. Their low thrust also makes them good candidates for accurate pointing of in-space telescopes, in which case large changes can actually be bad.

One of the most prominent DC electromagnetic thrusters is called the Hall thruster[8]. The geometry is much more complicated than the previous systems, but it has the potential[9] for providing propulsion for high-power systems needed for space exploration. A schematic of the Hall thruster is shown in Figure 8.1.4. The Hall thruster utilizes a radial magnetic field over which an axial electric field is applied. The field strength of the magnetic field is typically set such that the electrons are magnetized (that is, their trajectories are bound to the magnetic field), while the ions remain unmagnetized. In this regime, the electron trajectories are in the azimuthal direction in the presence of both the magnetic and electric fields. The resultant azimuthal current produces acceleration that reinforces the electric field acceleration, so that ions experience strong axial acceleration. A video of the workings of a Hall thruster can be seen at http://www.youtube.com/watch?v=TCLJe_IE58A.

7 http://en.wikipedia.org/wiki/Cubesat

8 http://en.wikipedia.org/wiki/Hall_effect_thruster
9 http://io9.com/5401436/the-best-sub+light-propulsion-system-this-side-of-luyten-726+8b

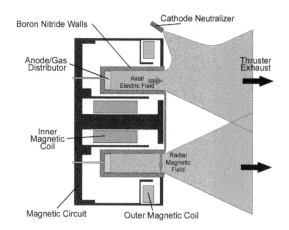

FIGURE 8.1.4. SCHEMATIC OF A HALL THRUSTER[11].

These systems are able to support more density than their electrostatic counterparts, and, because the electrodes are solid, they can withstand much higher power with little erosion to gridded systems. Typical exhaust speeds are between 15 to 20 km/s, with power efficiencies of present-day systems comparable to that of electrostatic thrusters. Hall thrusters that can operate at several hundred kilowatts of power are under development. These systems have been typically used for station keeping, with over 240 spacecraft using Hall thrusters. Hall thrusters have also been used as the primary propulsion unit for the European space agency *SMART-1*[10] spacecraft, which orbited the Moon before it was deliberately crashed to its surface in 2006.

Another highly prominent electromagnetic propulsion system is the variable specific impulse magnetoplasma rocket (VASIMR[12]). This system, shown in Figure 8.1.5, does not use any electrodes whatsoever. Instead, it uses intense radio frequency (RF) waves to produce the ionization of the propellant (typically xenon). The initial ionization is produced by waves at high frequency that drive the electrons into azimuthal motion without an axial

guide magnetic field. This preheating system uses about 30 kW of power. This preheated plasma then moves down the axial magnetic field when more intense waves at lower frequencies produce strong heating of the ions. This second stage uses about 200 kW. The heated plasma is then expelled out the back of the magnetic nozzle to produce a very intense plasma stream. A video of the operation of the system can be seen at http://www.youtube.com/watch?v=GIg6pWwezEU.

A laboratory version is being developed, and a flight-ready version has been proposed for use on the space station. A high-speed mission scenario for a manned mission to Mars[13] has also been developed. This scenario moves away from electric propulsion systems that use solar panels for power systems and instead would use nuclear power plants.

8.2. Nuclear Propulsion

All the above electric propulsion systems have the potential for providing much more efficient propellant utilization than conventional chemical rockets. However, it also brings up the important question of where the power could come from. The easiest candidate would be from solar power. The Sun produces approximately 1361 W/m² at 1 AU. This value is known as the solar constant[14]. The best solar panels have a current efficiency of about 30%.[15] The solar panels on the International Space Station[16] are of an older design (though fully space qualified) and produce 75–90 kW utilizing about 3000 m² of collectors. This yields

10   http://en.wikipedia.org/wiki/SMART-1
11   http://io9.com/5401436/the-best-sub+light-propulsion-system-this-side-of-luyten-726+8b
12   http://www.adastrarocket.com/aarc/VASIMR

13   http://www.youtube.com/watch?v=Zj53rVWK5z0
14   http://en.wikipedia.org/wiki/Solar_constant
15   http://www.extremetech.com/extreme/142962-princetons-nanomesh-nearly-triples-solar-cell-efficiency
16   http://www.nasa.gov/mission_pages/station/main/onthestation/facts_and_figures.html

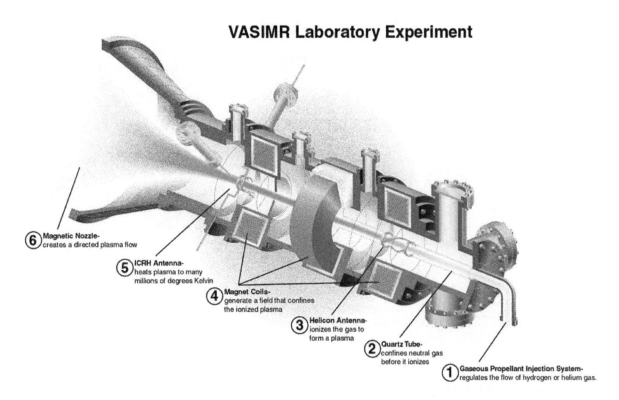

VASIMR Laboratory Experiment

⑥ Magnetic Nozzle- creates a directed plasma flow

⑤ ICRH Antenna- heats plasma to many millions of degrees Kelvin

④ Magnet Coils- generate a field that confines the ionized plasma

③ Helicon Antenna- ionizes the gas to form a plasma

② Quartz Tube- confines neutral gas before it ionizes

① Gaseous Propellant Injection System- regulates the flow of hydrogen or helium gas.

FIGURE 8.1.5. SCHEMATIC OF A VASIMR THRUSTER[17].

only a net of 30 (electrical) W/m^2, or about 2% efficiency. The point is that to produce even kilowatts of electrical power will require several square meters of solar panels, leading to moderately bulky systems and increased mass. The problem becomes worse with increasing distance from the Sun, as one moves to the planets beyond the Earth's orbit.

There are a few different alternatives that are being considered. One of these is nuclear power, which comes in three flavors:

1. Nuclear electric, where the energy converted directly to electricity can then be used for onboard systems as for space propulsion;
2. Nuclear thermal propulsion, where the energy is used to heat the propellant (as opposed to just using chemical reactions);

3. Nuclear pulsed propulsion, where the direct products of nuclear solutions are useful propulsion.

8.2.1. Nuclear Electric Propulsion

We already introduced nuclear electric systems when discussing RTGs in Chapter 3. RTGs have been used successfully in several deep-space missions, including the *Voyager* 1 and 2 spacecraft, which are close to the edge of the solar system. That we can still hear from them is due to the fact that they do not use solar power. More recent spacecraft using RTGs include *Cassini*[18] (to Saturn) and *Galileo*[19] (to Jupiter) and the Mars Science Lab Rover, *Curiosity*[20].

---

17 http://www.adastrarocket.com/aarc/Technology

18 http://saturn.jpl.nasa.gov/spacecraft/overview/
19 http://nssdc.gsfc.nasa.gov/planetary/galileo.html
20 mailto:http://mars.jpl.nasa.gov/msl/

GPHS-RTG

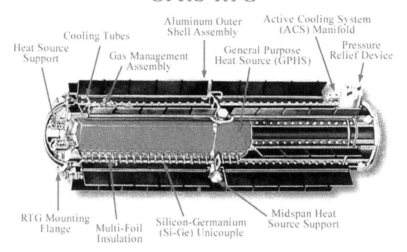

FIGURE 8.2.1. DIAGRAM OF A RADIOISOTOPE THERMAL GENERATOR (RTG) USED ON THE *CASSINI* PROBE[22].

These spacecraft all use radioisotope thermal generators (RTGs)[21] for their power.

RTGs use the decay of radioactive elements like Pu238 to generate heat. This is not a naturally occurring element, but rather is the by-product (or waste) of a type of nuclear power plant (specifically, one called a breeder reactor). Thermocouples are then used to convert this heat into electricity. They are relatively inefficient with 3% to 7% efficiencies and are capable of generating power levels of a few tens to a few hundreds of Watts, with about 0.5 kW produced per kilogram. Pu238 has the lowest shielding requirements combined with the longest half-life, of nearly 90 years, of human-produced radioactive elements. The long half-life is the reason for the continuing success of the *Voyager* spacecraft, which were launched in the late 1970s. There is a problem with this method, though—most countries no longer produce Pu238, partly due to signing nonproliferation nuclear treaties.

Because of the scarcity of Pu238, a more efficient system called the advanced Stirling radioisotope generator[23] (ASRG) is being developed. A diagram of the essential components and operating principles is shown in Figure 8.2.2. Similar to the RTG, a radioactive element such as Pu238 is the source of heat. But in the case of the ASRG, this heat is used to drive a piston connected to a generator. The generator converts the motion of the piston into electricity. In some sense, this system is very much like a car engine, with the difference being that the gas driving the motion of the piston is not vented. Instead, it must be cooled and recycled the engine so that it is a closed system. It is capable of generating nearly 140 W of power using less than 1 kg of Pu238, thus making more efficient use of our limited supply of Pu238.

---

21 http://en.wikipedia.org/wiki/
Radioisotope_thermoelectric_generator
22 http://en.wikipedia.org/wiki/
Radioisotope_thermoelectric_generator

23 http://spaceflightsystems.grc.nasa.gov/SSPO/
ASRG/

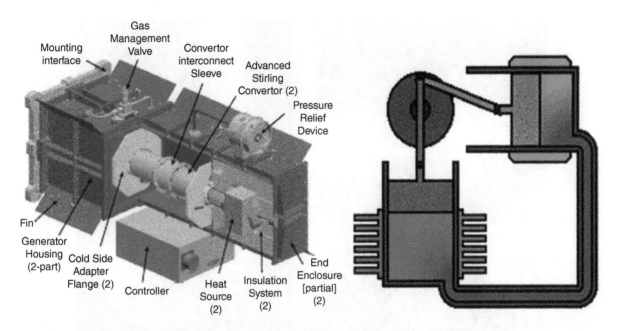

FIGURE 8.2.2. DIAGRAM OF AN ADVANCED STIRLING RADIOISOTOPE GENERATOR USED ON THE *CASSINI* PROBE. ANIMATION: HTTP://EN.WIKIPEDIA.ORG/WIKI/FILE:ALPHA_STIRLING.GIF

8.2.2. Space Nuclear Reactors

Larger power of requirements will require the flight of actual nuclear reactors. Nuclear reactors have an advantage, not only in terms of total amount of power available, but they are also much less radioactive than RTGs until the reactor is started up. So, in fact, there are some safety advantages to launching a nuclear reactor as opposed to a radioisotope system. The downside is that they are very much more massive. In a terrestrial nuclear reactor, coolant is passed through the core, where it is heated and used to drive electrical power generators, after which the coolant has to be either cooled before reentering the reactor (closed system) or new coolant has to be supplied (open system). For space reactors, one has essentially the same choices: use a closed system to generate electricity (nuclear electric), or use the heated coolant as the propellant (nuclear thermal).

The idea of flying nuclear power system in space was seriously considered as early as the late 1950s and continued until the early 1970s under the program called Nuclear Engine for

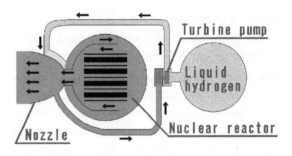

FIGURE 8.2.3. DIAGRAM OF A NUCLEAR THERMAL PROPULSION SYSTEM.

Rocket Vehicle Application (NERVA)[24]. This was a nuclear thermal system. Its operating principles are shown in Figure 8.2.3. Liquid hydrogen is passed through the nuclear reactor as coolant, where it becomes superheated and is then vented out a standard nozzle to produce propulsion. Because only hydrogen is being expelled, it can have a higher *Isp* than simply burning hydrogen as part of a bipropellant system.

The systems considered under NERVA were huge—the largest system was considered able to generate 4000 MW of thermal power. A scaled picture of engineers working in a cherry

---

24   http://en.wikipedia.org/wiki/NERVA

FIGURE 8.2.4.   NERVA MOTOR AND PROPELLANT PLUME.

picker is shown in Figure 8.2.4, along with the plume from the hydrogen propellant. NERVA nuclear rocket engine video can be seen at this link.[25] Research on NERVA was stopped, however, in the early 1970s, along with the cancellation of funding to the *Apollo* mission.

The idea of nuclear power received a resurgence in the early 2000s with the proposal to develop a spacecraft that could orbit the inner Galilean moons of Jupiter and produce detailed radar mapping of their surfaces and interiors. This mission was called the *Jupiter Icy Moons Orbiter* (JIMO), and instead of using nuclear thermal power, it was to use nuclear power to create electrical power. The propulsion side of the system was called Project Prometheus[26]. An artist's rendering of the JIMO spacecraft is shown in Figure 8.2.5. The electrical power was to drive several Hall thrusters, which are seen at the back end of the spacecraft. The large panels on the bulk of the length of the spacecraft are not solar panels, but are heat-rejection panels to take the heat from the coolant once it has been used to generate power onboard

FIGURE 8.2.5 ARTIST'S IMPRESSION OF THE *JUPITER ICY MOONS ORBITER*.

the spacecraft, so that it can be recirculated through the reactor. The nuclear reactor itself is at the front of the spacecraft to maximize the distance from the payloads, thereby reducing

25   http://www.youtube.com/watch?v=j6gKFvPjGpQ
26   http://nssdcftp.gsfc.nasa.gov/miscellaneous/
jupiter/JIMO_Background/JIMO.pdf

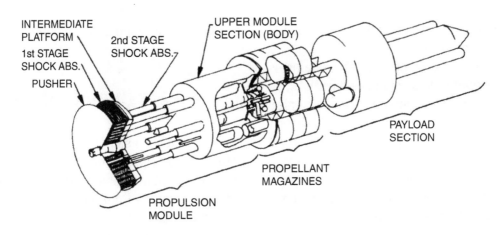

FIGURE 8.2.6. SCHEMATIC FOR THE *ORION* SPACECRAFT.

the radiation effects on the scientific and communications equipment, which are at the back end of the spacecraft. A video of this can be seen at the Operation of Prometheus for the *Jupiter Icy Moons Orbiter* (JIMO)[27].

8.2.3. Nuclear Pulsed System

A less subtle approach for nuclear propulsion is to use the direct products of a nuclear blast to propel the spacecraft. This approach was studied in the late 1950s and early 1960s at the height of the Cold War and was called Project Orion[28]. A schematic of the system is shown in Figure 8.2.6. In this concept, a nuclear sudden-impulse device (aka nuclear bomb) is detonated behind the spacecraft. The blast wave from the explosion impacts a pusher plate. Through this interaction, momentum is transferred from the blast wave to the spacecraft, propelling the spacecraft forward. The pusher plate also absorbs some of the momentum, as 100% transfer of momentum from the blast wave to the spacecraft would generate g forces too large

for humans to withstand. The advantage of this system is that the products from the blast usually have very high *Isp* equivalent to exhaust speeds of 20–30 km/s. The downside is that propulsion produced in this fashion tends to be unstable. There were always issues about maintaining the integrity of the pusher plate. The partial Test Ban Treaty of 1963 brought the end of nuclear devices in space.

Nevertheless, with the resurgence of future human missions to Mars, the possibility of developing an *Orion*-type spacecraft for a Mars mission has reappeared. A video showing current thoughts can be seen at this link: Project Orion Video[29]. Keeping the concept alive is the high thrust generated by this system. Using existing technologies, a spacecraft could be accelerated up to 0.1 times the speed of light. Suddenly, human spaceflight out of the solar system became plausible.

If controlled fusion were ever to be developed, it also would be a viable possibility for future space missions. The concept was studied in detail by the British Interplanetary Society in the 1970s under the title of Project Daedalus.[30] Fusion reactions offer significantly higher *Isp* propellants and energy densities than via fission processes, discussed earlier. Their designs indicated that with controlled

27   http://www.youtube.com/watch?v=JlCCXl-I-wA
28   http://en.wikipedia.org/wiki/
Project_Orion_(nuclear_propulsion)

29   http://www.youtube.com/watch?v=V1vKMTYa40A
30   http://en.wikipedia.org/wiki/Project_Daedalus

fusion, a 50-year mission to the closest star is theoretically possible.

The last category of nuclear systems is that of antimatter propulsion systems.[31] As we saw in Chapter 2, antimatter can be created through various nuclear reactions. Moreover, many of the antimatter particles tend to have charge so that they can be stored in a magnetic bottle without reacting with matter that dominates our universe. Because all the mass of a matter-antimatter mixture is converted into energy, such systems have the highest energy density and the highest specific impulse of any of the systems in this category. It is projected that only 10 g of antimatter would be needed to drive a fast mission to Mars.

The downside, beyond just being able to safely store large quantities of antimatter, is that the world's production from its nuclear power plants of antimatter is only between one and ten nanograms per year. Antimatter is the most expensive substance on Earth—worth approximately $60 trillion per gram. Thus, major technological developments will have to occur before antimatter systems can be treated as even a distant contender for future space propulsion systems.

8.3. Advanced Propulsion Systems

One does not necessarily have to nuke it in order to obtain greater access to space beyond present limitations of chemical and electrical propulsion systems. These systems are referred to as advanced propulsion systems because they take advantage of known technologies, but have yet to be fully proven in space. They fall into three categories:

1. Sails – solar and magnetic/plasma sails;
2. Beamed energy – lasers or plasmas;

3. Tethers, including space elevators.

8.3.1. Sail Technology

The idea of a solar sail[32] has been around even before rockets were developed. The basic principle is that momentum can be obtained by reflecting photons from the Sun. This has the advantage that no fuel is required; the concept is very simple. And despite the fact that solar radiation is always pointed outward, solar cells can be used to steer both toward the Sun and away from the Sun. How this is done is illustrated in Figure 8.3.1. To move into the solar system, one wants to drop spacecraft with angular momentum so that one would fall into the inner solar system. This can be achieved by ensuring that momentum gained from the reflection of the light is such that it opposes the orbital motion of the spacecraft. Similarly, for one to move outward into the solar system, the solar sail is directed such that the orbital speed of the spacecraft is increased.

There are two problems with solar sails. First, the pressure from solar photons is only about 10^{-5} N/m² at Earth orbit. To obtain sufficient thrust, several tens of square meters for even small spacecraft is required. If the solar

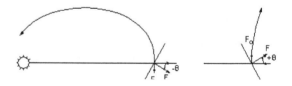

FIGURE 8.3.1.   A SOLAR SAIL CAN MOVE EITHER ON AN INWARD OR OUTWARD ORBIT IN THE SOLAR SYSTEM. IN BOTH IMAGES F IS THE NET FORCE FROM THE SUNLIGHT. TO MOVE TOWARD THE SUN, THE SAIL IS POSITIONED SO THAT THE COMPONENT OF THE NET FORCE TANGENTIAL TO THE ORBIT IS IN THE OPPOSITE DIRECTION OF THE ORBITAL PATH, F$_O$. TO MOVE AWAY FROM THE SUN, THE SAIL IS ANGLED SO THAT THE COMPONENT OF THE NET FORCE TANGENTIAL TO THE ORBIT IS IN THE SAME DIRECTION OF THE ORBITAL PATH, F$_O$.

---

31   http://en.wikipedia.org/wiki/Project_Daedalus

32   http://en.wikipedia.org/wiki/Solar_sail

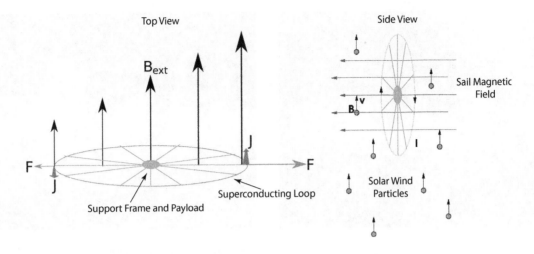

FIGURE 8.3.2.   SCHEMATIC OF THE WORKING OF A MAGNETIC SAIL.

sail material has too high a density, then the solar sail itself can outweigh the spacecraft, and no efficiencies would really be achieved. So, the emphasis on the development of solar sails is presently trying to find material that can be easily deployed, efficiently reflect light, and still maintain the lowest possible density. Examples include Mylar sails with a 5-µm thickness as a mass density of 7 gm/m² and aluminized Kapton films with a mass density of 12 gm/m². With these materials, a 100 m² reflective sail could at best generate 1 mN of thrust while weighing 1 kg. A 10-kg spacecraft would then obtain an acceleration of 10^{-4} m/s². Thus, to produce a ΔV of 1 km would require 10^7 sec, or nearly four months. Consequently, if solar sails are to be a significant player, the density of the solar sail material must be dropped by nearly an order of magnitude if bigger payloads and shorter mission times are to be supported.

The push to drop the solar sail density raises the second problem with solar sails, in that if the material is ultrathin, then the space plasma environment can lead to degraded performance. Nevertheless, the Japanese successfully launched a small satellite, IKAROS[33], which utilizes the solar sail to generate both power and propulsion. It has traveled from the Earth to a flyby of Venus. Future launches by NASA and by the Planetary Society are planned in the future.

The alternative to solar sail is the magnetic sail[34] (or magsail), where instead of reflecting sunlight, one reflects the solar wind or uses the plasma winds within the magnetosphere to produce the propulsion. In some sense, the problem is much more difficult than solar sails because the dynamics pressure from the solar wind is only about 4 nPa, or about 10^{-3} of that from solar photons. The advantage, though, is that one does not have to use a solid surface to produce the reflection. Instead, the reflection is produced by magnetic fields as shown in Figure 8.3.2. Such a magnetic field could be as simple as a magnetic loop.

In the original design of a magsail, a superconductor[35] was required to avoid power losses over the required large loop (10s to 100s km). The development of an appropriate superconductor still needs to occur, but this field is rapidly evolving, and hopes remain that large-scale, high-temperature conductors could be developed in the near future for space applications.

An alternative to using a superconductor is to produce an inflated magnetic field using the injection of low-energy plasma to create a magnetosphere analogous to the planetary

33   http://www.jspec.jaxa.jp/e/activity/ikaros.html

34   http://en.wikipedia.org/wiki/Magnetic_sail
35   http://en.wikipedia.org/wiki/Superconductivity

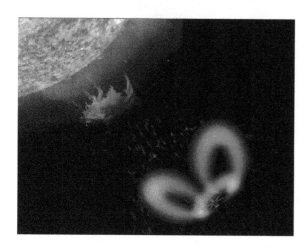

FIGURE 8.3.3. ARTIST'S IMPRESSION OF A MAGNETIC/PLASMA SAIL, OR M2P2, OPERATING IN THE SOLAR WIND.

FIGURE 8.3.4. A LASER LIGHT SAIL WOULD USE A SPACECRAFT SIMILAR TO A SOLAR SAIL (LIKE THIS ONE SHOWN) BUT THE PRIMARILY LIGHT SOURCE WOULD INSTEAD BE A LASER BEAM FROM THE EARTH, OR SOME OTHER PLATFORM.

magnetospheres discussed in Chapter 6, but on a much smaller scale size. This alternative, called mini-magnetospheric plasma propulsion (M2P2)[36] (shown in Figure 8.3.3), has the advantage in that it requires no massive structures to be deployed in space, nor does it require any superconducting magnets. It also has the advantage that the size of the system increases with distance from the Sun so that it would produce almost constant thrust. Research was performed in the early 2000s, where there were laboratory demonstrations of the process. A video of the laboratory operation can be seen at http://www.ess.washington.edu/Space/M2P2/HPH_M2P2_Bvary_web.avi. Research is not currently supported by NASA, but is continuing in Japan and in Europe.

8.3.2. Beam Energy

One of the main problems with solar sails and magsails is that the energy density from the solar photons or solar wind is very low; large reflecting areas are needed in order to gather sufficient momentum flux. The need for large reflecting areas can be removed if the energy

is beamed to the sail. For example, lasers (light) and masers (microwave) have been proposed to provide the propulsion on sails. These systems are called light sails[37] (as opposed to solar sails). They have the potential of reaching sub-light speeds with the propellant (photons) traveling at the speed of light. The downside is that the systems need very intense lasers or masers (at least in the terawatt range).

Laser lightcraft are not restricted to in-space propulsion only. The potential for using them for ground-launched systems has been demonstrated. The laser lightcraft[38] in these applications creates a superheated atmosphere under the mirror system as shown in Figure 8.3.5. This superheated atmosphere produces the propulsion for the system. A video of a launch of a laser lightcraft can be seen at http://www.youtube.com/watch?v=4vbXRP5lN7o. A video of a Russian version can be seen at http://www.youtube.com/watch?v=SPM7wJAhovM.

The advantage is that the spacecraft itself does not have to carry the fuel, since it is provided by the ambient medium, and the power

---

36   http://www.ess.washington.edu/Space/M2P2/

37   http://ffden-2.phys.uaf.edu/213.web.stuff/scott kircher/lightsails.html

38   http://www.lightcrafttechnologies.com/newsletter.html

unit remains on the ground. The disadvantage is that even for a few kilogram payload, lasers of several hundred kilowatts are required. The reason for these high-consumer requirements is that photons carry a significant amount of energy, but very little momentum. This mismatch between energy momentum means that you have to pay the penalty in terms of power required to produce the needed thrust.

An alternative to using lasers and masers is to use particle or plasma beams for the propulsion. These systems can only be used for in-space propulsion, since the presence of any neutral atmosphere would provide significant scattering and absorption of the particles. The advantage, though, is that significantly less power (hundreds of kW to MWs) is required to provide the required thrust. Collimation of the beam would be produced by a series of magnets, with reflection of the particles also performed by magnets on the payload.

This system, known as a MagBeam[39], is shown conceptually in Figure 8.3.6. This illustration highlights one of the important advantages of beamed systems, in that you leave all the heavy infrastructure behind so that only the payload (without significant power and propulsion) is transported to the destination. This has the potential for major savings in terms of mass need to be lifted into space, particularly if the system is reused for other orbital transfers. With the reduction in mass, 90-day round trips to Mars become possible. The main drawback at this time is trying to demonstrate that the beam collimation can be maintained over very large distances (hundreds of km). An animation showing deployment of the system for a Mars mission can be found at http://earthweb.ess.washington.edu/space/magbeam/NIAC2005/magbeam2.wmv.

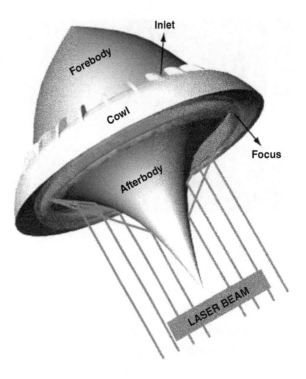

FIGURE 8.3.5. WORKINGS OF A LASER LIGHTCRAFT. THE INCIDENT LASER LIGHT IS FOCUSED TO A SMALL RING UNDER THE COWLING, WHICH PRODUCES A SUPERHEATED ATMOSPHERE, WHICH THEN PROPELS THE SPACECRAFT FORWARD. THE SPACECRAFT IS SPIN STABILIZED[40].

8.3.3. Space Tethers

The last form of propulsion discussed here is by the use of space tethers[41] or cables. These systems also fall under the category of propellantless propulsion systems, in that the payload itself does not have to carry any onboard propulsion. Instead, there is a main spacecraft, which has its own propulsion system to maintain its orbit. The spacecraft then deploys a tether as shown in Figure 8.3.7. This tether is envisaged to be several km to tens of km in length. The tether is then spun up so that the tip has the appropriate angular velocity. The payload is then captured, and the spin of this combined unit continues until you

40   Hybrid continuum/DSMC computation of rocket mode lightcraft flow in near space with high temperature and rarefaction effect" by Shan-Shu Xua, Zi-Niu Wua, Qian Lib, Yan-Ji Hongb, Computers and Fluids, Volume 38, Issue 7, August 2009, Page 1

39   http://en.wikipedia.org/wiki/MagBeam

41   http://en.wikipedia.org/wiki/Space_tether

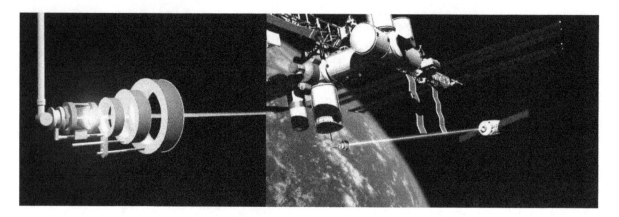

FIGURE 8.3.6. ARTIST'S IMPRESSION OF THE MAGNETIC NOZZLE NEEDED TO COLLIMATE THE PLASMA BEAM AND ITS USAGE FOR ORBITAL TRANSFERS, USING A SPACE STATION AS THE LAUNCHING POINT.

have sufficient angular momentum, at which point the payload is released to go into orbit. The main craft will change orbital parameters at release, so that its own propulsion units have to be utilized to return to its desired orbit.

There are two forms of tethers that have been proposed. One is where the tether acts as an insulator and is only used for capture and release of the payload. The other form is by use of a tether conductor known as the electro-magnetic tether[42], so that the currents that are

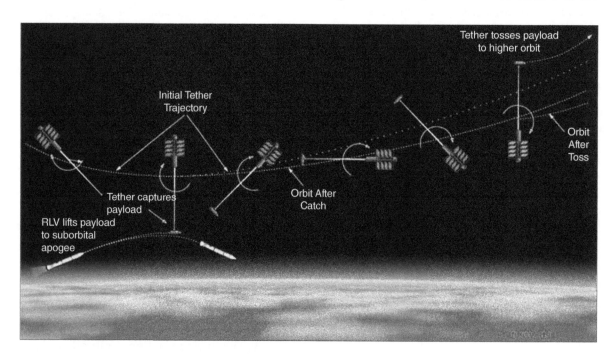

FIGURE 8.3.7. ARTIST'S IMPRESSION OF A SUBORBITAL PAYLOAD BEING CAPTURED BY A TETHER AND THEN BEING LAUNCHED INTO ORBIT.

---

42 http://en.wikipedia.org/wiki/Electrodynamic_tether

induced along the tether can provide electrical power and assist in orbital transfers for the main spacecraft, in addition to providing capture and release of the payload. Electromagnetic tethers were flown on the Space Shuttle (STS-46[43] and STS-75[44]). A video of the launch of STS-75 and the launch of the tethered satellite is at http://www.youtube.com/watch?v=pQTMliO1JVc.

The concept of the space elevator[45] takes the use of tethers to very much larger scale lengths. In this scheme as shown in Figure 8.3.8, a cable is run from the Earth to a point beyond geosynchronous orbit. Geosynchronous is important here, as it is a point in space that rotates at the same speed as the point on the Earth holding down the tether. It has to be slightly longer than geosynchronous, in order to attach a counterweight so that the center of mass of the full system is at or above geosynchronous orbit. This requirement means that the cable will have to be over 36,000 km in length.

The concept of the space elevator was first developed by Konstantin Tsiolkovsky[46] in 1895. The advantage of this system is that, like any elevator, high speeds are not required to reach the desired altitude. The energy can be put in at a much slower rate. Moreover, the power source remains on the ground. Both these factors reduce the amount of mass that must be taken into space, producing major cost savings. Crawlers that are able to scale long cables have recently been developed; lasers pointed at photocells power the crawler as it moves up a cable. Technology developments are presently focused on trying to find cables with sufficient tensile strength and low mass from which the tether can be constructed. It is thought that possibly carbon nanotubes or boron nitride

Space Elevator

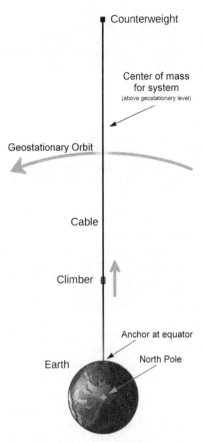

FIGURE 8.3.8. SCHEMATIC FOR THE OPERATION OF A SPACE ELEVATOR[47].

tubes could provide the base materials of the tether.

Solving the technical problems involving deployment of a space elevator at Earth still remain daunting, mainly involving the atmosphere of the Earth. However, for the Moon or Mars, requirements may be less stringent, which provides a more suitable environment for development.

43 http://en.wikipedia.org/wiki/STS-46
44 http://en.wikipedia.org/wiki/STS-75
45 http://en.wikipedia.org/wiki/Space_elevator
46 http://en.wikipedia.org/wiki/Konstantin_Tsiolkovsky

47 http://en.wikipedia.org/wiki/File:Space_elevator_structural_diagram--corrected_for_scale%2BCM%2Betc.TIF

Image Credits

Chapter 9

Planetary Destinations

The Inner Solar System

Now that we know how to travel throughout the solar system, how to power our spaceship, and the hazards we have to deal with while away from the Earth, where should we go? The solar system is probably most distinguishable by the fact that there is no repetition in planetary environments. Indeed, a common statement in describing any of the planetary environments around the solar system is that "it is "unique." With all this uniqueness, the question is "If there are limited resources for space travel, where should the top priority be?" Maybe this question is ill posed. The analogy could be that of a family trying to pick its next destination for a vacation. One could go over the next hill for the holiday, which would be affordable, but not necessarily an enriching experience. One could go several states over to find a more enriching experience, but still stay in budget. And maybe going to a different country would be vastly enriching but completely too costly; it may be something that will always stay high on the bucket list. We face the same dilemma in space travel.

In this chapter, we review components of the inner solar system from the viewpoint of the potential for space exploration, particularly surface exploration. We do not provide a full review from the viewpoint of planetary science, and we refer readers to solar system textbooks for such perspectives. And with current missions at several planets, new things are discovered every day. Our role here is to describe the potential for future surface exploration, not just by remote sensing, but by the placement of at least robotic instrumentation on the surface. Much of the potential for true surface exploration must await the development of advanced propulsion as described in the previous sections. Therefore, it is appropriate to describe what might be if such developments do indeed occur.

We suggest that reasons for surface exploration will be motivated by one of four factors:

a. Scientific, in terms of the origins of the solar system;
b. Economic, in terms of valuable resources not easily found on Earth;
c. Biological, in terms of life beyond Earth;
d. Technological, in terms of being the first or providing new data or system demonstrations.

We will let the future grade our choices as to which, and how, solar system objects described below will be most explored in the rest of this century. Our objective here is to stimulate discussions so that future developments can be placed into perspective.

9.1. Mercury

Named after the messenger to the gods in Roman mythology, Mercury is the closest planet to the Sun, yet due to its lack of thick atmosphere, it is not the hottest planet. That honor goes to Venus. However, it is one of the densest planets, with its core extending almost three quarters of its radius. This combination of no atmosphere but high density has been a point of discussion for models of the solar system. There are three main theories for its formation[1].

- Mercury formed in the region of the solar system where there were few volatiles to form an atmosphere;

- It formed with an atmosphere, but this was boiled off due to Mercury's proximity to the Sun; and
- Mercury formed in much the same way as the rest of the inner rocky planets, but was subject to a massive collision with another solar system object early in its history. This object was thought to be about one sixth the size of Mercury, and the collision stripped away its atmosphere. This latter model also explains the fact that Mercury's core extends out to almost three quarters of its radius.

One of the reasons for different competing models is that definitive observations of Mercury are more difficult than it seems. The planet's close proximity to the Sun means that it typically leads a sunrise or trails a sunset by only a short distance. This means the sky is usually not completely dark when one can see Mercury. It also means one must look at Mercury when it is close to the horizon, as it should not be observed once the Sun has risen or before the Sun sets. These restrictions make telescopic viewing of Mercury very difficult and typically requires a horizon free of mountains or buildings.

One obstacle that cannot be overcome, however, is that observations of Mercury from the surface of the Earth will be much more distorted by the atmosphere than observations of other planets. Figure 9.1.1 shows that when observing a planet on the horizon, the path the light from the planet travels through the Earth's atmosphere (segment b) is much longer than the path the light would travel if the planet were directly overhead (segment a). The Earth's atmosphere can distort and alter the light coming from an object in space on very short timescales. This is why stars appear to twinkle when we look up at them in the night sky. It also means that to get good observations, we must put our telescopes in orbit around the Earth—or better still, in orbit around the object we want to look at.

Thus, if Mercury is to be fully explored, it will have to involve spacecraft. The first satellite sent

---

1 http://www.universetoday.com/14021/formation-of-mercury/

to Mercury was the U.S. spacecraft *Mariner* 10, launched in 1973. *Mariner* 10 made three flybys of Mercury before it ran out of fuel and was shut down. *Mariner* 10's trajectory was such that it could only photograph a little less than half of the surface of Mercury. It did discover that Mercury possessed a global magnetic field. This was a surprise to scientists, as the slow rotation of Mercury was thought to prevent it from sustaining a dynamo magnetic field.

Mariner 10 also discovered that Mercury has a tenuous atmosphere made up of hydrogen, helium, carbon, oxygen, neon, and argon [2]. The presence of the light elements is thought to arise at least in part by absorption of solar wind particles that directly impact the surface and are eventually leached from the surface to produce components of a tenuous atmosphere. Other sources of the light elements may be from radioactive decay of heavy elements. The follow-up missions to Mercury, *Mariner* 11 and *Mariner* 12 were renamed *Voyager* 1 and *Voyager* 2. They were sent on a grand tour of the outer solar system and beyond in 1977, instead of going to Mercury.

The *MESSENGER*[2] mission to Mercury was launched by NASA in August 2004. It flew past Mercury three times before entering orbit in March 2011. Within a year, *MESSENGER* collected over 10,000 images, mapping the entire surface of the planet. *MESSENGER* is now operating in an extended-mission phase. After the use of all the fuel onboard for station keeping, *MESSENGER* will spiral toward the planet, eventually crashing into the surface.

Major discoveries so far by *MESSENGER* include the variations in the surface composition due to past volcanic eruptions [3, 4], confirmed that the planetary magnetic field is due to an internal dynamo and the discovery that it is offset from the center of the planet [5]. *MESSENGER* has also confirmed the presence of water ice in the polar regions, with the possible presence of organic compounds [6]. The latest results from *MESSENGER* can be seen at http://www.youtube.com/watch?v=AGZW4MeX-7I.

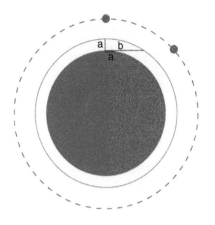

Figure 9.1.1. The green circle is the Earth. The blue circle represents the top of the Earth's atmosphere. The black dashed circle represents the apparent trajectory of a planet in the sky due to Earth's rotation. The two line segments, a and b, indicate the path length of light through the atmosphere when observing the planet at two different locations. Segment a is repeated underneath segment b to show the difference in length.

MESSENGER has also provided new insights into Mercury's origins. One way to distinguish the different models is through the relative abundance of different elements[3]. Mercury has high concentrations of heavy elements, including potassium, thorium, and uranium. If the ratio of potassium, a volatile metal, to thorium or uranium is similar to that on Earth, then Mercury most likely formed under cool conditions. Conversely, if potassium is depleted, then presumably Mercury would have formed under higher temperatures that would have prevented a sustainable atmosphere. The results from Mercury *MESSENGER* indicate that the relative abundance of potassium is Earthlike, and it for this reason that the impact model for the formation of Mercury is the most widely accepted model.

Reasons for returning to Mercury in the future probably will involve focus on (a) origins

---

2   http://messenger.jhuapl.edu/index.php

3   http://www.rsc.org/chemistryworld/News/2011/September/30091103.asp

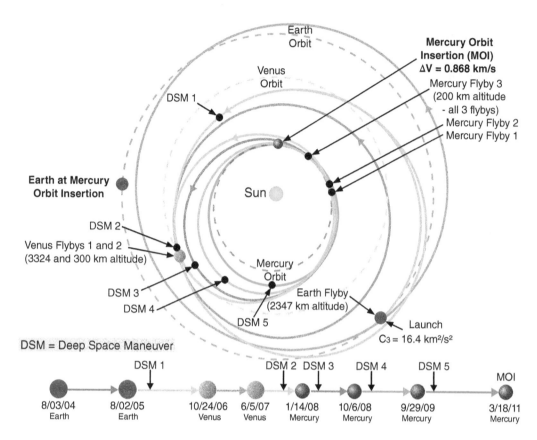

FIGURE 9.1.2. THE CONTORTED TRAJECTORY FOR *MESSSENGER* TO ATTAIN ORBIT AROUND MERCURY.

of the solar system through its geology and through its ice in the polar regions; (b) search for life in its polar cap regions; (c) economic possibilities in terms of its heavy metals and a source of He3 to support controlled fusion; and (d) technology developments, since no landing mission has occurred—yet national prestige may provide motivation for landing a spacecraft on the surface of Mercury.

Getting to Mercury is not easy, however. While it is relatively easy to fall into the inner part of the solar system, it is actually very difficult to go into orbit around Mercury due to the need to gain sufficient speed for orbital capture. As it is so close to the Sun, Mercury is one of the more difficult objects in the solar system to send a spacecraft to. *Mariner* 10 did not orbit around Mercury; it orbited around the Sun in a manner that would have allowed it to make multiple passes by Mercury. The *MESSENGER* spacecraft did enter orbit

around Mercury, but only after a six-and-a-half-year journey and multiple gravity assists by the Earth, Venus, and Mercury. This trajectory is shown in Figure 9.1.2. For comparison, the *New Horizon*'s mission will take nine years to reach Pluto (having traveled a distance of approximately 32 AU) and will use only one gravity assist by Jupiter.

While it may be difficult to observe detailed characteristics of Mercury from Earth due to the lack of total darkness when observable, we can still see enough to use observations to prove part of Einstein's Theory of General Relativity. As early as 1859, Urbain Le Verrier found that Mercury's orbit does not follow Newton's laws. People came up with many ideas to explain the deviation, including the hypothetical planet Vulcan, which orbited between the Sun and Mercury in such a way that we could not see it from Earth. It was not until Albert Einstein unveiled his Theory of General Relativity in

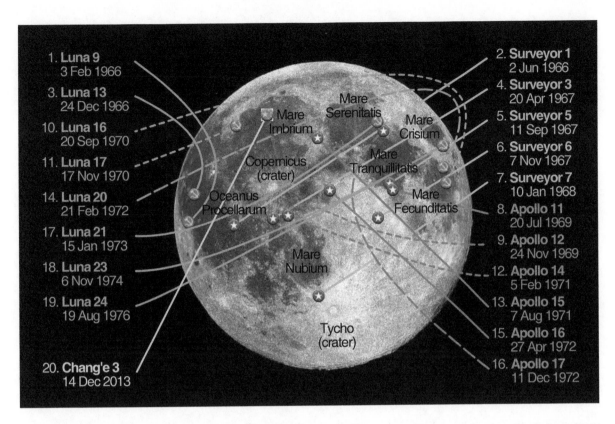

FIGURE 9.2.1. PICTORIAL HISTORY OF MISSIONS TO THE MOON. A FULL LIST OF ALL LUNAR MISSIONS CAN BE SEEN AT HTTP://WWW.LPI.USRA.EDU/LUNAR/MISSIONS/

1915 that the deviation in Mercury's orbit was explained. One part of the Theory of General Relativity states that objects with mass will distort the fabric of space-time around them—the more massive the object, the more it will distort space-time. The deviation in Mercury's orbit is due to the warping of space-time by the Sun. The orbits of all the planets in the solar system are affected by this distortion of space-time, but the effect decreases with distance from the Sun; thus, Mercury is the most strongly affected.

9.2. The Moon

The Moon represents the first place humans walked other than the Earth and remains a contender for human colonization. Its proximity makes it the easiest place to travel to beyond the Earth and a place to test out new technologies.

Missions for the exploration of the surface of the Moon have been numerous as seen in Figure 9.2.1, which shows a pictorial history of the lunar missions. The high point, of course, was the *Apollo* missions, which saw the first humans set foot on another solar system object beyond the Earth in 1969. During the course of all the *Apollo* landings on the Moon, humans spent over three days exploring the Moon and returned with almost 1000 pounds of lunar rocks. One of the key findings from analysis of the lunar rock is that much of it has a chemical composition similar to the Earth's mantle [7]. This led to much debate about the origin of the Moon.

The leading theory for the formation is attributed to the collision of the Earth with a Mars-sized object (a list of the different theories is at http://www.universetoday.com/19718/

FIGURE 9.2.2. SIDE-BY-SIDE COMPARISON OF MERCURY AND THE MOON. BOTH ARE HEAVILY CRATERED, THOUGH THE MOON HAS LARGE BASALTIC FLOWS CALLED MARES ON ITS SURFACE.

formation-of-the-moon/). Material ejected (depleted in iron) from the collision was thrown into orbit around the Earth, where the material eventually coalesced to form the Moon. An excellent video demonstrating the formation of the Moon can be seen at http://www.youtube.com/watch?v=fUOzWfC5wPg. A similar process is thought to have occurred for Mercury, the main difference being that Mercury, like the Earth, ended up with the majority of the heavy ions. The fate of the object that may have collided with Mercury is unknown. However, for both the Moon and Mercury, with no atmosphere present and therefore no significant erosional processes occurring, both solar system objects retain the scars from the period of bombardment[4] that occurred early in the formation of our solar system.

The lack of atmosphere around the Moon means the surface of the Moon closely resembles that of Mercury as seen in Figure 9.2.2. One difference, though, is that the surface of the Moon has large mares (or seas of basaltic

flows). These mares are thought to have occurred shortly after the formation of the Moon, when the interior of the Moon was still hot and molten. Large impacts would have then allowed the molten material to reach the surface and produce filling-in of the oldest craters, creating the smooth surfaces of the mares. In the case of Mercury[5], the surface cooled sufficiently quickly that the heavy bombardment did not pierce its crust, so mares on Mercury are relatively small. However, Mercury has large scarps, where the core eventually cooled and contracted, causing the crust to crack and fall inward. It is still unresolved as to why the mare regions all face the Earth.

The Moon will play a central role in future human exploration efforts, mainly as a technology demonstration point, particularly due to its proximity to the Earth. In testing our ability to live off of the Earth, the Moon represents our proverbial backyard in which colonists can escape back home with only a few days' travel in the event of a major problem. The Moon also represents a

---

4   http://en.wikipedia.org/wiki/Late_Heavy_Bombardment

5   http://www.uni.edu/morgans/astro/course/Notes/section4/new18.html

possible jumping-off point for our exploration of the rest of the solar system, as launching materials from the Moon is much easier than from the Earth due to the reduced gravity.

In addition, interest in the Moon will continue, since the potential for ice has been discovered in the craters in the polar regions [8]. These permanently shadowed craters remain hidden from sunlight year round and could trap any water in the regolith. At this point, exploration from a resources point of view is unlikely unless controlled fusion is successful, and the need for He3 becomes important.

9.3. Venus

Venus, named for the Roman goddess of love, remains problematic for space exploration. A variety of spacecraft[6] has visited Venus, including: *Sputnik 7*[7], *Venera 1*[8], *Mariner 1*[9], *Sputnik 19*[10], *Mariner 2*[11], *Sputnik 20*[12], *Sputnik 21*[13], *Venera 1964A*[14], *Venera 1964B*[15], *Cosmos 27*[16], *Zond 1*[17], *Venera 2*[18], *Venera 3*,[19] *Venera 4*[20], *Mariner 5*[21], *Cosmos 167*[22], *Venera 5*[23], *Venera 6*[24], *Venera 7*[25], *Cosmos 359*[26], *Venera 8*[27], *Cosmos 482*[28], *Mariner 10*[29], *Venera 9*[30], *Venera 10*[31], *Pioneer Venus 1*[32], *Pioneer Venus 2*[33], *Venera 11*[34], *Venera 12*[35], *Venera 13*[36], *Venera 14*[37], *Venera 15*[38], *Venera*

---

6   http://nssdc.gsfc.nasa.gov/planetary/planets/venuspage.html
7   http://www.planetary.org/explore/space-topics/space-missions/missions-to-venus-mercury.html
8   http://www.planetary.org/explore/space-topics/space-missions/missions-to-venus-mercury.html
9   http://planetary.org/explore/space-topics/space-missions/missions-to-venus-mercury.html
10   http://www.planetary.org/explore/space-topics/space-missions/missions-to-venus-mercury.html
11   http://www.planetary.org/explore/space-topics/space-missions/missions-to-venus-mercury.html
12   http://www.planetary.org/explore/space-topics/space-missions/missions-to-venus-mercury.html
13   http://www.planetary.org/explore/space-topics/space-missions/missions-to-venus-mercury.html
14   http://www.planetary.org/explore/space-topics/space-missions/missions-to-venus-mercury.html
15   http://www.planetary.org/explore/space-topics/space-missions/missions-to-venus-mercury.html
16   http://www.planetary.org/explore/space-topics/space-missions/missions-to-venus-mercury.html
17   http://www.planetary.org/explore/space-topics/space-missions/missions-to-venus-mercury.html
18   http://www.planetary.org/explore/space-topics/space-missions/missions-to-venus-mercury.html
19   http://planetary.org/explore/space-topics/space-missions/missions-to-venus-mercury.html
20   http://www.planetary.org/explore/space-topics/space-missions/missions-to-venus-mercury.html
21   http://www.planetary.org/explore/space-topics/space-missions/missions-to-venus-mercury.html
22   http://planetary.org/explore/space-topics/space-missions/missions-to-venus-mercury.html
23   http://www.planetary.org/explore/space-topics/space-missions/missions-to-venus-mercury.html
24   http://www.planetary.org/explore/space-topics/space-missions/missions-to-venus-mercury.html
25   http://planetary.org/explore/space-topics/space-missions/missions-to-venus-mercury.html
26   http://www.planetary.org/explore/space-topics/space-missions/missions-to-venus-mercury.html
27   http://www.planetary.org/explore/space-topics/space-missions/missions-to-venus-mercury.html
28   http://www.planetary.org/explore/space-topics/space-missions/missions-to-venus-mercury.html
29   http://www.planetary.org/explore/space-topics/space-missions/missions-to-venus-mercury.html
30   http://www.planetary.org/explore/space-topics/space-missions/missions-to-venus-mercury.html
31   http://www.planetary.org/explore/space-topics/space-missions/missions-to-venus-mercury.html
32   http://www.planetary.org/explore/space-topics/space-missions/missions-to-venus-mercury.html
33   http://www.planetary.org/explore/space-topics/space-missions/missions-to-venus-mercury.html
34   http://www.planetary.org/explore/space-topics/space-missions/missions-to-venus-mercury.html
35   http://www.planetary.org/explore/space-topics/space-missions/missions-to-venus-mercury.html
36   http://www.planetary.org/explore/space-topics/space-missions/missions-to-venus-mercury.html
37   http://www.planetary.org/explore/space-topics/space-missions/missions-to-venus-mercury.html
38   http://www.planetary.org/explore/space-topics/space-missions/missions-to-venus-mercury.html

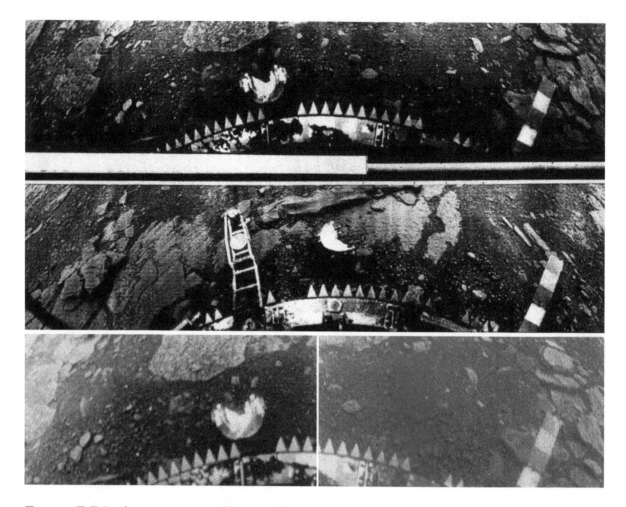

FIGURE 9.3.1. IMAGES FROM THE VENERA 13 LANDER.

16[39], *Vega 1*[40], *Vega 2*[41], *Galileo*[42], *Magellan*[43], *Cassini*[44], and *Venus Express*[45]. Most of the dedicated missions to Venus (in particular the *Venera* series) have been from the former Soviet Union; several of these missions were unsuccessful.

The thick clouds around Venus mean that in order to "see" the surface, a satellite with an active radar system must be put in orbit. The *Magellan* mission succeeded in mapping the

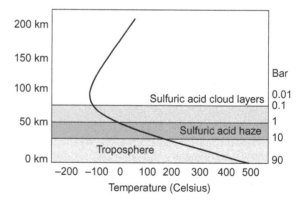

FIGURE 9.3.2. THE ATMOSPHERIC PROFILE FOR VENUS. THE UNIT OF ONE BAR IS EQUIVALENT TO ONE ATMOSPHERE AT EARTH AT SEA LEVEL.

39 http://www.planetary.org/explore/space-topics/space-missions/missions-to-venus-mercury.html
40 http://www.planetary.org/explore/space-topics/space-missions/missions-to-venus-mercury.html
41 http://planetary.org/explore/space-topics/space-missions/missions-to-venus-mercury.html
42 http://www.planetary.org/explore/space-topics/space-missions/missions-to-venus-mercury.html
43 http://www.planetary.org/explore/space-topics/space-missions/missions-to-venus-mercury.html
44 http://www.planetary.org/explore/space-topics/space-missions/missions-to-venus-mercury.html
45 http://en.wikipedia.org/wiki/Venus_Express

entire surface of Venus with radar and found something quite surprising—the surface appears to be only 300–600 million years old [9]. This suggests that Venus has had resurfacing by volcanic activity some 300–600 million years ago, so in comparison with Mercury and Mars, it is still very active.

Taking pictures on the surface of Venus is even more challenging than taking pictures from space. The former USSR is the only country that has put a lander on Venus, and it took them several tries. At 90 atmospheres, being on the surface of Venus is equivalent to being over 900 meters below the surface of the ocean on Earth. The *Venera* spacecraft that reached the surface had an operation time of only about two hours. Flat vistas are seen on the images taken by *Venera* 9, 10, 13, and 14. An example from *Venera* 13 is shown in Figure 9.3.1.

And to just make it a little more interesting for exploration purposes, Venus has clouds of sulfuric acid. The atmospheric composition at its surface is nearly 96.5% CO_2, with the remainder being primarily nitrogen. Because of the predominance of CO_2, which is a greenhouse gas, the average surface temperature is about 450° C. A profile showing the changes with altitude is shown in Figure 9.3.2. The atmospheric pressure does not decline between the terrestrial pressure until about 50 meters in height.

Extremophiles[46] have been detected on Earth that are able to live in exceeding acidic and high-pressure regions that are present near sea floor vents. However, the absence of water, at least on the surface, indicates that the chances of life on the surface is small. There is potential for life below the hot surface or the possibility of it in the high-altitude clouds, since the pressure is still high there.

However, the extreme conditions on Venus suggest that at this time, it is unlikely to be heavily explored. There is a chance of limited

46   http://en.wikipedia.org/wiki/Extremophile

FIGURE 9.4.1.   HUBBLE IMAGES SHOWING THE DEVELOPMENT OF A GLOBAL DUST STORM ON MARS.

astrobiology and science investigations over the next couple of decades, but the authors predict that it will not be in the mainstream of exploration for some time in the future.

9.4. Mars

Mars is named after the Roman god of war. It remains, and will continue to remain, a primary target for space exploration. Conditions for exploration are no more extreme than on the Moon, except for the travel distance. Mars, though, offers significantly more targets that can provide detailed information on

Mission Name	Launch Country	Launch Date	Arrival
Mariner 3	USA	Nov. 1964	Faring failure, never arrived
Mariner 4	USA	Nov. 1964	Flyby July 1965
Mariner 6	USA	Feb. 1969	Flyby July 1969
Mariner 7	USA	March 1969	Flyby August 1969
Mariner 8	USA	May 1971	Failure during launch
Mariner 9	USA	May 1971	Orbital insertion November 1971
Mars 2	USSR	May 1971	Orbital insertion and landing, November 1971
Mars 3	USSR	May 1971	Orbital insertion and landing, December 1971
Viking 1	USA	August 1975	Landed June 1976
Viking 2	USA	Sept. 1975	Landed August 1976
Phobos 1	USSR	July 1988	Lost during cruise
Phobos 2	USSR	July 1988	Orbital insertion of Mars, January 1989; lost contact during trajectory change to Phobos
Mars Observer	USA	Sept. 1992	Lost contact just prior to orbital insertion
Mars Pathfinder	USA	Dec. 1996	Landed July 1997
Mars Global Surveyor	USA	Nov. 1996	Orbital insertion September 1997
Nozomi	Japan	July 1998	Never achieved orbital insertion
Mars Climate Orbiter	USA	Dec. 1998	Lost contact during orbital insertion
Mars Polar Lander	USA	Jan. 1999	Lost contact during landing, December 1999
Mars Odyssey	USA	April 2001	Orbital insertion October 2001
Mars Express/Beagle Lander	ESA	June 2003	*Mars Express* orbital insertion December 2003; *Beagle* lander lost contact upon landing
Mars Exploration Rover – *Spirit*	USA	June 2003	Landed January 2004
Mars Exploration Rover – *Opportunity*	USA	July 2003	Landed January 2004
Mars Reconnaissance Orbiter	USA	Aug. 2005	Orbital insertion March 2006
Phoenix	USA	Aug. 2007	Landed May 2008
Mars Science Lab – *Curiosity*	USA	Nov. 2011	Landed August 2012

Sources:
http://www.nasa.gov/mission_pages/mars/missions/index-past.html
http://spider.seds.org/mars/mars-l.html

the formation of the solar system, planetary processes, including climate change aspects, and the possibility of life other than that on the Earth. It is for these reasons that exploration efforts of Mars continue to grow.

However, surface exploration does pose some interesting problems. When one thinks of hazards to robots and humans in space, they usually do not think of dust, but previous missions have shown this little thing can collectively become a big problem. We have known since humans began looking at Mars through a telescope that Mars experiences large dust storms. The *Mariner* 9 mission had the misfortunate of spending seven months flying to Mars, only to arrive for orbital insertion during the middle of a global dust storm. Once the dust storm subsided, however, *Mariner* 9 went on to make many ground-breaking discoveries as the first satellite in orbit around Mars. The Hubble Space Telescope captured such a storm in 2001 (Figure 9.4.1). Dust in the atmosphere can be deposited on solar panels. This was believed to be one of the scenarios that would end the life of the Mars Exploration Rovers. In fact, it might have ended *Spirit*'s mission, had it not been for the serendipitous passing of some

dust devils. In 2005, a little over a year into its mission, the energy output of the solar panels had become dangerously low. Then, one day, the output jumped back up to 93% efficiency. Analysis of the camera images taken by *Spirit* at the same time showed the passage of multiple dust devils past the rover. It is believed that one or more of those dust devils passed directly over the rover, sweeping the dust off the solar panels. A clip of dust devils moving past *Spirit* can be seen at http://marsrovers. nasa.gov/gallery/press/spirit/20050819a.html.

Dust is not only a problem on Mars—it is also a significant worry for sending humans back to the Moon. It was well known from the *Apollo* missions that soon after setting foot on the Moon, astronauts would become covered in statically charged dust. The astronauts driving the lunar buggies reported that the vehicles generated a large rooster tail of dust behind them. At the time, nothing had been planned to mitigate any hazardous effects from the dust. Besides being a hazard, if it becomes lodged in mechanical parts or the joints of airlocks on space suits, there is the potential health hazard. *Apollo* astronauts returning from the Moon reported that during the return trip to Earth, they had a strange

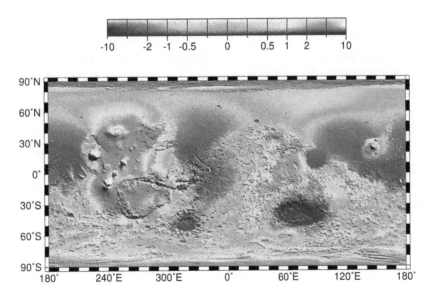

FIGURE 9.4.2. THE TOPOGRAPHY OF MARS. AS THERE IS NO "SEA LEVEL" AT MARS, 0 KM IS THE MIDPOINT BETWEEN THE HIGHEST ALTITUDE AND THE LOWEST ALTITUDE. THIS ALTITUDE OF 0 KM IS CALLED THE "REFERENCE GEOID."

metallic taste in their mouths, most likely due to the continual ingestion of lunar dust that they had brought aboard the return vehicle.

Here is a lengthy history of missions to Mars. Note: Only successful USSR missions prior to 1988 are listed, including:

A Martian day is only 36 minutes longer than an Earth day. This has interesting implications for the scientists and engineers working on missions that land on the surface of Mars. During the first few weeks of a lander or rover mission, the scientists and engineers try to make the most of every minute that the lander or rover can be operational—that is, during a Martian day. This means the scientists and mission planners are awake when the rover or lander is "awake," and sleeping during the Martian night. Therefore, for the first few weeks of a mission, the scientists and engineers live according to a Martian day. At first, this does not disrupt their lives too much; they get up at a normal time and go to bed when it gets dark, but after only a couple of weeks, the scientists have to wake up in the middle of the late afternoon and are eating dinner at 3:00 A.M. NASA has started to track and monitor the scientists and engineers who live a Martian day while on the Earth to study how the human body responds to having its natural 24-hour cycle disrupted. They are using the data to guide what future human explorers of Mars will need to do in order to adapt to a different day/night cycle.

The Martian topography is one of a tale of two hemispheres (Figure 9.4.2). The southern hemisphere is heavily cratered, and except for two very large impact basins, higher in altitude relative to the reference geoid. As a result, the southern hemisphere is typically referred to as the "southern highlands." The northern hemisphere, by contrast, has a smoother surface and is on average lower in altitude. It is referred to as the "northern lowlands." The origin of this dichotomy is still unknown. One recent theory suggests that the northern lowlands are the result of a large impact early in the formation of Mars [10]. As to why the northern lowlands are so much smoother than the southern

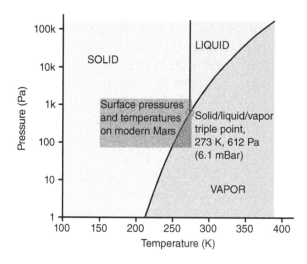

Figure 9.4.3. The phase diagram for water, with the conditions found on Mars overlaid in the purple box.

highlands, it goes back to the question of how the lowlands formed. The relative lack of craters in the northern hemisphere can either mean the rock is much younger than that in the southern highlands, or it can mean that many of the older craters have been erased by some weathering process that only occurred in the northern lowlands. Researchers have studied very high-resolution images of the boundaries in the northern hemisphere between low altitudes (blue and purple regions in Figure 9.4.2) and higher altitudes (yellow and orange regions in the same figure). In several places, they claim to see evidence of wave action [11]. Long-term wave motion on a lake shore or ocean shore will leave very distinctive marks in the sand, which then can turn into sandstone rock, preserving the wave markings. These results suggest that the northern lowlands were once a large ocean that both erased craters and prevented new ones from forming.

Another notable geologic feature on Mars is the very high altitude region on the left-hand side of Figure 9.4.2. This is referred to as the Tharsis Montes region. It is the location of several extinct volcanoes, including Olympus Mons—the tallest volcano in the solar system—and Valles Marineris, a large canyon that, at 4000 km long, is nearly equivalent to the width

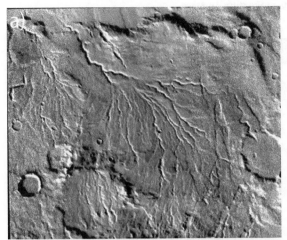

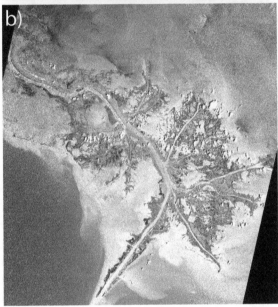

FIGURE 9.4.4. TOP: A PICTURE FROM MARS. BOTTOM: A LANDSAT 3 PICTURE OF THE MISSISSIPPI RIVER DELTA. SOURCE: HTTP://WWW.LPI.USRA.EDU/ PUBLICATIONS/SLIDESETS/REDPLANET2/SLIDE_26. HTML

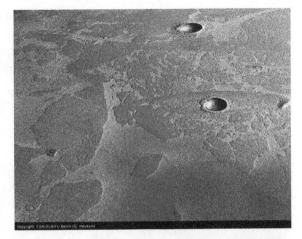

FIGURE 9.4.5. TOP: MARTIAN SURFACE STRUC-TURES. BOTTOM: ICEBERGS, AS SEEN FROM SPACE, OFF OF ANTARCTICA.

of North America. The origin of Valles Marineris is unknown, but is most likely tied to the origin of the entire Tharsis region. One leading theory proposes that at some point, a large magma plume rose up underneath the crust of the now Tharsis region. This magma plume both created and fed the volcanoes of the region while simultaneously pushing the crust up, producing an expansive landslide (the region to the lower left of Valles Marineris) [12]. Repeated volcanic eruptions lead to the cooling of the magma

underneath the region and the subsistence of the crust. When crust subsided, a rift formed, creating Valles Marineris.

One of the main questions concerning Mars is "Is there now, or was there ever, life on Mars?" This question is intimately tied to the question of how long liquid water existed and was stable on the surface of Mars and how prevalent it was when it existed. Figure 9.4.3 shows the water phase diagram with the range of temperatures and pressures that can be found presently on Mars. Only in a very small range of conditions, typically found near the lowest altitudes, is liquid water stable on current-day Mars. Figure 9.4.3 also shows that, in order for liquid water to have been prevalent in the past, it is not just a matter of Mars having been warmer—Mars had to have had a much thicker atmosphere.

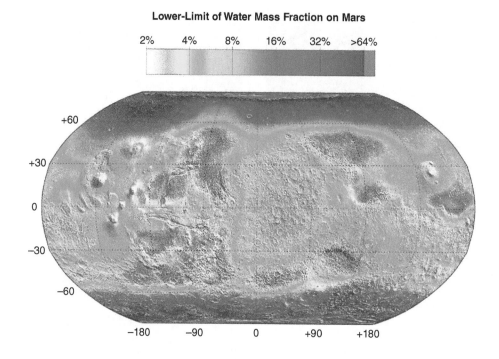

Lower-Limit of Water Mass Fraction on Mars

FIGURE 9.4.6. ESTIMATED CONCENTRATION OF BURIED WATER (AKA PERMAFROST) FROM SATELLITE OBSERVATIONS OF EPITHERMAL NEUTRONS DETERMINED BY *MARS ODYSSEY*.

But what evidence do we have for liquid water having been prevalent on Mars? It's not the "canale" seen by Percival Lowell [13]. Some of the first evidence for lakes and rivers on Mars from satellite images was not conclusive. Figure 9.4.4a is an example of the types of images that orbiters around Mars have captured. The figure appears very much like the image of the Mississippi River Delta (Figure 9.4.4b), also known as a fluvial fan. A fluvial fan forms when water from a river or channel flows into a region where it can spread out in many directions. While the similarity of the structure on Mars to the one on Earth suggests an ancient river on Mars, it is not proof. The structure could have been formed by the very prevalent wind storms that develop on Mars.

More circumstantial evidence of water on Mars came from the image in Figure 9.4.5. This image appears to be one of ancient Martian icebergs, frozen in time and covered in dust. While the similarity of the picture from Mars to a picture of icebergs at the Earth, also seen from

space, is suggestive, the two impact craters seen in the image from Mars help further the case that the image from Mars is one of buried water ice. The craters are unusually smooth and round when compared to craters formed by an impactor hitting a surface made of rock. This suggests that the impactors that formed the craters in Figure 9.4.5a hit a material that could melt during impact, leading to much smoother crater walls.

The arrival of *Mars Odyssey* in 2002 allowed for the measurement of subsurface hydrogen (and thus water) via the detection of backscattered neutrons. As the atmosphere of Mars is considerably thinner than the Earth's, cosmic rays can punch through the atmosphere and interact with the surface regolith. During that process, neutrons are created that can travel back up into space, where they can be detected by a satellite in orbit. The energy of the neutrons is characteristic of the material the cosmic rays interact with. Through this process, the concentration of hydrogen (and

FIGURE 9.4.7. IMAGES OF MARTIAN "BLUEBER-
RIES," OR GRAY HEMATITE.

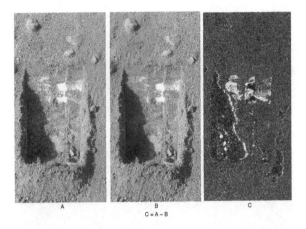

FIGURE 9.4.8. CHANGES IN A TRENCH DUG BY
PHOENIX. LOOK IN THE LOWER LEFT SIDE OF THE
TRENCH ON SOL 20 FOR LITTLE WHITE PEBBLES THAT
DISAPPEARED FOUR DAYS LATER. NOTE THAT THE
WATER ICE VISIBLE AT THE TOP OF THE TRENCH
WOULD HAVE BEEN SO COLD IT WOULD HAVE BEEN AS
HARD AS CONCRETE.

water) in the first meter of the Martian surface can be remotely estimated. *Mars Odyssey* found significant deposits of subsurface water in the Martian poles, particularly the north pole (Figure 9.4.6).

The first direct measurement of past liquid water from the surface of Mars came soon after the Mars Exploration Rover *Opportunity* landed in 2004. The landing site for *Opportunity* was selected due to the high abundance of gray hematite as seen from space. Gray hematite is an iron mineral that only forms in the presence of liquid water (Figure 9.4.7). When *Opportunity* landed in Eagle Crater, it found a preponderance of "blueberries"—spherically shaped rocks called concretions, which consist entirely of gray hematite (Figure 9.4.7a). Concretions form when iron-rich rock becomes saturated

with water for long periods of time. The iron is picked up by the water and precipitates out of the surrounding rock-forming hematite. When an outcrop of rock was analyzed that contained concretions that had not yet broken free (Figure 9.4.7b), the surrounding rock was determined to be jarosite [14]. The combination of jarosite and gray hematite has been found to form on the Earth, but it does so only when the water saturating the rock has a pH less than 5, but more typically has a pH between 1 and 3, making it essentially battery acid! So, *Opportunity* found conclusive proof of a region in which liquid water had been present for a long period of time, although that water was probably so acidic, it could not have supported life or the development of life.

This did not bode well for the search for life on Mars. But then the *Phoenix* lander touched down near the north pole of Mars. The *Phoenix* lander arose out of the ashes of the failed *Mars Polar Lander*. It did not roam around Mars, but rather landed in an area near the polar cap. *Phoenix* had a large arm on it, with which it could scoop up surrounding soil and dump the material into chambers to analyze the chemical makeup of the soil. One of the first holes left behind, after *Phoenix* scooped up some soil, is

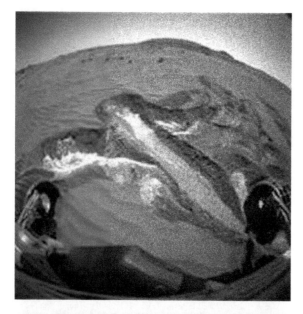

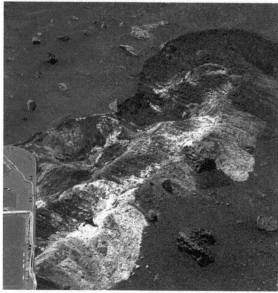

FIGURE 9.4.9. TRENCHES DUG BY THE WHEELS OF *SPIRIT*.

turn to vapor in a process called sublimation. This is exactly what had happened to the little pebbles. When *Phoenix* analyzed the chemistry of the surrounding soil, it found material with a pH of 8–9. This is much better for life. In fact, the chemistry and pH of the soil would be perfect for growing asparagus, turnips, or bacteria.

The history of liquid water on Mars was further added to by the Mars Exploration Rover *Spirit*. The *Spirit* landing site was selected because it appeared from space that the Gusev Crater had been filled in with sediment from a flood. This seemed like a good place to look for evidence of water and life. Unfortunately, such evidence was not forthcoming from Gusev Crater. And once out of the crater, *Spirit* had the seeming misfortune to break a front wheel over two years into its three-month mission. In order to continue on its way, the engineers programmed *Spirit* to drive backward, dragging its broken wheel behind it. On a particularly fateful day, the engineers told *Spirit* to stop and take a panoramic image of where it had been and where it was going. When the images came up at mission control at the Jet Propulsion Laboratory, the scientists and engineers were stunned. *Spirit* had churned up some sort of white material (Figure 9.4.9).

The engineers then sent *Spirit* instructions to begin doing donuts to churn up more of the material. Subsequent analysis showed that the white material was not water ice, but rather salt. *Spirit* serendipitously found evidence of past hydrothermal activity on Mars—a sort of Yellowstone Park on Mars. This has become an ultimate example of "when life gives you lemons, make lemonade." Had *Spirit* not broken a wheel and been dragging it behind, the rover would have never churned up the material below the surface crust it was traversing over and never discovered former hot springs on Mars.

The *Curiosity* mission presents a new path for rovers. This mission forgoes the use of solar panels and the problems with dust accumulation, instead using radiothermal

shown in Figure 9.4.8. Left behind were some white material and little white pebbles. Just because the material was white, the scientists could not assume that it was water ice (as we will see with a discovery made by *Spirit*). But in this case, the material *was* water ice. The little white pebbles that were seen on mission day 20 (referred to as a Sol) had disappeared by Sol 24. As water ice was not stable when exposed to sunlight and air at that time and place for Mars, any exposed water ice would

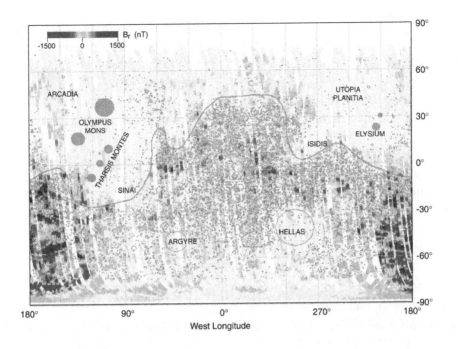

FIGURE 9.4.10. A MAP OF THE MAGNETIC ANOMALIES SUPERIMPOSED ON A TOPOLOGY OF MARS. THESE ANOMALIES ARE CONCENTRATED AROUND THE CRATERED (OLDER) SOUTHERN HEMISPHERE.

generators (RTGs) for power. This design, however, meant that *Curiosity* was much too heavy to use the airbag technology previously used by *Spirit*, *Opportunity*, and *Pathfinder*. Instead, it used a newly developed sky-crane technology for landing. An animation of this process can be seen at http://www.youtube.com/watch%3Fv=E37Ss9Tm36c. *Curiosity* is now roving Mars, sure to make many fascinating discoveries in the years to come.

When discussing how the solar wind interacts with planets, we mentioned that Mars does not currently possess a global magnetic field. This is one of the key reasons that its atmosphere is now too thin for liquid water to be stable on the surface. Without the protection of a global magnetic field, the solar wind can directly impact the Martian atmosphere, driving the loss of atmospheric components to space. That liquid water was once stable on the surface, as proven by Mars Exploration Rover discoveries, means the Martian atmosphere was once much thicker than it is now. What that atmosphere may have been like is largely unknown.

At the earliest stages of the planet's history, the Martian atmosphere was most likely protected by a global magnetic field. Early missions to Mars provided inconclusive evidence regarding the nature of a magnetic field at Mars, with early measurements suggesting possibly a weak global magnetic field, while others argued that the signals may have been due to the moon Phobos being magnetized. The arrival of *Mars Global Surveyor* resolved the question, showing that instead of a global magnetic field, Mars possesses an extensive region of magnetized rock called magnetic anomalies (Figure 9.4.10). The magnetic anomalies have total magnetic field strengths on the order of 1500 nT at satellite orbital altitudes [15]. This is only an order of magnitude smaller than the Earth's global magnetic field at the surface. These are very strong magnetic anomalies. That they are concentrated in the southern highlands (Figure 9.4.10) suggests they date from a time when Mars was young and still geologically active.

These discoveries all highlight that the more we investigate Mars, the more questions arise.

References

[1] http://pds.jpl.nasa.gov/planets/special/planets.htm

[2] http://history.nasa.gov/SP-423/mariner.htm

[3] Evans, L. G., et al. (2012). Major-element abundances on the surface of Mercury: Results from the *MESSENGER* Gamma-Ray Spectrometer, *J. Geophys. Res.*

doi:10.1029/2012JE004178.

[4] Head, J. W., et al. (2011). Flood Volcanism in the Northern High Latitudes of Mercury Revealed by *MESSENGER*, S*cience*, 30 September 2011: Vol. 333 no. 6051 pp. 1853–1856.

doi:10.1126/science.1211997

[5] Anderson, B. J., et al. (2011). The Global Magnetic Field of Mercury from *MESSENGER* Orbital Observations, *Science*, 30 September 2011: Vol. 333, no. 6051 pp. 1859–1862,.

doi:10.1126/science.1211001

[6] Submitted to *Science*, not yet published. Published at LPSC 2012, Paige, et al.

[7] Engel, A. E. J., & Engel, C. G. (1970). Lunar rock compositions and some interpretations, *Geochimica et Cosmochimica Acta Supplement*, Volume 1. Proceedings of the *Apollo* 11 Lunar Science Conference held 5–8 January, 1970, in Houston, Texas. Volume 2: Chemical and Isotope Analyses. Edited by A. A. Levinson. New York: Pergamon Press, p.1081.

[8] Paige, D. A., et al., (2010). Diviner Lunar Radiometer Observations of Cold Traps in the Moon's South Polar Region, *Science*, 330 (6003), 479–482.

doi: 10.1126/science.1187726

[9] Arvidson, R. E., Greeley R., Malin, M. C., Saunders, R. S., Izenberg, N., J. J. Plaut, J. J., E. R. Stofan, E. R., & Shepard, M. K. (1992). Surface modification of Venus as inferred from *Magellan* observations of plains, *J. Geophys. Res.*, 97(E8), 13303–13317.

doi:10.1029/92JE01384[47].

[10] Andrews-Hanna, J. C., & Zuber, M. T. (2008). THE DICHOTOMY-FORMING IMPACT ON MARS: EVIDENCE AND IMPLICATIONS, Workshop of the Earth Solar System Impact Bombardment, November 19–20, 2008, Abstract #3015[48]

[11] Kreslavsky, M. A., & Head, J. W. (2002). Fate of outflow channel effluents in the northern lowlands of Mars: The Vastitas, Borealis Formation as a sublimation residue from frozen ponded bodies of water, *J. Geophys. Res.*, 107 (E12), 5121.

doi:10.1029/2001JE001831

[12] Bigot-Cormier, F., & Montgomery, D. R. (2007). Valles Marineris landslides: Evidence for a strength limit to Martian relief? *Earth and Planetary Science Letters*, 260 (1–2), 179–186.

http://dx.doi.org/10.1016/j.psl.2007.05.028[49]

[13] Lowell, P. (1911). Mars and its canals. Macmillan and Company Limited.

---

47   http://dx.doi.org/10.1029/92JE01384
48   http://www.lpi.usra.edu/meetings/bombardment2008/pdf/3015.pdf
49   http://dx.doi.org/10.1016/j.epsl.2007.05.028

[14] Squyres, S., et al. (2004). The *Opportunity* Rovers, Athena Science Investigation at Meridiani Planum, Mars, *Science*, 306 (5702), 1698–1703.

doi:10.1126/science.1106171

[15] Connerney, J. E. P., et al. (2001). The global magnetic field of Mars and implications for crustal evolution, *Geophys. Res. Lett.*, 28 (21).

doi:10.1029/2001GL013619

An excellent resource for planetary process is **Exploring the Planets, 2nd Edition.**[50]

Image Credits

---

50 http://www.explanet.info/

Planetary Destinations

Asteroids and Beyond

Missions to the outer planets will always be few and far between (at least in the first half of this century). Neptune and Uranus have only been visited once by *Voyager* 2[1]. Pluto will shortly be visited by *New Horizons*[2] in 2015, after nearly a nine-year trip, the first spacecraft to visit Pluto. Given the relatively small occurrence of missions to the outer planets, we will only discuss the potential out to as far as Saturn. We recognize that not considering the outermost planets and beyond is a limitation, but the question here is the timescale over which this exploration will occur. With the present trip time in excess of a decade and mission development of several years, it is the view of the authors that missions beyond Saturn will not occur within the next two decades; therefore, it is an acceptable omission at this time, and we leave it up to the readers to try and disprove our hypothesis.

10.1. The Asteroids

Thus, the next stopping-off point must be the asteroid belt. Asteroids have received significant attention due to the Earth's close encounter with Asteroid 2012 DA14 and the

---

1 http://en.wikipedia.org/wiki/Voyager_2
2 http://en.wikipedia.org/wiki/New_Horizons

FIGURE 10.1.1. EXAMPLES OF DIFFERENT-SIZED ASTEROIDS.

explosion of a meteor in 2013 over Chelyabinsk in Russia (video of the event at https://www.youtube.com/watch?v=9OOmh7_I8vI). This asteroid was considered small, only 20 m in diameter, weighing an estimated 11,000 tons.

The asteroid belt[3] is located between Mars and Jupiter. It is thought that planet formation began to occur in this region along with the rest of the solar system. However, the emergence of Jupiter, with its large mass, causes the asteroids to continuously undergo pulverizing collisions, which prevents the formation of a full planet. It was once believed that there was between two and ten Earth masses in the Asteroid Belt, but through collisions and ejection of material, the mass is presently 0.1% of its original mass.[4]

Asteroids come in all shapes and sizes[5] as shown in Figure 10.1.1. About half the mass of the asteroid belt is contained in four asteroids: Ceres, Vesta, Pallas, and Hygiea. It is estimated that there are 200 asteroids over 100 km in diameter and over 1 million asteroids[6] bigger than 1 km in diameter.

The asteroids are characterized by three main categories[7]:

- Chondrite asteroids, which are carbon, calcium, and aluminum rich, with a composition similar to that of the early solar system, indicating unmodified components;
- Achondrites, silicate-rich asteroids. They lack the light elements, indicating that they have been modified through melting and reformation, possibly from being ejected from moons and planets;
- Iron asteroids that may have been associated with protoplanets, which were able to differentiate into an iron core and crust, but which were subsequently disrupted.

(A more detailed classification of the asteroids can be seen at this link.)[8]

3   http://en.wikipedia.org/wiki/Asteroid_belt
4   http://en.wikipedia.org/wiki/Asteroid_belt
5   http://www.space.com/11093-photos-asteroids-deep-space-rocks.html
6   http://en.wikipedia.org/wiki/Asteroid
7   http://en.wikipedia.org/wiki/Asteroid_belt
8   http://www.space.com/15948-asteroid-belt-space-rocks-infographic.html

Components of the asteroid belts have been investigated by several missions passing through the region to other destinations. The first spacecraft to traverse the asteroid belt was *Pioneer* 10[9], which entered the region on July 16, 1972, on its way to Jupiter. This mission was followed by *Pioneer* 11[10], *Voyagers* 1 and 2[11], *Galileo*[12], *Cassini*[13], and *New Horizons*[14], as they too investigated heading out toward the outer planets. *Ulysses*[15] provided high-latitude observations of the Sun and also had to pass this region in order to attain gravitational assists from Jupiter to reach its high-inclination orbit. *Stardust*[16] (1999) and *Rosetta*[17] (2004) studied asteroids as they made rendezvous with comets.

Dedicated missions to the asteroids include *NEAR*[18], launched in 1996 and ending with a touchdown landing on the near-Earth asteroid Eros[19]. The *Hayabusa*[20] spacecraft, launched in 2003, used electric propulsion to reach the asteroid Itokawa and return a few tiny grains back to the Earth in 2010. The *Dawn*[21], launched in 2007, entered orbit around Vesta in 2011. It left Vesta in 2012 and is presently on a journey to Ceres, with arrival due in 2015. Vesta is a metal-rich asteroid while Ceres is carbonaceous, though there are arguments as to whether both Ceres and Vesta are dwarf planets or asteroids. Videos of the *Dawn* mission[22] (using electric propulsion) and its images of Vesta[23] can be found at the embedded hyperlinks. It is important to note that the objectives of *Dawn* could only be achieved through the use of electric propulsion similar to *Hayabusa*[24].

Our predictions for the future is that we will see more missions to the asteroids. These missions will focus around technology demonstrations, the origins of the solar system, and hopefully in-situ resource utilization. Because gravitational forces associated with these objects are relatively small, missions returning significant quantities of materials are necessary in the next 20 years if humans are going to have a substantial footprint beyond low Earth orbit. It is projected that advanced propulsion techniques play an important role, as demonstrated by the *Hayabusa* and *Dawn* missions.

10.2. Jupiter and Its Moons

Jupiter[25] is the largest planet in the solar system and is named after Jove, the Roman king of the gods (the Greek counterpart is Zeus). Its general properties are listed in Table 10.1. Jupiter makes up most of the 0.1% of mass in the solar system not contained in the Sun. That large mass is good for life on Earth. Jupiter acts as a large solar-system vacuum cleaner, sucking up comets that enter the solar system, preventing them from impacting Earth [3]. An example of this process was seen when Comet Shoemaker Levy 9 impacted Jupiter in 1994. An excellent video describing this impact can be seen at http://www.youtube.com/watch?v=J-Ld9eaVtkM. Jupiter's presence is not completely benign, however. It can also disrupt the orbits of asteroids in the asteroid belt, sending them hurtling into the inner solar system, where they can then impact the terrestrial planets [3].

---

9   http://en.wikipedia.org/wiki/Pioneer_10
10   http://en.wikipedia.org/wiki/Pioneer_11
11   http://en.wikipedia.org/wiki/Voyager_program
12   http://en.wikipedia.org/wiki/Galileo_(spacecraft)
13   http://en.wikipedia.org/wiki/Cassini%E2%80%93Huygens
14   http://en.wikipedia.org/wiki/New_Horizons
15   http://en.wikipedia.org/wiki/Ulysses_probe
16   http://en.wikipedia.org/wiki/Stardust_(spacecraft)
17   http://en.wikipedia.org/wiki/Rosetta_(spacecraft)
18   http://en.wikipedia.org/wiki/NEAR_Shoemaker
19   http://en.wikipedia.org/wiki/433_Eros
20   http://en.wikipedia.org/wiki/Hayabusa_%28spacecraft%29
21   http://en.wikipedia.org/wiki/Dawn_(spacecraft)
22   http://www.youtube.com/watch?v=jHp9w8N0mcw
23   http://www.youtube.com/watch?v=BO2mb-ucHBk

24   http://en.wikipedia.org/wiki/Hayabusa_%28spacecraft%29
25   http://www.explanet.info/Chapter09.htm

Table 10.1. General properties of Jupiter.

Mass[1]	1.9×10^{27} kg
Average distance from the Sun[1]	5.2 AU
Length of Day in Earth days[1]	0.41
Length of Year in Earth years[1]	11.86
Orbital eccentricity[1]	0.048
Cloud Top Mean Temperature[1]	120 K
Radius	71,500 km
Atmospheric Composition[1]	90% H, 10% He, 0.07% CH_4

Its composition is very similar to that of the Sun, but its smaller mass means the center of Jupiter does not have high enough pressures to initiate fusion. If it did, we would be living in a binary star system! To actually generate fusion, its mass has to be about 80 times higher[26], in which case it could be classified as a brown dwarf[27]. However, Jupiter appears to reemit more energy than it receives from the Sun [5, 6], indicating that it is still cooling off from its formation 4.6 billion years ago.

As noted above, the composition of Jupiter is mostly hydrogen and helium, and while Jupiter is known as a gas giant, most of its structure is believed to be not gaseous as shown in Figure 10.2.1. Its mass (and pressure) is sufficiently high that the bulk of the planet may be in the form of metallic hydrogen[28]—hydrogen in a liquid state, but at sufficiently high pressures that if the electrons are stripped of the hydrogen and the resulting fluid is able to be an electrical conductor. Metallic hydrogen would support the very strong magnetic field of Jupiter, which is ten times stronger[29] than the terrestrial magnetic field. At its very center, there is most likely a core made of rock and heavy elements or compounds that is possibly the size of the Earth.

Jupiter[30] has a huge variety of processes associated with it, including fast rotation (a period of 10.6 hours); a magnetosphere that is larger than the Sun; aurora[31]s that completely outshine the terrestrial auroras; giant atmospheric storms, including the Giant Red Spot[32] that lasted for decades to centuries; and radiation belts[33] significantly more lethal than the terrestrial radiation belts. Jupiter has been visited by several flyby missions, including *Pioneer* 10[34], *Pioneer* 11[35], *Voyager* 1[36], *Voyager* 2[37], *Ulysses*[38], *Cassini*[39], and *New Horizons*[40]. There has been only one mission that has gone into orbit around Jupiter: the *Galileo*[41] orbiter, though a second mission, called *Juno*[42], is expected to arrive in 2016.

---

30   http://en.wikipedia.org/wiki/Jupiter
31   https://www.google.com/search?q=jupiter+aurora&hl=en&qscrl=1&rlz=1T4GGHP_enUS524US526&source=lnms&tbm=isch&sa=X&ei=ycFEUYfyOoHJrQGyjYDoDA&sqi=2&ved=0CAcQ_AUoAQ&biw=1151&bih=689
32   https://www.google.com/search?q=jupiter+aurora&hl=en&qscrl=1&rlz=1T4GGHP_enUS524US526&source=lnms&tbm=isch&sa=X&ei=ycFEUYfyOoHJrQGyjYDoDA&sqi=2&ved=0CAcQ_AUoAQ&biw=1151&bih=689
33   http://airandspace.si.edu/exhibitions/exploring-the-planets/online/jupiter/jupmag.html
34   http://en.wikipedia.org/wiki/Pioneer_10
35   http://en.wikipedia.org/wiki/Pioneer_11
36   http://en.wikipedia.org/wiki/Voyager_1
37   http://en.wikipedia.org/wiki/Voyager_2
38   http://en.wikipedia.org/wiki/Ulysses_probe
39   http://en.wikipedia.org/wiki/Cassini%E2%80%93Huygens
40   http://en.wikipedia.org/wiki/New_Horizons
41   http://en.wikipedia.org/wiki/Galileo_spacecraft
42   http://en.wikipedia.org/wiki/Juno_(spacecraft)

---

26   https://www.uta.edu/planetarium/astronomy-101/ask-the-astronomer/qa.php?question=29
27   http://en.wikipedia.org/wiki/Brown_dwarf
28   http://en.wikipedia.org/wiki/Metallic_hydrogen
29   http://www.universetoday.com/15185/jupiters-magnetic-field/

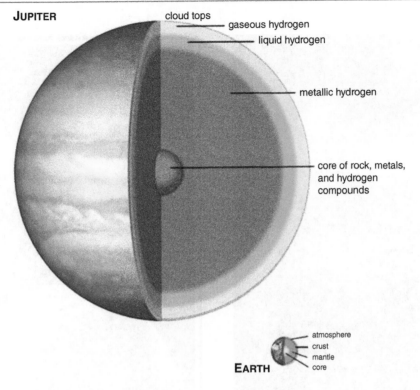

FIGURE 10.2.1. INTERNAL STRUCTURE OF JUPITER[43].

The fact that it is a gas giant means that the planet itself will not be explored. The moons of Jupiter, however, are a different story. Jupiter has 67 confirmed moons[44] and counting (as of 2013). Some of these moons have only been discovered[45] in the last couple of years as more powerful telescopes come online. The bulk of these moons are irregular satellites that have high-inclination orbits and eccentricities, and are thought to be captured asteroids or comets. There are only eight moons with regular orbits which probably formed early in the history of Jupiter. Of these eight moons, four of them form the inner group and have diameters less than 200 km and orbit within about one radii of the planet. The other four are called the Galilean moons, after their discovery by Galileo Galilei. These moons orbit from around six Jovian radii out to about 26 Jovian radii. They are so large that they are bigger than the dwarf planets

of our solar system and can be seen with an amateur telescope (as seen in Figure 10.2.2). If you have access to such a telescope, we highly recommended trying to see Jupiter if the time of year is correct.

It is these Galilean satellites that are most likely to be explored over the next few decades. They are home to some of the best examples of fire and ice outside the Earth and possibly offer the best potential for discovering life beyond our planet. High-resolution images of the four Galilean moons are shown in Figure 10.2.3.

Io[46] is the innermost of the Galilean satellites. Io sits at about six Jovian radii and is in an orbital resonance[47] with two of the other three Galilean moons. This means that every two times that Io orbits Jupiter, Europa orbits once, and for every four Io orbits around Jupiter, Ganymede orbits once. This alignment of orbits means that Io is constantly in a gravitational

43   http://www.lpi.usra.edu/education/explore/
solar_system/background/

44   http://en.wikipedia.org/wiki/Moons_of_Jupiter

45   http://news.nationalgeographic.com/
news/2012/02/120202-new-moons-jupiter-satellites-
swarm-space-science/

46   http://en.wikipedia.org/wiki/Io_moon

47   http://upload.wikimedia.org/wikipedia/
commons/8/83/Galilean_moon_Laplace_resonance_
animation.gif

FIGURE 10.2.2. THE GALILEAN MOONS[48] AS SEEN THROUGH AN AMATEUR TELESCOPE.

tug-of-war with   Jupiter, pulling on it from one side and either Europa or Ganymede pulling on it from the other. These gravitational forces flex and heat the interior of Io, leading to a partially molten interior and active volcanism. In fact, Io is the most volcanically active body in the solar system—more active than Earth!

These volcanoes produce not only sulfur-rich lava flows on the surface but also plumes of gas extending 100s of km above the surface [7] (Figure 10.2.4). The red, orange, and white features in the images are from condensed sulfur and frozen sulfur dioxide.

The gas in the plumes can become ionized by solar UV radiation or local high-energy particles. Once it becomes ionized, the gas becomes a plasma that is tied to the Jovian magnetic field, forming a torus of plasma at Io's orbit. Through this process, an average of

48 http://astronomyonline.org/solarsystem/
galileanmoons.asp

FIGURE 10.2.3. THE GALILEAN MOONS OF JUPITER: IO (LEFT); EUROPA, GANYMEDE, AND CALLISTO (RIGHT).

FIGURE 10.2.4. Volcanism on Io. Left-hand side shows the surface is covered with volcanoes (dark regions). Right-hand side shows a superimposed image of a gas plume from a volcanic eruption that extends hundreds of km into space. A full video of Io can be seen at http://www.youtube.com/watch?v=AHBe8F7akvw[49–50].

one ton/s of plasma is loaded into the Jovian magnetosphere [8]. The interaction of the plasma from Io with the Jovian magnetic field also modulates the radio emissions produced by Jupiter. Through radio observations of Jupiter, we can remotely detect Io and when it is volcanically active.

While Io is a high-priority target due to its active volcanism, it will be a hard place to explore because of its presence deep within the radiation belts of Jupiter. There may be robotic missions in the very distant future. One such scenario can be seen at http://www.youtube.com/watch?v=07aNZUhjrSQ. However, the requirements for going into orbit and landing on its surface are huge and beyond anything that is feasible with chemical rockets. Exploration

will have to wait for developments in advanced propulsion systems.

The next moon out is the icy body, Europa[51]. It sits at about 9.4 Jovian radii and has a radius of 2410 km—nearly 40% of that of Earth. The moon consists of rock and water very much like the Earth, and the components have separated out to have the internal structure shown in Figure 10.2.5. This includes a metallic core and a rocky interior. The surface is covered in water ice. The ice thickness is estimated to be a 100–200 km thick. As such, it contains more water than the Earth's oceans.

Even more tantalizing is that this ice is not stationary. This comes from observations of a region on the surface called the Conamara Chaos. The Conamara Chaos is a region in the icy crust in which it appears that the crust was broken apart into ice floes that rearranged themselves and then refroze into place (Figure 10.2.6). Had the melting occurred due to an impact, then the original terrain that can be seen in the form of ridges would have been erased in the impact. Instead, the fact that

49 http://lasp.colorado.edu/education/outerplanets/moons_galilean.php

50 http://www.google.com/url?sa=i&source=images&cd=&cad=rja&docid=byiRWCmOeLSuSM&tbnid=QMidjr7xBaVnEM:&ved=0CAgQjRwwAA&url=http://starchild.gsfc.nasa.gov/docs/StarChild/solar_system_level2/io_volcano.html&ei=vvdEUerUE8qLqwH-r4HIDg&psig=AFQjCNFiTTky2W0A9k0D0wnaZnBCZdwmig&ust=1363560766367780

51 http://en.wikipedia.org/wiki/Europa_(moon)

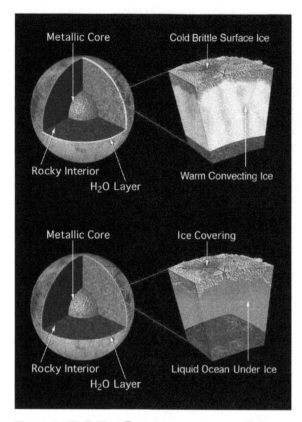

Metallic Core   Cold Brittle Surface Ice

Rocky Interior
H₂O Layer   Warm Convecting Ice

Metallic Core   Ice Covering

Rocky Interior
H₂O Layer   Liquid Ocean Under Ice

FIGURE 10.2.5. POSSIBLE INTERIOR OF EUROPA. EUROPA HAS THE POTENTIAL FOR A LIQUID WATER OCEAN UNDERNEATH ITS ICY CRUST[52].

much of the original terrain remains intact implies[52] that the region was heated from below. The question of what heated the ice from below is still an open question, but Europa undergoes the same type of orbital resonance that Io experiences, just to a lesser degree. Every other orbit Europa makes around Jupiter will have Jupiter and Io gravitationally tugging on it from one side and Ganymede tugging on it from the other. As this process leads to volcanism on Io, it is thought that Europa could possess volcanoes too, but these would be under the ice layer.

The ridges are created by the gravitational tug-of-war that Europa undergoes. The gravitational forces cause the ice to flex and crack. The ridges form when liquid or slushy material squirts up from below (Figure 10.2.6). This process allows us to get a sense for what the

subsurface material may be like. The ice near the ridges appears to be colored—this discoloring is associated with salts from below (like magnesium) being deposited on the surface.

Other evidence that there are oceans on Europa comes from the observations of an induced magnetosphere around Europa, produced by the sweeping of the Jovian magnetic field around the moon. When a changing magnetic field interacts with a conductor, a magnetic field will be induced in that conductor. The *Galileo* spacecraft observed a magnetic field around Europa that could only be an induced magnetic field being generated at the moon [9]. This appears to be further evidence of a briny subsurface ocean[53] at Europa.

The presence of oceans on Europa is not only important in itself, but there is also the possibility of extraterrestrial life[54]. This suggestion comes from the fact that life has been detected on Earth under similar conditions expected to be present on Europa, despite the extreme conditions. This includes the detection of life around the Earth's deep ocean hydrothermal vents and underneath the frozen Lake Vostok in Antarctica. The question then becomes, will we find a similar ecosystem in the subsurface oceans of Europa?

Because of the high potential for the detection of extraterrestrial life, Europa will remain a high-priority target. Possible mission scenarios to Europa can be seen at http://www.youtube.com/watch?v=kPPnPcPBNQg. The main features of such a mission require a spacecraft to make a soft landing on the surface and then deploy a "drill" to penetrate the surface. This drill will probably consist of some type of nuclear reactor, where the heat will melt the ice and allow the drill to fall through the ice. Since the ice is possibly 100 km thick [4], a tether will have to be deployed to allow communication with the surface from whence the data is either directly beamed back to Earth or transmitted to an orbital spacecraft, which then beams the

---

52   http://www.lpl.arizona.edu/undergrad/classes/spring2011/Hubbard_206/Lectures3/Mar24.htm

53   http://www.nature.com/nature/journal/v395/n6704/full/395777a0.html
54   http://en.wikipedia.org/wiki/Europa_(moon)

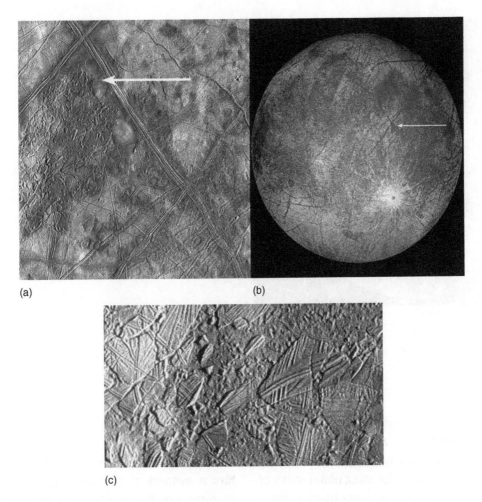

(a)   (b)

(c)

FIGURE 10.2.6. FORMATION AND MOVEMENT OF ICE RIDGES ON EUROPA. ON THE LEFT IS THE CONAMARA CHAOS REGION, IN WHICH RIDGES ARE BROKEN UP. IN THE MIDDLE IS AN UNDISTURBED REGION OF RIDGES. ON THE RIGHT IS A SCHEMATIC OF HOW THE ICE RIDGES ARE BELIEVED TO FORM[55].

information back. The vehicle will also have to withstand huge pressures of being under huge amounts of ice and water. On Earth, going to the bottom of the deepest oceans remains problematic, so trying in space at much larger depths also seems problematic. All the while, everything we send will have to be perfectly sterile so as not to potentially contaminate Europa with terrestrial life.

At this time, we are very far from being able to launch such a system cost effectively, let alone the cost of effectively going into orbit around Europa and softly landing a

several-hundred-kg payload on its surface. But hopefully in the near future (say two to three decades), these issues may be overcome so that when a mission does occur, we might be able to address the question of whether we are alone in the solar system.

Ganymede[56] is the third of the Galilean moons. It is the largest of these moons, with a diameter of 5268 km, and it sits at 15 Jovian radii. Ganymede has a composition that is very similar to that of Europa, except the question of an ocean remains a topic of debate. It is also the only moon we know of in the solar system with a global magnetic field. This magnetic field

55   http://lasp.colorado.edu/education/outerplanets/moons_galilean.php

56   http://en.wikipedia.org/wiki/Ganymede_(moon)

(a)

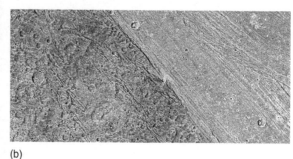

(b)

FIGURE 10.2.7.   A) A TRUE COLOR IMAGE OF GANYMEDE AND B) A ZOOMED IN IMAGE OF THE DICOTOMY BETWEEN THE DARK, HEAVILY CRATERED REGIONS (LEFT) AND THE LIGHT, GROOVED REGIONS (RIGHT).

is supported by an interior that is fully differentiated and most likely with an iron-rich liquid core. This core is surrounded by an inner rocky mantle (which accounts for most of the mass of the moon), and a warm icy outer mantle and a cold ice crust.

This ice crust differs from that seen at Europa in that it is heavily cratered, such that it more closely resembles the Moon. There are two different regions as shown in Figure 10.2.7. The darker regions are heavily cratered, indicating that those regions are billions of years in age. The surface appears dark due to dusk from micrometeorites. The lighter surfaces formed in a similar fashion as the mares on the Moon from the upwelling from the interior, which flooded or resurfaced some of the older regions before resolidifying. One difference from the Moon, however, is that the upwelling material is not lava, but rather liquid water.

In addition to these regions, it can be seen that the equator is darker than the polar regions. This difference (Figure 10.2.8) appears to be associated with the magnetic field of Ganymede. Plasma from the Jovian magnetosphere can impact the polar regions

of Ganymede, eroding the surface and leaving it a lighter color.

Another important feature is that Ganymede has a system of grooves and ridges. These features are thought to arise from processes similar to plate tectonics, like what occurs on Europa. If this hypothesis is correct, there is the possibility that liquid water may be present in the near-surface region. Moreover, the presence of Ganymede's magnetic field means that there is some radiation shielding, so there is potential for life in the near surface.

At this time, the priority for surface exploration of Ganymede would be lower than that of Europa because of the latter's subsurface oceans. However, if missions like *Juno* show that Ganymede's liquid water is closer to the surface than currently believed, this prioritization may change. Presently, the best estimate for surface exploration of Ganymede is probably not until the next century.

The outermost Galilean moon is Callisto[57], sitting at 26 Jovian radii. It is the third largest moon in the solar system and is only fractionally smaller than Ganymede. It is made up of

---

57   http://en.wikipedia.org/wiki/Callisto_(moon)

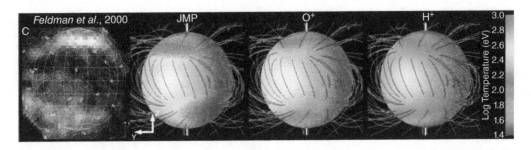

FIGURE 10.2.8. HST IMAGE OF AURORA ON GANYMEDE COMPARED WITH PREDICTIONS FOR THE MAGNETIC FIELD OF GANYMEDE [10][58].

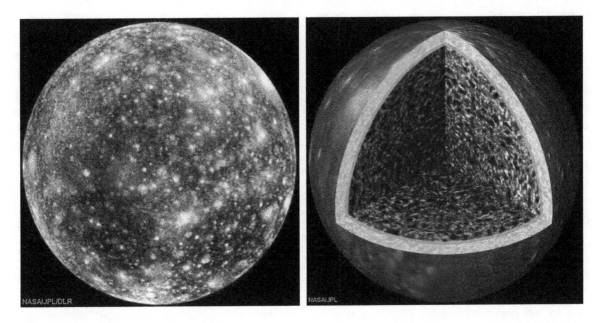

FIGURE 10.2.9. GANYMEDE: SURFACE AND INTERIOR. A HIGH-RESOLUTION IMAGE OF GANYMEDE'S SURFACE CAN BE SEEN AT THIS LINK[59–60].

ice and rock, similar to Ganymede, but it differs from Ganymede in that the material is non-differentiated as illustrated in Figure 10.2.9. The surface is highly cratered and appears very similar to Mercury's surface. This means that Callisto has had little geological activity since its formation. There is the potential of a liquid water layer between the crust and the undifferentiated mantle.

As far as surface exploration is concerned, Callisto has probably the lowest priority of all the Galilean moons. However, the fact that the surface is undifferentiated may mean that there is easier access to rocky material and hence the possibility of rare earth elements. Thus, there is the potential that Callisto may jump levels in the priority listings as more detailed data becomes available. Callisto may also have the best justification of having sufficient resources available for terra-forming, although such efforts are unlikely for the next couple of centuries.

58   http://www.ess.washington.edu/Space/SpaceModel/ganymede.html

59   http://www.lpi.usra.edu/galileoAnniv/img/hiRes/call-hemi.jpg

60   http://www.whillyard.com/science-pages/our-solar-system/callisto.html

10.3. Saturn and Its Moons

Saturn[61] is probably the most spectacular planet in the solar system with its rings[62] that extend from 7,000 km to 80,000 km above Saturn's equatorial surface. These rings can be seen with today's amateur telescopes (and again, we highly recommend to readers that if they have access to such a telescope to try viewing them yourself on an appropriate night). The rings were discovered by Christiaan Huygens[63] in 1655.

Saturn was first visited by *Pioneer* 11[64] in 1979. This mission sent back images of Saturn's cloud tops, icy rings, and some characteristics of a few of its moons. Shortly after, it was visited by *Voyager* 1[65] in 1980 (with a close flyby of Titan) and *Voyager* 2[66] in 1981 (with detailed observations of Saturn's atmosphere and rings). The latter missions identified new rings and moons that had not been previously identified by terrestrial telescopes.

The first and only mission to go into orbit around Saturn is the *Cassini–Huygens*[67] spacecraft, which arrived at Saturn in 2004. This mission has been providing continuous data to the present moment (2013) and with new findings available at this link[68].

The general properties of the planet are listed in Table 10.2. Saturn has almost the same composition as Jupiter and is only fractionally smaller in radius. However, despite the relatively small change in diameter, there are significant differences in the interior structure, as shown in Figure 10.3.1. In particular, the region of metallic hydrogen is very much smaller, and as a result, the magnetic field of

Table 10.2. General properties of Saturn.

Mass[1]	5.7×10^{26} kg
Average Distance from the Sun[1]	9.5 AU
Length of Day in Earth Days[1]	0.44
Length of Year in Earth Years[1]	29.5
Orbital Eccentricity[1]	0.056
Cloud Top Mean Temperature[1]	88 K
Radius	60,300 km
Atmospheric Composition[1]	97% H, 3% He, 0.05% CH_4

Saturn is much weaker, being only a twentieth of Jupiter's field, or slightly larger than the terrestrial magnetic field. The magnetosphere around Saturn is correspondingly smaller as are the radiation belts, but Saturn is still subject to intense auroras (Figure 10.3.2).

The atmosphere of Saturn is also very similar to that of Jupiter as shown in Figure 10.3.3. The lower atmosphere has water clouds, while at higher altitudes, there are clouds of ammonium hydrosulfide and ammonia. These latter clouds give Saturn and Jupiter their yellowish and red tinges. Uranus and Neptune, in comparison, are much colder, with methane atmospheres and a blue tinge.

Another similarity between Saturn and Jupiter is that both have a large number of moons. The present count for Saturn is 62 moons thus far identified. The position and images of some of the moons are shown in Figure 10.3.4. Identification of the moons is somewhat difficult as the moons found recently have been small, and it is hard to determine the difference between a moon and a large orbiting ice chunk. As such, these moons have been given numbers instead of names.

The composition of these moons, though, is very different from those of Jupiter. These differences make Saturn a continued destination for studies in the future. Some of the more interesting moons are discussed below. A gallery of images and information on most of the moons can be seen at http://saturn.jpl.nasa.gov/science/moons/.

61   http://www.explanet.info/Chapter10.htm
62   http://en.wikipedia.org/wiki/Rings_of_Saturn
63   http://en.wikipedia.org/wiki/Christiaan_Huygens
64   http://en.wikipedia.org/wiki/Pioneer_11
65   http://en.wikipedia.org/wiki/Voyager_1
66   http://en.wikipedia.org/wiki/Voyager_2
67   http://en.wikipedia.org/wiki/Cassini%E2%80%93Huygens
68   http://saturn.jpl.nasa.gov/

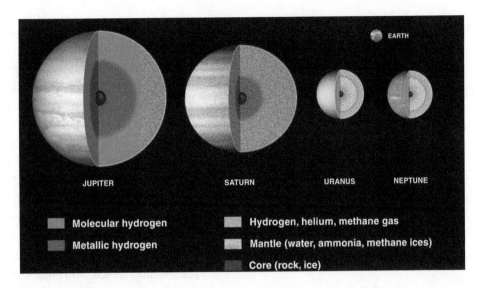

FIGURE 10.3.1. INTERIOR STRUCTURE OF THE OUTER PLANETS.

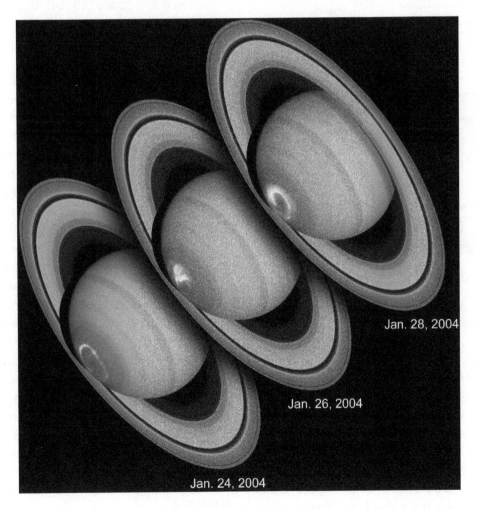

FIGURE 10.3.2. HUBBLE TELESCOPE IMAGES OF THE AURORAS ON SATURN.

a) Jupiter Tropospheric Profile

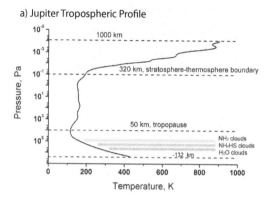

b) Uranus Tropospheric Profile

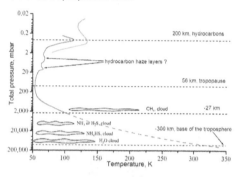

c) Interior Composition of the Outer Planets

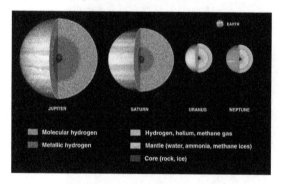

FIGURE 10.3.3. ATMOSPHERIC PROFILES FOR JUPITER AND URANUS, AS WELL AS MODELS OF INTERIOR COMPOSITION FOR THE FOUR LARGEST PLANETS IN THE SOLAR SYSTEM.

The moon Mimas[69] (Figure 10.3.5a) is nicknamed the Death Star due to a large cratering, giving it a striking resemblance to the structure in the *Star Wars* films. It has a diameter of only 400 km and is mainly water ice, with a small amount of rock. It is responsible for creating the gap between the A and B rings of Saturn.

Iapetus[70] also has a large impact crater (Figure10.3.5b), but it also has a curious ridge

structure running along its equator. The origin of this ridge structure is still a mystery to scientists, with many hypotheses suggesting it is associated with a complex formation scenario (such as an early rapid rotation [11] or a ring system of its own [12]). The optical dichotomy of bright white polar regions and trailing hemisphere versus dark brown/red leading hemisphere is believed to be the result of uneven heating of the surface by the Sun. Iapetus's slow rotation (79 days) is believed to result in an uneven sublimation of ice from the surface, with the dark material being a lag (or residue) of organic compounds left behind when the water ice in the region evaporated into space [13, 14]. But even these moons cannot compete with their sisters, Enceladus[71] and Titan[72], when it comes to capturing our imagination.

The flybys of Enceladus[73] by the *Voyager* missions showed the moon to have a relatively youthful surface when compared to the other moons nearby [15, 16]. This, plus the fact that Enceladus is centrally located in the E-ring, leads scientists to believe that Enceladus is somehow the source of the material in the E-ring [15]. But how? It wasn't until *Cassini* arrived at Saturn almost 25 years later that the mystery would begin to be solved. The first image *Cassini* took of Enceladus is shown in Figure 10.3.6a. Initially, scientists and engineers thought the wispy feature above the surface of the moon was an image artifact and not real, so they did not immediately release the image. It was only after subsequent images were taken that showed the same feature that scientists understood it was real. But what is it? Subsequent flythroughs of the material by

69   http://saturn.jpl.nasa.gov/science/moons/mimas/
70   http://saturn.jpl.nasa.gov/science/moons/iapetus/

71   http://saturn.jpl.nasa.gov/science/moons/enceladus/
72   http://saturn.jpl.nasa.gov/science/index.cfm?SciencePageID=73
73   http://saturn.jpl.nasa.gov/science/moons/enceladus/

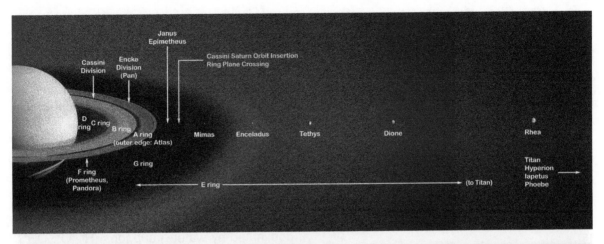

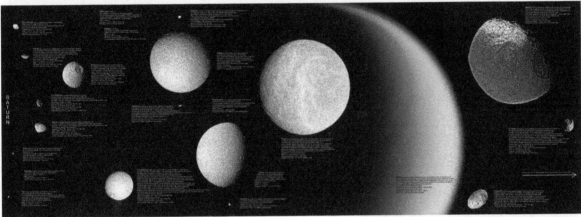

FIGURE 10.3.4. POSITION AND IMAGES OF SOME OF THE MOONS ABOUT SATURN.

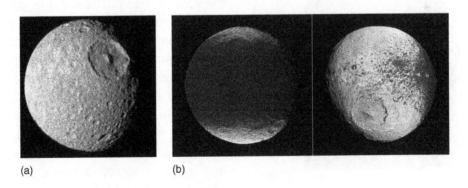

(a)   (b)

FIGURE 10.3.5. IMAGES OF (A) MIMAS AND (B) IAPETUS.

Cassini showed that it is a collection of jets of water and organic material being shot out of the surface of the moon. The material also seems to be originating from a formation in the icy surface of the southern hemisphere, dubbed the tiger stripes (Figure 10.3.6b). Thermal imaging of the tiger stripes indicates they are warmer than the surrounding ice (Figure 10.3.6c). But with a maximum temperature at the center of the stripes no more than 160 K (well below the melting point of water) [17], it is still unknown what physical process can produce the jets of water coming from the tiger stripes [18]. The observations of the jets from the tiger stripes

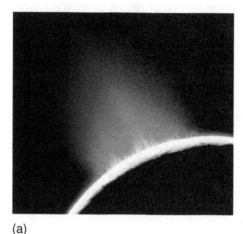

(a)

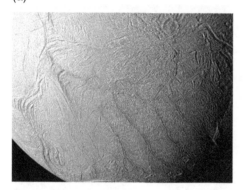

(b)

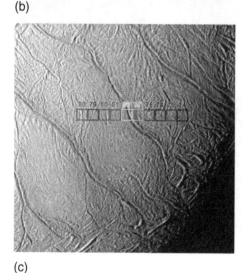

(c)

FIGURE 10.3.6. (A) CYROVOLCANOES ON ENCELADUS; (B) TIGER STRIPES OR CRACKS IN THE ICE SURFACE; AND (C) A CLOSE-UP OF THE TIGER STRIPES.

did help us gain insight into one question scientists were stumped by upon orbital insertion of *Cassini*—namely, why is the Kronian magnetosphere so saturated with water-group ions?

Saturn's moon Titan[74] is so large that it is slightly larger than Mercury—making it planet size. (Video of Titan at this link.)[75] Its classification as a moon only comes about due to its orbiting Saturn and not the Sun. Titan is the only moon in the solar system with a thick atmosphere. The base of Titan's atmosphere[76] is mostly nitrogen. It is for this reason that scientists initially believed that the magnetosphere of Saturn should be permeated with nitrogen ions. Instead, they see a magnetosphere dominated by water-group ions (H^+, O^+, OH^+), which we now know most likely originated from Enceladus.

But this does not mean Titan is not without importance. Its thick atmosphere of methane and ethane are believed to be similar to that of the early Earth's atmosphere, prior to photosynthetic life converting it to an oxygen-rich atmosphere [19, 20]. It is for this reason, in addition to the observation of complex hydrocarbons in its atmosphere, that Titan is of great interest to astrobiologists. With a mean temperature of 94 K [21], it is probably too cold for life to exist on the surface of a current-day Titan, but as we saw with the moons of Jupiter, the surface may not be the only place that life could be found. The temperature does mean that methane and ethane can condense out of the atmosphere into a liquid, potentially forming lakes or rivers of liquid methane.

Titan's thick methane/ethane atmosphere leads to the formation of a smog-like layer covering the entire planet (Figure 10.3.7a). This makes it impossible to see the surface using only passive remote-sensing techniques. In order to see the surface, we need to either land something or use radar—both of which have been done by *Cassini*. The *Cassini* spacecraft carried with it a probe called *Huygens* that was designed to land on the surface of Titan soon after *Cassini* arrived at Saturn. Not only was

(a)   (b)

FIGURE 10.3.7. (A) OPTICAL IMAGE OF TITAN. ITS METHANE ATMOSPHERE PRE-VENTS IMAGING OF ITS SURFACE. (B) *HUYGENS* LANDER IMAGE OF TITAN'S SURFACE, SHOWING PEBBLES OF WATER ICE.

Huygens designed to land on the surface, take pictures, and make other scientific measurements on its way through Titan's atmosphere, it was also designed to float! Because we could not see the region *Huygens* would be landing in, we had no idea if it might be a methane lake or a dry surface. The landing site turned out to be a dry surface (Figure 10.3.7b) surrounded by boulders made of water ice and as hard as concrete. When *Huygens* landed, the science instruments detected a brief burst of water vapor, suggesting the probe, hot from entry in the atmosphere, melted an ice crust below it, partially sinking into the surface.

While *Huygens* failed to see any evidence of methane lakes, subsequent radar measurements by *Cassini* did. Figure 10.3.8a shows a full radar mapping of one hemisphere of Titan. High-resolution radar mapping of the north pole (Figure 10.3.8b) (and later the south pole) showed regions of low radar return, the same behavior expected when imaging a liquid surface. These results were interpreted to mean methane lakes with sizes comparable to or larger than the Great Lakes existed in the polar regions of Titan [22]. That the features were lakes of liquid methane or ethane was later confirmed when *Cassini* observed sunlight glint off the surface of Titan [23]—a process that only happens when sunlight reflects off a liquid surface.

Similar to Jupiter, the moons of Saturn are expected to remain as high-priority targets for a deeper understanding of the origins of life and the solar system, as plans for future missions[77] to Titan have been developed. Unfortunately, the potential for a new mission to arrive at Saturn is probably 30 years away. In the very long time frame of a couple of centuries, the huge water and organic compound resources may be of interest for planetary resource utilization.

---

77 http://www.jpl.nasa.gov/video/index.php?id=810

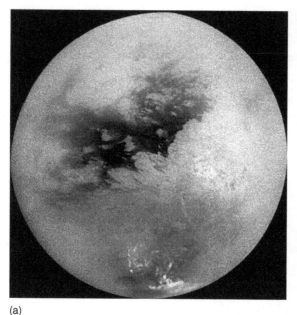

(a)

(b)

FIGURE 10.3.8. RADAR IMAGES OF TITAN (A) FULL DISK AND (B) CLOSE-UP OF METHANE LAKES.

10.4 The Future

With this, we conclude our grand tour of the solar system and investigation of how we could explore it—both robotically and with humans. As we, the human race, decide where we should explore and how often we explore, the question is not just about science discovery and what is technologically possible. It is also one regarding the track that the human species takes. Our past history has shown that it is someone or several people, pushing the boundaries, trying to accomplish something new or go someplace uncharted that leads to the advances that allow us to take that next step. It is a discovery fortuitously happening that allows us to chart a new course. You, dear reader, get to help us decide: Where is that next step going to take us?

Other Reading:

[1]　http://pds.jpl.nasa.gov/planets/special/planets.htm

[2]　Horner, J., & Jones, B. W. (2010). "Jupiter: Friend or foe? III: The Oort Cloud comets," *International Journal of Astrobiology*, 9 (1).

[3]　Schenk, P. M., Chapman, C. R., Zahnle, K., and Moore, J. M. (2004). *Chapter 18: Ages and Interiors: The Cratering Record of the Galilean Satellites*[78]. In *Jupiter: The Planet, Satellites and Magnetosphere* Cambridge University Press.

[4]　Hubbard, W. B. (1977). The Jovian surface condition and cooling rate[79], *Icarus*, 30, (2), 305–310.

78　http://books.google.ca/books?id=8GcGRXlmxWsC&pg=PA427
79　http://www.sciencedirect.com/science/article/pii/0019103577901646

[5] Bagenal, F., Dowling, T., & McKinnon, W. (Eds.). (2004). *Jupiter: The planet, satellites and magnetosphere*. Cambridge University Press.

[6] http://news.nationalgeographic.com/news/2007/05/070502-volcano-io.html

[7] Schneider, N. M., & Bagenal, F. (2007). "Io's neutral clouds, plasma torus, and magnetospheric interactions." In Lopes, R. M. C., & Spencer, J. R. *Io after Galileo*. Springer-Praxis. pp. 265–286.

ISBN: 3-540-34681-3[80].

[8] Khurana, K. K., et al. (1998). Induced magnetic fields as evidence for subsurface oceans in Europa and Callisto, *Nature*, 395, 777–780, doi:10.1038/27394

[9] Paty, C., & Winglee, R. (2004). Multi-fluid simulations of Ganymede's magnetosphere, *Geophys. Res. Lett.*, 31, *L24806*,

doi:10.1029/2004GL021220[81]

[10] Kerr, R. A. (2006-01-06). "How Saturn's Icy Moons Get a (Geologic) Life." *Science* 311 (5757): 29.

doi: 10.1126/science.311.5757.29[82].

PMID[83]: 16400121[84]

[11] Ip, W.-H. (2006). *On a ring origin of the equatorial ridge of Iapetus. Geophysical Research Letters*, Volume 33, L16203,

doi:10.1029/2005GL025386[85]

[12] Denk, T., et al. (2010-01-22). "Iapetus: Unique Surface Properties and a Global Color Dichotomy from *Cassini* Imaging." *Science*[86] (AAAS[87]) 327 (5964): 435–439.

Bibcode: 2010Sci … 327..435D[88].

doi:10.1126/science.1177088[89].

PMID: 20007863[90]

[13] Spencer, J. R., & Denk, T. (2010-01-22). "Formation of Iapetus' Extreme Albedo Dichotomy by Exogenically Triggered Thermal Ice Migration." *Science*[91] (AAAS) 327 (5964): 432–435.

Bibcode: 2010Sci … 327..432S[92].

doi:10.1126/science.1177132[93].

PMID: 20007862[94].

[14] Terrile, R. J., & Cook, A. F. (1981). *Enceladus: Evolution and Possible Relationship to Saturn's E-Ring*[95]. 12th Annual Lunar and Planetary Science Conference, Abstract 428.

[15] Rothery, D. A. (1999). *Satellites of the Outer Planets: Worlds in their own right*. Oxford University Press.

80 http://en.wikipedia.org/wiki/Special:BookSources/3-540-34681-3
81 http://dx.doi.org/10.1029/2004GL021220
82 http://dx.doi.org/10.1126%2Fscience.311.5757.29
83 http://en.wikipedia.org/wiki/PubMed_Identifier
84 http://www.ncbi.nlm.nih.gov/pubmed/16400121
85 http://dx.doi.org/10.1029%2F2005GL025386

86 http://en.wikipedia.org/wiki/Science_%28journal%29
87 http://en.wikipedia.org/wiki/American_Association_for_the_Advancement_of_Science
88 http://adsabs.harvard.edu/abs/2010Sci … 327..435D
89 http://dx.doi.org/10.1126%2Fscience.1177088
90 http://www.ncbi.nlm.nih.gov/pubmed/20007863
91 http://en.wikipedia.org/wiki/Science_%28journal%29
92 http://adsabs.harvard.edu/abs/2010Sci … 327..432S
93 http://dx.doi.org/10.1126%2Fscience.1177132
94 http://www.ncbi.nlm.nih.gov/pubmed/20007862
95 http://articles.adsabs.harvard.edu//full/seri/LPICo/0428//0000010.000.html

[16] Brown, R. H., et al. (2006). Composition and physical properties of the Enceladus surface, *Nature*, 311, (5766), 1425–1428.

[17] Waite Jr., J. H., et al. (2006). *Cassini* ion and neutral mass spectrometer: Enceladus plume composition and structure, *Nature*, 311 (5766), 1419–1422.

[18] Kasting, J. F., and Howard, M. T. (2006). Atmospheric composition and climate on the early Earth, *Phil. Trans. R. Soc. B,* 361 (1474), 1733–1742.

    doi: 10.1098/rstb.2006.190

[19] Trainer, M. G., et al. (2006). Organic haze on Titan and the early Earth, *PNAS*, 103, (48), 18035–18042.

[20] Mitri, G., Showman, A. P., Lunine, J. I., & Lorenz, R. D. (2007). "Hydrocarbon Lakes on Titan," *Icarus* 186 (2): 385–394.

    Bibcode: 2007Icar..186..385M[96]

    doi:10.1016/j.icarus.2006.09.004[97].

[21] Stofan, E. R.[98], Elachi, C., et al. (January 4, 2007). "The lakes of Titan." *Nature* 445 (1): 61–64.

    Bibcode: 2007Natur.445 … 61S[99]

    doi:10.1038/nature05438[100].

    PMID: 17203056[101].

[22] http://www.nasa.gov/mission_pages/cassini/whycassini/cassini20091217.html

Image Credits

Chapter 10 Opening Image: NASA, Holland Ford (JHU), the ACS Science Team and ESA, "Hubble's newest camera images ghostly star-forming pillar of gas," http://www.space-telescope.org/images/heic0206c/. Copyright in the Public Domain.

Figure 10.1.1: NASA/JPL-Caltech/JAXA/ESA, "Comparative Sizes of 9 Asteroids," http://www.nasa.gov/multimedia/im-agegallery/image_feature_2010.html. Copyright in the Public Domain.

Figure 10.2.1: Lunar and Planetary Institute, "Internal Structure of Jupiter," http://www.nasa.gov/mission_pages/juno/education/explore.html. Copyright © 2012 by Lunar and Planetary Institute. Reprinted with permission.

Figure 10.2.2: Copyright © stewartde (CC BY-SA 2.0) at http://commons.wikimedia.org/wiki/File:Jupiter_and_Galilean_moons.jpg

Figure 10.2.3: NASA, "Galilean Moons from Voyager," http://commons.wikimedia.org/wiki/File:Galilean_moons_from_Voyager.jpg. Copyright in the Public Domain.

Figure 10.2.4a: NASA, "Iosurface gal," http://commons.wikimedia.org/wiki/File:Iosurface_gal.jpg. Copyright in the Public Domain.

Figure 10.2.4b: NASA, "PIA00703," http://commons.wikimedia.org/wiki/File:PIA00703.jpg. Copyright in the Public Domain.

Figure 10.2.5: JPL, "EuropaInterior1," https://commons.wikimedia.org/wiki/File:EuropaInterior1.jpg. Copyright in the Public Domain.

Figure 10.2.6: NASA, "Europa's Chaos Terrains," http://svs.gsfc.nasa.gov/vis/a010000/a011100/a011176/. Copyright in the Public Domain.

Figure 10.2.7a: NASA, "Ganymede g1 true," http://commons.wikimedia.org/wiki/File:Ganymede_g1_true.jpg. Copyright in the Public Domain.

Figure 10.2.7b: NASA, "Ganymede terrain," http://commons.wikimedia.org/wiki/File:Ganymede_terrain.jpg. Copyright in the Public Domain.

Figure 10.2.8: Feldman, et al., "Ganymede temperatures," http://earthweb.ess.washington.edu/space/SpaceModel/ganymede/ganymede.jpg. Copyright © 2000 by John Wiley & Sons, Inc.

Figure 10.2.9a: NASA/JPL/DLR, "Callisto," http://whillyard.com/science-pages/our-solar-system/upload-images/jupiter-moon-callisto-1.jpg. Copyright in the Public Domain.

Figure 10.2.9b: NASA/JPL, "Callisto, with interior cut," http://whillyard.com/science-pages/our-solar-system/upload-images/jupiter-moon-callisto-2.jpg. Copyright in the Public Domain.

Figure 10.3.1: NASA, "Gas Giant Interiors," http://commons.wikimedia.org/wiki/File:Gas_Giant_Interiors.jpg. Copyright in the Public Domain.

---

96   http://adsabs.harvard.edu/abs/2007Icar..186..385M

97   http://dx.doi.org/10.1016%2Fj.icarus.2006.09.004

98   http://en.wikipedia.org/wiki/Ellen_Stofan

99   http://adsabs.harvard.edu/abs/2007Natur.445 … 61S

100   http://dx.doi.org/10.1038%2Fnature05438

101   http://www.ncbi.nlm.nih.gov/pubmed/17203056

Figure 10.3.2: NASA/ESA, "Saturn.Aurora.HST.UV-Vis," http://commons.wikimedia.org/wiki/File:Saturn.Aurora.HST.UV-Vis.jpg. Copyright in the Public Domain.

Figure 10.3.3a: Copyright © Ruslik0 (CC BY-SA 3.0) at http://en.wikipedia.org/wiki/File:Structure_of_Jovian_atmosphere.png

Figure 10.3.3b: Copyright © Ruslik0 (CC BY-SA 3.0) at http://en.wikipedia.org/wiki/File:Tropospheric_profile_Uranus.png

Figure 10.3.3c: NASALPI, "Gas Giant Interiors," http://en.wikipedia.org/wiki/File:Gas_Giant_Interiors.jpg. Copyright in the Public Domain.

Figure 10.3.4a: NASA, "Saturn's Rings PIA03550," http://en.wikipedia.org/wiki/File:Saturn%27s_Rings_PIA03550.jpg. Copyright in the Public Domain.

Figure 10.3.4b: : Francesco Ruspoli/ NASA, "oons of Saturn 2007," http://en.wikipedia.org/wiki/File:Moons_of_Saturn_2007.jpg. Copyright in the Public Domain.

Figure 10.3.5a: NASA, "Saturn Moon," http://saturn.jpl.nasa.gov/multimedia/images/moons/images/PIA06258-th200.jpg. Copyright in the Public Domain.

Figure 10.3.5b: NASA/JPL/Space Science Institute, "Global View of Uapetus' Dichotomy," http://commons.wikimedia.org/wiki/File:Global_View_of_Iapetus%27_Dichotomy.jpg. Copyright in the Public Domain.

Figure 10.3.6a: NASA, "Enceladus," http://apod.nasa.gov/apod/image/0710/PIA08386_enceladus_r.jpg. Copyright in the Public Domain.

Figure 10.3.6b: NASA, "Enceladus Cassini," http://apod.nasa.gov/apod/image/0603/enceladus_cassini_PIA07800c16.jpg. Copyright in the Public Domain.

Figure 10.3.6c: NASA/JPL/GSFC/Space Science Institute, "Enceladus polar temps," https://commons.wikimedia.org/wiki/File:Enceladus_polar_temps.jpg. Copyright in the Public Domain.

Figure 10.3.7a: NASA, "Purple Titan," http://solarsystem.nasa.gov/multimedia/gallery/Purple_Titan.jpg. Copyright in the Public Domain.

Figure 10.3.7b: ESA/NASA/JPL/University of Arizona, "Huygens surface color," http://commons.wikimedia.org/wiki/File:Huygens_surface_color.jpg. Copyright in the Public Domain.

Figure 10.3.8a: NASA/JPL/Space Science Institute, "Titan Globe," http://commons.wikimedia.org/wiki/File:Titan_globe.jpg. Copyright in the Public Domain.

Figure 10.3.8b: NASA / JPL-Caltech / USGS, "Liquid lakes on titan," http://en.wikipedia.org/wiki/File:Liquid_lakes_on_titan.jpg. Copyright in the Public Domain.

CPSIA information can be obtained
at www.ICGtesting.com
Printed in the USA
BVHW05s0552050418
512525BV00006B/70/P